INTRODUCTION
TO COLLOID
CHEMISTRY

INTRODUCTION TO COLLOID CHEMISTRY

KAROL J. MYSELS, *Chemistry Department,*
University of Southern California, Los Angeles, California

19 59

INTERSCIENCE PUBLISHERS, INC., NEW YORK
INTERSCIENCE PUBLISHERS, LTD., LONDON

INTERSCIENCE PUBLISHERS, INC., 250 Fifth Avenue, New York 1, N. Y.
For Great Britain and Northern Ireland
INTERSCIENCE PUBLISHERS, LTD., 88/90 Chancery Lane, London, W. C. 2

PRINTED IN THE UNITED STATES OF AMERICA
BY MACK PRINTING COMPANY, EASTON, PA.

PREFACE

This book is the outgrowth of teaching courses in Colloid Chemistry at various levels at the University of Southern California for more than a decade and of many years of study and research in this field. It is addressed to those who wish to acquire a broad acquaintance with colloids and gain an insight into the basic factors responsible for the observed phenomena and for the principal methods of investigation.

It has been written with two audiences in mind. One is the college senior or beginning graduate student who may use it as a textbook for a one-semester introductory course. The other is the industrial chemist or executive who desires a coherent and concise survey of a field neglected in his academic career. Simplicity of presentation and development of the subject from the fundamentals have therefore been the aim. A knowledge of only the basic principles of physical chemistry and physics should be a sufficient prerequisite. On the other hand, a mastery of the material presented should give a basis for understanding the main factors involved in most practical problems and also for delving into the more advanced treatment of the whole field or of special topics.

To help the reader check his grasp of the subject, problems are provided at the end of the chapters. The object should not be just to find or choose the correct answer—which is listed anyhow at the end of the book—but to be able to reach a conviction as to its correctness or incorrectness and to see clearly the reasoning behind it and how it fits into the whole picture. Some of these problems are rather simple, others may be found quite sophisticated, and some introduce applications not covered in the text itself.

The basic philosophy of this book is given in Chapter 1. Stemming from the belief that a qualitative understanding of principles is of most value, it required a novel approach and organization. Its development has been greatly encouraged by the reaction of many of my students, among whom Dr. I. Reich, Prof. I. Fatt, and Mr. M. Tuvell come especially to mind.

As originator of the "Textbook Errors" column of the *Journal of Chemical Education* I am painfully aware of the difficulty of avoiding errors and confusions when following an established pattern. Any break with tradition increases this difficulty manyfold. I am therefore especially grateful to my colleagues Prof. Robert D. Vold and Marjorie J. Vold and Arthur W. Adamson of the University of Southern California, and to Dr. W. H. Harwood of Continental Oil Co., who helped to remove many a weakness from the original manuscript. Drs. Piet Scholten's assistance was invaluable in checking proofs and figures. I have also been greatly helped by a Science Faculty Fellowship of the National Science Foundation which enabled me to study and clarify in my own mind a number of points.

Nevertheless, the reader must realize that a book is always a compromise between the evils of not writing any and of writing one that is imperfect. Help and suggestions for future improvement will be gratefully received.

K.J.M.

Los Angeles, California
June 1959

CONTENTS

CHAPTER I

Why Colloid Chemistry?

Chemistry is generally defined as that branch of science which studies the composition and transformations of matter. Chemistry, like all science, is made feasible only through a simplification of the systems studied. Historically, progress has been largely dependent on simplification. The recognition of primary factors, such as mass and its conservation in reactions; the isolation of materials showing simple behavior, such as the gases, elements, or acids; the development of hypotheses subject to test, such as Dalton's atoms or the kinetic theory—these are all simplifications on which chemistry is built. Simplification is also necessary today in the process of education, where the beginner must be introduced to the unbelievable variety and richness of the sum total of chemical knowledge through so-called principles and fundamentals.

This simplification, however necessary, is somewhat dangerous, for the student may be left with the impression that the picture is complete. Actually, of course, the process of education and research is endless, and the chemist constantly will encounter facts which do not fit his mental picture; he must modify that picture to fit reality better. Probably this process, and the illumination which it gives, is familiar to every reader, as when organic chemistry unfolded suddenly the unsuspected richness of carbon compounds or when thermodynamics gave a quantitative correlation of apparently unrelated facts. Can colloid chemistry open such new horizons?

1-1. Chemistry and Classical Chemistry

Classical chemistry, whose outline the student receives in Inorganic, Organic, and Physical, has obvious limitations and

1

omits from consideration many kinds of matter and many kinds of transformations. Probably the most striking examples are living matter and the processes involved in birth, growth, and death, which today have become a field of study large and important enough to bear the name of biochemistry. As we well know, biochemists have developed methods which differ widely from those of the classical chemist and study, with often astonishing results, phenomena whose existence he might not even suspect.

There are quite good reasons why the separation of chemistry and biochemistry is justifiable. If the chemist keeps his systems sterile and starts with inanimate matter, he is not likely to run into the kind of problems that biochemistry helps solve. Conversely, a biochemist is not likely to require a knowledge of reactions at high temperatures or in concentrated acids. Most important, perhaps, the systems studied by the biochemist tend to be more complicated and hence do not offer that simplicity which, as we have seen, is a requirement for establishing basic generalizations and principles.

On the other hand, one might rightly point out that biochemistry is based on chemistry and that all the classical laws of chemistry beginning with those of conservation of mass and of elements must apply there too. This is perfectly true, yet these laws alone are just as unable to explain the facts of biochemistry as the laws of mechanics and electricity alone are impotent when faced with most chemical systems. We need the body of chemical principles to handle chemical systems, although these systems certainly do no more than satisfy all of the requirements of mechanics and electricity.

More abstractly, one might say that the solution of any problem involves a given system and certain laws which describe its behavior. For simple systems the laws of physics can be applied to give a complete solution. When the system becomes sufficiently complicated, however, the application of these laws becomes impractical or impossible, and other generalizations become useful. These in turn become insufficient for still more complicated problems and have to be replaced by others. Each set of generalizations and systems is more or less self-contained and forms a correspondingly more or less self-contained branch of science, such as physics, or chemistry, or biochemistry.

Thus classical chemistry leaves out whole areas within the purview of chemistry. Sometimes, as in the case of biochemistry, this simply narrows the field without depriving the chemist of any essential tools; in other cases, however, it may limit materially his understanding of nature. A case in point seems to be the field of colloids.

1-2. Colloids

One of the characteristics of the particles (molecules and ions) of classical chemistry is their limited size. The formula of even the largest molecule of classical organic chemistry can be completely written on a single blackboard. The molecular weights of these particles seldom run into many hundreds. As a result, we can measure these weights by freezing point lowering and can easily observe the diffusion of the particles. Their solutions are clear, and even the electron microscope does not enable us to see their shape.

Yet particles can be, and frequently are, larger than that; they can even have macroscopic dimensions, since there is no intrinsic difference between the bonds holding together the carbon atoms of a diamond and those of a neopentane molecule. Whereas the small particles are the subject of classical chemistry, the macroscopic ones—steel balls and flexible ropes—are properly in the realm of physics. But there is an intermediate range where the particles are small enough to give solutions but large enough for their particle weight to range from tens of thousands to billions. Hence their solutions may show important peculiarities, such as a freezing point lowering which is undetectable, an easily visible turbidity, and negligible diffusion rates. It is this intermediate region of particle sizes which forms the heart of the field of colloids.

Concomitant with the size is the charge. Whereas classical chemistry deals with ions carrying one or a few electronic charges, the giant colloidal ions may carry dozens or thousands. Much stronger electric forces result, so that complete dissociation becomes the exception rather than the rule. Indeed, the interaction between colloidal particles is one of the determining factors of their behavior.

The particles of classical chemistry can generally be considered as rigid little spheres, although free rotation becomes of some importance in isomerism and in calculations of specific heats. As the particles become large, they may grow into giant spheres; they may retain one small dimension and grow into giant plates; they may retain two such dimensions to give giant threads or even giant networks. These dissymmetries have no analogy among classical structures yet are decisive when it comes to the behavior of the colloidal system in such obviously striking properties as high viscosities of dilute solutions or the formation of iridescent layers. Hence, the problem of the outer shape of particles, which is unimportant in classical chemistry, becomes central in colloids.

A molecule which is a thread a few atoms thick and many thousands long acquires flexibility as a characteristic property. Thermal motion no longer shifts the molecule as a whole: its parts can move independently of each other within relatively wide limits, so that one end can have only an approximate idea of the location of the other and indeed may not even differentiate parts of its own molecules from those of its neighbors. This type of behavior, which again poses no problem in classical chemistry, becomes important in the study of colloids and accounts for many of the peculiarities which make plastics, rubbers, and synthetic fibers such an important part of our daily lives.

Classical chemistry tends to deal with substances in the narrow sense of the word, i.e., with pure elements or compounds formed, if we neglect isotopic effects, by only a single or a few clearly distinct species of particles. Thus benzene is formed by one species and sodium hydrogen sulfate by four very dissimilar ones.

This simplicity of composition is natural because different substances lead to easily distinguishable properties, so that separation
and purification are, in principle, easy.   Although most practic-
ing chemists will probably disagree with this estimate, they will
have to admit that to separate homologs which may differ by two
carbon atoms out of ten thousand or a million would be a task of a
completely different order of magnitude.   Because separation
of species is so difficult, because mixtures often behave much as a
substance would, and also because, as we shall see, substances
often give a great many species in dynamic equilibrium, the
colloid chemist pays much attention to the separation of species
(fractionation) and to the interpretation of the behavior of mixtures of many similar species, the so-called polydisperse systems.

When an atom or a very small molecule interacts with another,
the whole of it is involved, as in $H_2 + Cl_2 = 2HCl$.   For larger
particles, classical chemistry often distinguishes groups which
react while the rest of the molecule remains unchanged; but,
in general, the whole of one particle is exposed to the other, and
it is the difference in reactivity of the groups which makes for
the difference of behavior.   When macroscopic particles interact with small ones, it is clear that only their surface is ever
involved, so that, unless the surface disintegrates, the interaction is strictly limited and unimportant.   This is the reason why
cooking utensils may be built of a metal having as high an affinity
for oxygen as aluminum.   In the case of colloids there are many
interactions which are similarly limited to the surface.   Here,
however, the proportion of atoms located in the surface may become very significant and their number huge, so that both the
total amount of interaction and its effect on the colloid often
become very important.   A close mutual interrelation between
surface and colloid chemistry must exist, because colloids readily
supply large areas on which surface phenomena are frequently
studied and also because most of the important interactions of
colloids are surface interactions.   It should be noted, however,
that surface phenomena may be studied, and sometimes are
best studied, on flat surfaces involving no colloids.   Surface

chemistry is therefore properly a separate field of chemistry but one which is of particular importance in the study of colloids.

Other points neglected by classical chemistry yet important in the study of large particles will be discussed later. At this point enough has been said, perhaps, to indicate that an understanding of colloids frequently requires emphasis on concepts which differ from those used customarily in classical chemistry.

1-3. Importance of Colloids

Given the fact that colloid chemistry is a distinct field, the question arises whether it is merely one of the many interesting things in life which one would like to study if provided with a 48-hr. day, or whether its fundamentals belong in the arsenal of basic tools of every chemist. Although expert opinions do differ on this point, and there certainly are problems in chemistry which may never bring one to grips with a colloid, there is little doubt that chemists having to deal with a variety of materials and their transformations, whether in research or in production, seldom get gray before facing problems involving colloids. It is then that their chances of being able to reach the best solution depend on their grasp of the fundamental factors involved, i.e., on their knowledge of colloid chemistry.

Among the most frequently encountered problems on which colloid chemistry may shed some light are the control of filterability, the purity of precipitates, the breaking of emulsions, the regulation of foam, the preparation of catalysts, and the cleaning of surfaces. Those who deal with proteins, starches, oils, rubbers, plastics, paints, pigments, soils, insecticides, air pollutants, dyes, or textiles, deal always with colloids whether or not they fully appreciate this fact.

The fact that colloids are frequently encountered, and that colloid chemistry helps in understanding them, does not mean that one can solve all the problems involved upon finishing this book, nor does it mean that one will be helpless without it. Colloid chemistry, like all science, always deals with many more unsolved mysteries than pat answers. In addition, what was a perplexing problem yesterday, if solved today will become obvious and barely worth mentioning tomorrow while new difficulties clamor for attention. On the other hand, many problems have been, and will be, solved empirically or by other scientific approaches, even where principles of colloid chemistry might have hastened the solution or reduced the effort. Colloid chemistry neither stands alone nor is omnipotent, but it is hoped that the reader will find it helpful.

1-4. The Simplifications

Even if we agree that a mastery of the principles and fundamentals of colloid chemistry is of value to the chemist, we are still faced with the choice of these principles and fundamentals. As always, these should be the ideas which are both readily grasped and give the best understanding of what matter is and how it behaves. Their selection has to be made anew by each generation and to some extent by each teacher in the light of new developments. There seems to be little unanimity among the authors of textbooks as to what these fundamentals should be in the field of colloid chemistry, so that the present course, although organized along new lines, is not really heterodox. It is based on the concept, given above, that colloid chemistry requires a different emphasis than classical chemistry but that fundamentally colloids are particles, just as the small ions and molecules. Thus, they are subject to thermal motion, to the effects of mechanical, gravitational, coulombic, and van der Waals forces and, like all particles, interact with electromagnetic radiation. What differs frequently is the relative importance and extent of these effects, their macroscopic manifestations, and the methods of studying them.

In order to give an understanding of as wide a field as possible, theory—that is, the behavior of idealized systems and hypothetical particles—will be emphasized. Descriptive material will be brought in for illustrative purposes rather than for its own sake. Further, the qualitative rather than the quantitative aspects of the theory will be emphasized, since unless one knows

what is occurring one cannot calculate it intelligently.   Moreover, in many applications quantitative treatment can give only
an illusion of accuracy because the qualitative aspects are not
fully understood.   Those who desire or need the more quantitative or more descriptive aspects can find them readily in more
advanced texts, in specialized reviews, and in the original
literature.*   Our qualitative discussion of principles should
give them an adequate basis and the references an initial guide
to further study.

1-5. The Outline

There is no doubt that gradual development from the simple to
the more complex facilitates the understanding of a subject.   In
an attempt to conform to this principle, we shall begin by introducing some of our structural elements and shall examine
their behavior when only gravitational, or only van der Waals
forces are important.   Then the effects of thermal agitation alone
will be studied, followed by the combined influences of these
factors.   Later, electric forces will be discussed at length; first
alone, then in relation to the previously described ones.   Finally,
we shall consider optical effects: refraction, interference, and
scattering.

* The literature of the field of colloids is very large and widespread.   The
following brief list gives the books which have been of greatest value to the
author.   The master's hand is still felt in the relatively old T. Svedberg, *Colloid
Chemistry* (ACS Monograph No. 16), Chemical Catalog Co. (Reinhold Publishing Corp.) New York, 1928;   and in H. Freundlich, *Colloid and Capillary
Chemistry*, many editions, Methuen and Co., London, 1926.   Recent advanced
texts are: H. R. Kruyt, *Colloid Science*, Elsevier Press, New York, Vol. I, 1952,
Vol. II, 1949;   and A. E. Alexander and P. Johnson, *Colloid Science*, Oxford
University Press, London, 1949.   A wealth of materials and original points of
view are in J. W. McBain, *Colloid Science*, D. C. Heath and Co., Boston, 1950.
Polymers are covered by P. J. Flory, *Principles of Polymer Chemistry*, Cornell
University Press, Ithaca, 1953.

CHAPTER II
Some Structural Elements

Our discussion will be centered on the behavior of colloidal particles in a fluid medium, especially in water. In this chapter we will describe briefly some of the outer characteristics, especially the shape and size of our particles, and in the next chapter proceed to a study of their behavior in water.

2-1. Aggregation

Before examining the outer appearance of the particles, there is one facet of their structure which should be introduced: the fact that a particle may be composed of smaller ones. A trivial aspect of this structure is that all particles are formed of atoms or ions. The important aspect for us is that small particles composed of atoms or ions can form larger ones, either in reality or at least on paper. It becomes particularly interesting if this formation of the larger particle, or its reverse, or both, occurs during the observation of a system.

Particles which are not formed of smaller ones are called "primary." This applies whether they are small or large. If one wishes to emphasize that they are building blocks for the larger ones, they may be called "monomers" or "monomeric." In the formation of larger ones the primary particles may be joined by covalent bonds, or by the less specific ionic bonds, or by the much weaker van der Waals forces.

The nomenclature of the larger particles is not uniform, but generally if the large particle is held together by covalent bonds it is called a "polymer," and if it is composed of many monomers the term "high polymer" applies. "Aggregate" may be used as the most general term, but occasionally it is opposed to polymer to indicate weaker, noncovalent bonding and the continued independent existence of the primary particles.   If the larger particles are readily formed from the smaller ones, and vice versa, so that a dynamic equilibrium exists between the two, we speak of "association colloids," and the aggregate is generally called a "micelle."   When the smaller particles keep much of their individuality, and especially when there is no dynamic equilibrium, the aggregates are often called "secondary particles."

Not all colloidal particles are formed of smaller ones, and even when they are this structure will not often concern us.   Hence we shall generally discuss the particles as units and bring in their structure only when necessary.

Figure 2-1. Spherical particles of polystyrene latex (large) and of bushy-stunt virus (small).   Shadowed electron micrograph.   (*Courtesy of Prof. R. C. Williams, Virus Laboratory, University of California, Berkeley.*)

2-2. The Shape

The exact shape of colloidal particles is most often unknown or determined only approximately. Frequently, too, it is likely to be highly complex. As a first approximation, however, we can consider relatively simple shapes whose behavior can be more readily interpreted and which will come close to most real shapes.

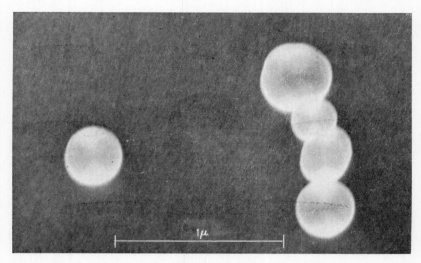

Figure 2-2. Spherical particles of carbon black. Dark field electron micrograph. (*Courtesy of Hitachi-Erb and Gray Scientific, Los Angeles, Calif.*)

In fact, the difference will frequently be less than the experimental error.

The simplest possible shape is the sphere, characterized by its radius r. This shape not only is often the easiest to treat theoretically but also represents exactly or approximately many real cases. Thus it is the shape always expected from particles which are essentially fluid, such as the droplets of one liquid dispersed in another, i.e., an emulsion. The particles of dispersions of plastics and rubbers in water—the so-called latexes or lattices often used in the preparation of paints—are also generally spherical. Figure 2-1 shows an example of such

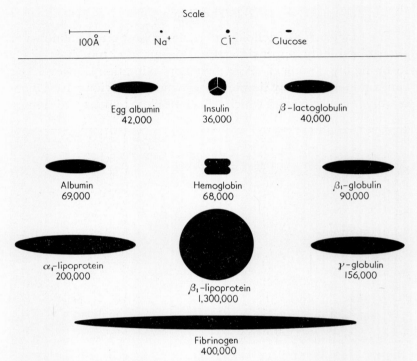

Figure 2-3. The probable shape and particle weight of some proteins.   (*Courtesy of Prof. J. L. Oncley, Harvard Medical School.*)

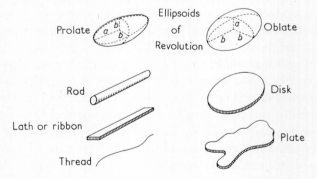

Figure 2-4. Some schematic models for nonspherical particles and their relation.

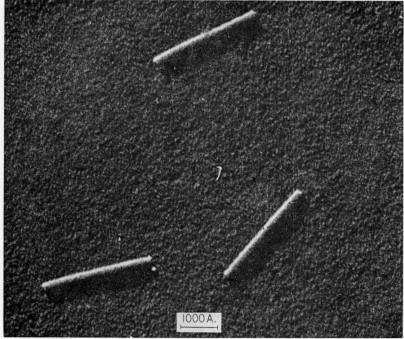

Figure 2-5. Rod-shaped particles of Tobacco Mosaic virus. Shadowed electron micrograph. (*Courtesy of Prof. R. C. Williams, Virus Laboratory, University of California, Berkeley, California.*)

particles. Many carbon blacks are also composed of particles which are essentially spherical (Fig. 2-2). This is also the shape of certain viruses, such as the bushy stunt virus shown in Fig. 2-1. Occasionally a large organic molecule such as the β_1-lipoprotein has a shape which appears to be spherical as far as is known today (Fig. 2-3).

Frequently we have good reasons to believe that a particle must have a different shape—for example, that a crystal is certainly angular—yet, if it is symmetrical enough, it will behave like a sphere for many purposes.

When the shape deviates somewhat from spherical, we can consider as models the ellipsoids of revolution. This is the

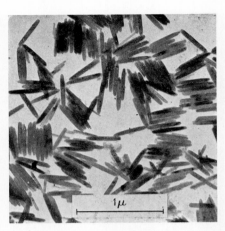

Figure 2-6. Electron micrograph of lath-shaped ferric oxide particles capable of forming irridescent layers. (*Courtesy of John H. L. Watson, the Edsel B. Ford Institute for Medical Research, Henry Ford Hospital, and Wilfried Heller and Wesley Wojtowicz, Chemistry Department, Wayne State University, Detroit, Michigan.*)

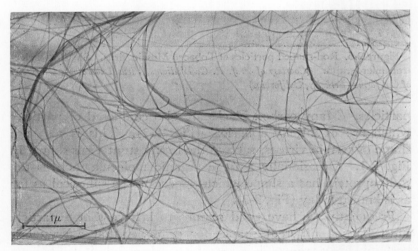

Figure 2-7. Filaments from a V_2O_5 sol on a collodion film. Electron micrograph. (*Courtesy of Prof. C. E. Hall, Massachusetts Institute of Technology, Cambridge; from "Introduction to Electron Microscopy," McGraw-Hill Publishing Co., N. Y., 1953.*)

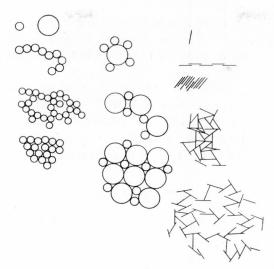

Figure 2-8. An almost infinite variety of shapes and structures can be formed by aggregation of simple particles.

probable shape of many proteins (Fig. 2-3). As shown in Fig. 2-4, ellipsoids may be oblate (like a disk) or prolate (like a cigar). Such ellipsoids are characterized by two dimensions: their single half-axis a and their largest radius of revolution b. The deviation from sphericity is generally expressed as their "axial ratio," a/b. If the axial ratio becomes unity, the ellipsoid becomes a sphere. If the ratio is less than unity it is disk shaped, and if the ratio is larger it is cigar shaped. If the particle becomes very flat, we can regard it as a flat disk characterized by its radius and thickness; if it becomes very long, we may consider it as a rod of a given radius and length. The tobacco mosaic virus shown in Fig. 2-5 belongs to this type. Particles that are both long and flat, like the ferric oxide particles of Fig. 2-6, we call laths. When the elongation becomes extreme compared to the other two dimensions, like the vanadium pentoxide shown in Fig. 2-7 or like many high polymers such as polyethylene or rubber, we can call it a thread or filament.

The ovoid is a more general model for less symmetrical but compact particles, while an irregular plate can approximate flat particles such as those of the clay bentonite shown later in Fig. 8-11.

The shape of aggregates or polymers need not have a simple relation to that of the primary particles forming them.   Spherical aggregates can be formed from small rods or plates, while rods may be formed by a string of spheres or a stack of disks.   Figure 2-8 indicates some of the variety of shapes and structures due to aggregation.

2-3. Flexibility

A spherical or ellipsoidal particle can certainly be considered rigid for most of our purposes.   A very thin plate or a lath may show some deformations when subjected to relatively strong

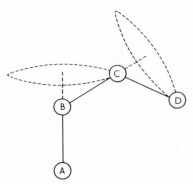

Figure 2-9. The possible positions of successive carbon atoms in a hydrocarbon chain.   Free rotation around the *AB* bond allows *C* to be anywhere on the dotted circle.   For one of these possible positions of the *BC* bond, *D* can again assume any of the positions indicated by the dotted circle.   (*From J. J. Hermans: Flow Properties of Disperse Systems, Interscience Publishers, N. Y., 1953.*)

forces, but these deformations are generally not very important in quiescent systems.   On the other hand, a long thread-like particle exhibits considerable flexibility.   The factor which makes this flexibility particularly important is not an elastic

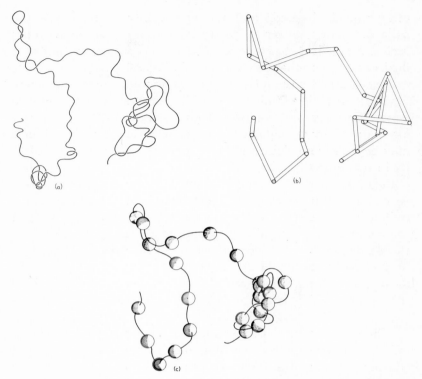

Figure 2-10. A short random coil (*a*) and its schematic representation as a sequence of rigid segments (*b*) and as a string of pearls (*c*).

deformation of a definite shape but the more or less free twisting due to rotation around carbon-carbon and other bonds, so that the particle has no single, definite shape but alters it spontaneously even in a quiescent system.

We know that the two carbons of ethane can rotate around their common bond, so that in propane the third carbon may point anywhere along a 71° cone, as shown in Fig. 2-9. The next carbon again will be somewhere along a cone beginning at the third carbon, and the process continues for each successive one. Hence, even if we know where one end of such a molecule is and how it is oriented, there is uncertainty as to where the other end is located, and the uncertainty increases as the molecule grows longer. The picture of a rigid rod becomes useless for such a structure and must be replaced by that of a flexible thread or chain, as indicated in Fig. 2-10a.

On the other hand, a chain of carbon atoms is not completely flexible; there is a limit to the radius around which it can be bent. Furthermore, rotation around bonds is often hindered, for example, by steric factors, so that short lengths of the chain may be somewhat rigid and only longer lengths show flexibility in the sense that the position of one end does not define that of the other end. To render this situation more easily tractable, we can use a model formed by short, completely rigid "segments" united by completely flexible joints (Fig. 2-10b). For a given total length of the chain, as the over-all flexibility increases, the segments become shorter. As a further simplification we may concentrate all the matter of each segment into a sphere located at its center and connect these spheres by long, infinitely thin strings. This is the so-called "bead necklace" or "string-of-pearls" model (Fig. 2-10c).

When a very long, slender, flexible molecule of this type, a string of many hundreds or thousands of beads, is left to itself without any directing force except thermal motion, there is no reason why one segment should assume any particular orientation with respect to another, nor is there any reason why the string should be either tightly coiled or completely stretched; it is most likely to assume some nondescript, loosely coiled, and constantly changing shape as indicated in Figs. 2-10 and 2-13 for relatively very short lengths. Later we shall look in some detail at this arrangement of segments, but for the time being it may suffice to give it a highly descriptive name: the "random coil."

2-4. The Size

There are several ways of describing the size of colloids, and depending on the problem involved some may be preferable to

TABLE 2-1

Conversion of Some Units (Approximate)[a]

	Inch	Centimeter	Millimeter	Thousandth in.	Micron	Millionth in.	Milli-micron	Angstrom
Inch	1	2.5	25	1000	2.5×10^4	10^6	2.5×10^7	2.5×10^8
Centimeter	0.4	1	10	394	10^4	4×10^5	10^7	10^8
Millimeter	4×10^{-6}	0.1	1	39	10^3	4×10^4	10^6	10^7
Thousandth in.	10^{-3}	2.5×10^{-3}	2.5×10^{-2}	1	25	10^3	2.5×10^4	2.5×10^5
Micron	4×10^{-5}	10^{-4}	10^{-3}	4×10^{-2}	1	39	10^3	10^4
Millionth in.	10^{-6}	2.5×10^{-6}	2.5×10^{-5}	10^{-3}	2.5×10^{-2}	1	25	254
Millimicron	4×10^{-8}	10^{-7}	10^{-6}	4×10^{-5}	10^{-3}	4×10^{-2}	1	10
Angstrom	4×10^{-9}	10^{-8}	10^{-7}	4×10^{-6}	10^{-4}	4×10^{-3}	0.1	1

[a] This table is based on the ratio 1 in. = 2.5 cm. which introduces an error of less than 2%. The exact (international) value is now 2.54 while until recently it was 2.54000508 in the U.S. and 2.5399956 in Britain (*Science* **129**, 260 (1959)).

others, although in principle they are generally equivalent. The most useful are their dimensions and their mass.

As mentioned above, dimensions such as the radius of a sphere or the axes of an ellipsoid suffice to define the particle if its shape is known.   These dimensions may be expressed in microns, μ, (10^{-3} mm.), millimicrons, mμ (10^{-3} μ), or angstroms, A. (10^{-4} μ).   Table 2-1 gives a comparison of these units with the customary ones.   For the sake of consistency we shall use angstroms as far as possible, since this is the unit generally used in the description of atomic, molecular, and optical phenomena.

The amount of matter in a particle is generally expressed by chemists as particle weight.   This is a dimensionless number relating the weight (or the mass) of a single particle to that of an oxygen atom taken as 16, or relating the weight (or the mass) of a mole of material, i.e., Avogadro's number of particles, to that of a mole of oxygen atoms taken as 16.   This number represents also, on a macroscopic scale, the weight (or the mass) of a mole expressed in grams.   We will give to the particle weight M any of these meanings depending on context.   However, when it comes to quantitative expressions involving the c.g.s. system, M will always mean the mass of a mole since in this system the gram is only a unit of mass whereas the weight, i.e., the force exerted by gravity, is measured in dynes.

We will often deal also with the microscopic behavior of a single particle.   Then, in addition to the particle weight, M, we will have use for the weight of the particle, m.   This weight (or mass) of the single particle will be expressed in grams and, again, when used in c.g.s. expressions, it will always refer to the mass of the particle.

The relation between the mole and the individual particle, between M and m is, of course, Avogadro's number $\mathbf{N}$.   For our purposes, $\mathbf{N} = 6.0 \times 10^{23}$.

Thus the particle weight M, of H_2, is 2; the force exerted on it by gravity is $M\mathbf{g} = 2 \times 981 \approx 2 \times 10^3$ dynes, whereas the weight of the particle H_2, m, is $M/\mathbf{N} = 2/(6 \times 10^{23}) = 3.33 \times 10^{-24}$ g. and the force exerted by gravity on it is $m\mathbf{g} = 3.3 \times 10^{-21}$ dynes.

TABLE 2-2

Effect of Size and Shape upon Weight, Assuming a Density of 2

Radius or half-length			Sphere		Disc 10 A. thick		Rod 10 A. diameter	
mm.	μ	A.	Weight of a particle, g.	Particle weight	Weight of a particle, g.	Particle weight	Weight of a particle, g.	Particle weight
1	10^3	10^7	8.4×10^{-3}	5×10^{21}	6.3×10^{-9}	3.7×10^{15}	1.6×10^{-14}	9.5×10^9
0.1	10^2	10^6	8.4×10^{-6}	5×10^{18}	6.3×10^{-11}	3.7×10^{13}	1.6×10^{-15}	9.5×10^8
10^{-2}	10	10^5	8.4×10^{-9}	5×10^{15}	6.3×10^{-13}	3.7×10^{11}	1.6×10^{-16}	9.5×10^7
10^{-3}	1	10^4	8.4×10^{-12}	5×10^{12}	6.3×10^{-15}	3.7×10^9	1.6×10^{-17}	9.5×10^6
10^{-4}	0.1	10^3	8.4×10^{-15}	5×10^9	6.3×10^{-17}	3.7×10^7	1.6×10^{-18}	9.5×10^5
10^{-5}	10^{-2}	100	8.4×10^{-18}	5×10^6	6.3×10^{-19}	3.7×10^5	1.6×10^{-19}	9.5×10^4
10^{-6}	10^{-3}	10	8.4×10^{-21}	$5,000$	6.3×10^{-21}	$3,700$	1.6×10^{-20}	$9,500$
10^{-7}	10^{-4}	1	8.4×10^{-24}	5	6.3×10^{-23}	37	1.6×10^{-21}	950

In contrast, if we consider a particle whose individual weight, m, is at the limit of sensitivity of today's ultramicro weighing[1], i.e., 0.001 γ or 10^{-9} g., its particle weight, M, would be **N** times larger, i.e., 6×10^{14}, almost a thousand million millions.   If the density of this particle were 1, it could be a cube 10 μ on edge.

The mass of a particle depends of course on its dimensions, its shape, and its average density.   The first two are predominant, and Table 2-2 shows what happens as a sphere becomes larger, a disk broader, and a rod longer, while their density remains the same.

If a particle is formed of smaller units of known mass its size can be measured in a still different way by simply counting the smaller units.   The number obtained fully determines the mass of the particle and, if the arrangement of the units is also known, its dimensions.   This number is generally called the "degree" of polymerization, or of association, or of aggregation, as the case may be.

2-5. The Field of Colloids

While discussing size, one should perhaps attempt to define the field of colloids.   Such definitions are frequently given and generally require that one dimension of the particle fall into a range whose lower limit varies between about 10 and 100 A. and the upper between about 10^3 and 10^4 A.   These are good orders of magnitude to keep in mind, but obviously properties change continuously with size, shape, and density, so that sharp limits should not be expected.   In fact, even their approximate position is mostly a question of emphasis.   Depending on the property studied and the point of view, the colloidal approach may be useful over different ranges of size and weight.

A scale which should be kept in mind for comparison is given by the limits of resolution of the ordinary and of the electron microscope.   For reasons which we shall later try to understand (Chapter 19), the microscopes fail to distinguish objects that are too close together.   This occurs, even under best conditions, at the so-called limit of resolution of a microscope. For the ordinary light microscope this limit is of the order of 2000 A. and is not likely to change in the near future. For the electron microscope it is now about 10 A. and is being reduced at a rather rapid pace. Today at any rate, the colloidal range is mainly located between these two limits of resolution.

In terms of particle weights we can also think of the colloidal range as being between thousands and billions or so, depending on density and, again, upon the point of view.

2-6. Polydispersity

Thus far we have discussed the size and shape of a single particle, yet this is an entity we seldom encounter in practice. Most of our experiments and problems deal with macroscopic amounts of materials representing billions upon billions of particles. If these particles are all alike, then we can speak of a well-defined particle size or molecular weight of the material. These concepts, however, lose their simple meaning if the particles differ, especially if they differ widely, in size and mass.

Let us look for example at a familiar element, sulfur. When heated, as we all know, the yellow S_λ turns brown and partially changes into S_μ, insoluble in CS_2 and most common solvents. This is explained as due to the opening of the S_8 rings of ordinary S_λ to from S_8 chains which break and reunite to form chains containing from two up to a very large number of S atoms. What is the molecular weight of S_μ? No simple answer can be given to this question, although there can be no doubt about the chemical purity, since we are still dealing with an element.

One possible way out of this difficulty is to subdivide (fractionate) the material into fractions, each formed by uniform particles. The particle weight of each fraction is then well defined. We can then characterize our material, e.g., in terms of these fractions, by a table or a graph giving the relative amounts and particle weights. Each such fraction is said to be "monodisperse"; if the number of fractions is small we call the material

"paucidisperse," and if their number is very large, "polydisperse."   The latter is by far the most frequent case in practice.

Immediately we may notice a possible ambiguity: How do
we describe the amount of each fraction?   In terms of the total
weight or in terms of the number of particles?   Actually, the
two are equivalent since quite generally, if fraction i has a total
weight W_i and consists of n_i particles, each weighing m_i, we have

$$n_i m_i = W_i \qquad (2\text{-}6.1)$$

Therefore it is a matter of convenience which basis is used, al-
though the results for a given material may look very different.
This is shown by Fig. 2-11a for two simple paucidisperse systems.
In each graph the height of a line represents the number or the
weight of particles having the corresponding particle weight.
The over-all impression is very different in the two cases.

2-7. Other Presentations

Figure 2-11a shows what is probably the simplest presentation
of the composition of a polydisperse system; it shows the amount

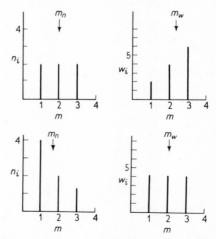

Figure 2-11a. Top and bottom: two simple size distributions, each shown
according to the number of particles on the left and according to their weight
on the right.   Vertical arrows indicate the corresponding averages.

of material in each fraction.   Another frequently used method presents instead the total amount of material in a given fraction and those below it.   Figure 2-11b shows again the distributions of Fig. 2-11a but by this second "cumulative" method.

Thus far we have assumed that it is possible to fractionate a material into truly monodisperse fractions.   There are, how-

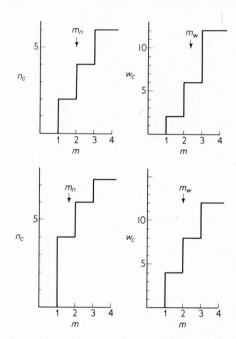

Figure 2-11b. Top and bottom: cumulative representation of the two distributions of Fig. 2-11$a;$ on the left according to the number of particles, on the right according to their weight.

ever, great practical difficulties in the fractionation of poly-diperse colloids.   They become particularly apparent when we remember that polydispersity is often due to the difference in the degree of aggregation or polymerization of the particles involved. Hence the particles may differ solely by the successive addition of one monomeric unit out of hundred or thousands or more, so that their properties are extremely similar and their separation correspondingly difficult.

In addition, the particles may be too unstable to undergo the

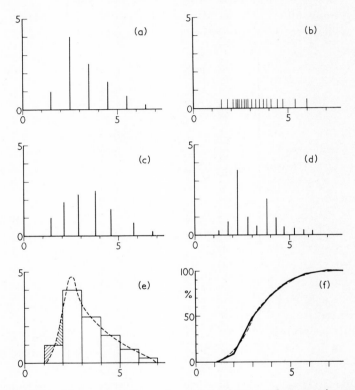

Figure 2-12. *Bottom*:   representation of a polydispersed system, in terms of broad fractions and of a continuous distribution, (*e*) on a differential, (*f*) on a cumulative basis.   *Above*;   detailed distributions equivalent to the bottom ones. (*a*) and (*b*) are reasonably well represented;   (*c*) and (*d*) are quite poorly represented by the smooth lines.   Note that the smooth line of (*e*) is drawn so that the shaded areas are equal.

rigors of fractionation procedures without changing.   Fractionation may also be impossible in principle, as when the different sizes are in rapid dynamic equilibrium with each other so that any fraction, however isolated, reverts immediately to the equilibrium distribution.

In practice, therefore, fractionation generally produces at best "narrow" and overlapping fractions. Hence, instead of being represented by lines, the distribution should be represented by thick bars or steps showing the amount and approximate breadth of a fraction.

Figures 2-12 *e* and *f* are such step graphs of a distribution. A number of more detailed distributions, each of which is equivalent to these step graphs, is shown by line graphs *a* to *d* in Fig. 2-12. Thus we see that the separation of broad fractions cannot give us any detailed information about the actual distribution of individual species. Therefore, for the sake of simplicity one frequently assumes that the distribution is a continuous one and that it can be represented by a smooth line. How such a smooth line is constructed from the step graph is shown in *e* and *f*. Although a step graph or smooth line may often describe quite well the real distribution of particle sizes (*a* and *b*), at other times it may give only a rough approximation (*c* and *d*).

It may be noted that the smooth line of *e* is the derivative of the smooth line of the cumulative graph *f*. Hence the former type of graph is often called a differential presentation of the distribution.

Thus, although a description of polydisperse systems in terms of a particle-weight distribution may be very informative, it is seldom available or complete. Less perfect methods must be sought.

2-8. The Averages

A very useful way of looking at a particle weight is to consider it as the result obtained by performing a molecular weight determination experiment, such as a freezing point or a gas density determination experiment, and applying the proper formula to the measured value. The result may be called the particle weight M of the material, be it monodisperse or polydisperse. In the former case M has its simple meaning, and in the latter it will be an average of the particle weights of all its fractions. We are thus led to the concept of average particle weight and have to consider more closely what is meant by "average."

For example, let us try to average the weights of the paucidisperse material formed by ten particles weighing 1 and one particle weighing 10. One possible line of reasoning is that the heavy particle weighs 9 more but it is only one out of 11; hence $9/11 = 0.82$ should be effectively added to each of the lighter ones and the average weight should be 1.82. The same result is obtained by noting that the total number of particles is 11 and their total weight 20. Division gives again 1.82.

There is, however, another approach. Half the weight of the material has a particle weight of 1 and the other half of 10. Since the two halves are equal, we should take the simple average of 1 and 10 which is 5.5.

Both approaches seem reasonable, but the results certainly differ. We could decide arbitrarily to use only one, but we shall see later that different methods of determining particle weights give different averages of the real particle-weight distribution, so that both must be kept. (For a fuller discussion of other averages, see, for example, reference 2.)

The first type of average, based on the number of particles, is called the number-average weight, m_n. It can be defined generally in terms of the composition of the material as the total weight W_t divided by the total number n_t of particles

$$m_n = W_t/n_t \qquad (2.8.1)$$

If we bring in the individual fractions this is equivalent to

$$m_n = \Sigma\ W_i/\Sigma\ n_i \qquad (2-8.2)$$

since the sum of the weights of all fractions equals the total weight, and the sum of the numbers in all fractions is the total number. Another equivalent form, in view of the relation between W_i, n_i and m_i, is

$$m_n = \Sigma\ n_i m_i/\Sigma\ n_i \qquad (2-8.3)$$

The second type of average, based upon the weight of each fraction, is called the weight-average weight m_w. It is defined as the sum of the particle weights times their weight for all fractions divided by the total weight, i.e.

$$m_w = \Sigma \ W_i m_i / W_t \tag{2-8.4}$$

We can transform this into the equivalent expression

$$m_w = \Sigma \ n_i m_i^2 / \Sigma \ n_i m_i \tag{2-8.5}$$

For simplicity we have kept the above discussion in terms of the weights m of the individual particles. The reader can easily verify that the corresponding particle weights M can be obtained by strictly analoguous expressions in terms of the number of moles N

$$M_n = W_t / N_t = \Sigma \ W_i / \Sigma \ N_i = \Sigma \ N_i M_i / \Sigma \ N_i \tag{2-8.6}$$

$$M_w = \Sigma \ W_i M_i / W_t = \Sigma \ N_i M_i^2 / \Sigma \ N_i M_i \tag{2-8.7}$$

Since the number of moles is proportional to the number of particles, they can be substituted for each other if they occur in both numerator and denominator. Thus

$$M_n = \Sigma \ n_i M_i / \Sigma \ n_i \quad \text{and} \quad M_w = \Sigma \ n_i M_i^2 / \Sigma \ n_i M_i \tag{2-8.8}$$

As we shall see later, the number-average particle weight, M_n, is obtained by colligative measurements, such as the determination of the freezing point lowering (Chapter 6), whereas the weight-average, M_w, is obtained from light scattering (Chapter 20).

In Fig. 2-11 both averages, m_n and m_w, are indicated by arrows for each distribution. It may be noted that the former is always lower. This is due to the fact that the larger fractions are always weighted more heavily in computing the weight-average. Only for a monodisperse system do the weight- and number-averages coincide.

2-9. Hydration

In relating, earlier, the weight to the size, we have used the term "average density" of the particle. This, obviously, is the correct value to use but implies that the density of a particle might not be uniform.   If we consider the nature of a particle carefully, we find indeed that variations of density may become quite significant.   We shall not worry about the differences of density within an atom due to the concentration of almost all its mass in the nucleus, but shall consider only the differences occurring over somewhat larger distances and due to the inter-action of the particle with the solvent: the so-called "solvation" or, in case of water, "hydration."

Hydration is not peculiar to colloid chemistry.   We all know that if $AlCl_3$ is placed in water, a vigorous reaction occurs and the anhydrous product cannot be recovered from the solution by any simple drying.   The aluminum ion has become strongly hydrated, and although we describe it conventionally as Al^{3+} it would be more correct probably to write $Al(H_2O)_6^{3+}$.   The weight of the ion is no longer 27 but about 135, and its radius not the 0.5 A. encountered in crystals but some 3.5 A.   Hence the question of dimension and weight of an aluminum ion is ambiguous unless one specifies whether it pertains to the hy-drated or the unhydrated ion.   Similarly, the density of the unhydrated ion is of the order of 10 g./cc., whereas that of the hydrated ion is an average of about 10 for the anhydrous ion and of about 1 for the water of hydration, or about 1.2 g./cc.

Related phenomena involving tightly bound water are fre-quently faced in the study of colloids, where a particle may be covered with a layer of water of about molecular thickness and very tightly held.   Often, however, one encounters much larger amounts of water of hydration which are held much less tightly.   In fact, this water may be simply entrapped mechanically within the particles.   Thus an aggregate of primary particles will often, as shown in Fig. 2-8, have crevices and cavities that can be occupied by water.   This water is not bound to the par-ticles by any appreciable forces yet is mechanically entrapped so that it will move along with the aggregate.   If we now measure the outside dimensions of the aggregate, we will be measuring the sum of the volumes occupied by the primary particles and

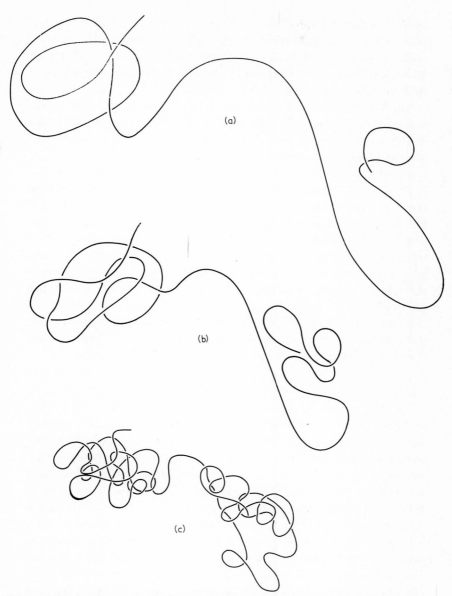

Figure 2-13. Random coils of same length and same general configuration, but of increasing tightness and decreasing freedom of drainage from *a* to *c*.

by this water.   Hence the particle will appear to be hydrated and the extent of hydration may even be very large.

The voluminous flocculent precipitates of hydroxides which we all remember from analytical chemistry are typical examples of structures heavily hydrated by entrapment.

Similarly, a random coil formed by a flexible string-of-beads molecule will entrap within its involutions amounts of solvent which may be very large.   How firm the entrapment of this solvent is depends on how long the chain and on how tightly it is coiled.

Figure 2-13 shows different degrees of tightness for coils of the same total length and same general configuration.   It can be easily seen that a loose coil, especially if it is also short, will not entrain much solvent.   We may then speak of a "free draining," weakly solvated coil.   If the chain is tightly coiled, and especially if it is also long, it becomes "nondraining"; the solvent is firmly entrapped and follows the movements of the particle.   Most real long-chain molecules will, of course, be intermediate in their properties and correspondingly more difficult to treat;   they can at least be given a simple name: "partially draining."

Summary

Among the most useful models for colloidal particles are spheres, ellipsoids, disks, rods, laths, and flexible coils—especially random coils.   The particles may be primary or they may be aggregates.   If they interact strongly with the solvent, and especially if they entrap it, their hydration becomes important. Polydisperse systems can be characterized by their distribution among more or less well defined fractions or by average characteristics.   Depending on whether the averaging is done according to the number of particles or according to their weight, number-averages or weight-averages such as M_n or M_w are obtained.   These values can be very different for polydisperse systems but coincide for monodisperse ones.

References

1. P. L. Kirk, *Quantitative Ultramicroanalysis*, John Wiley & Sons, Inc., New York, 1950, Chap. 4.
2. E. K. Fischer, *Colloidal Dispersions*, John Wiley & Sons, Inc., New York, 1950, pp. 7–15; or S. Singer, *J. Polymer Sci.*, **1,** 445 (1946).

Problems

(Answers to all problems are on p. 439)

10. If a cube is subdivided into 1000 cubes, the surface of each smaller cube is _____ times smaller.
21. The total surface of the subdivided material in problem 10 is _____ times larger.
5. The weight of a particle of gold (ρ = 19.3) having a radius of 10 A. is _____ g.
15. The particle weight of the particle of problem 5 is _____.
25. The degree of aggregation of gold atoms in the particles of problem 5 is about _____.
18. A system is formed by equal numbers of spheres whose radii are in the ratio $1:2:3$. Assuming that the M of the smallest sphere is 100, the M_n of the system is _____.
7. The M_w of the system in problem 18 is _____.
26. The average particle weight of a system is reported to be 100×10^3 as measured by light scattering (which gives the weight-average) and for the same system it is also reported to be 150×10^3 as measured by osmotic pressure (which gives the number-average). This leads to the conclusion that (*1*) the most likely particle weight is about 125,000, (*2*) the system is monodisperse, (*3*) the system is polydisperse, or (*4*) something is wrong with the reports.
30. If three solutions have equal numbers of particles per unit volume but their weight concentrations are in the ratio of $1:4:16$, then one can calculate the ratio of (*1*) radii, (*2*) M_n, (*3*) M_w of the particles.
36. The quantities which can be calculated according to problem 30 for the three systems are in the ratio (*1*) $1:4:16$, (*2*) $16:4:1$, (*3*) $64:8:1$, or (*4*) $4:2:1$.
28. *A* and *B* are monodisperse systems of spheres having the same weight concentration. M_n of *A* is twice that of *B*. The ratio of

the total surface in A compared to that in B is therefore (1) 2, (2) 1.414, (3) 1.126, (4) 1, (5) 0.794, (6) 0.707, (7) 0.5 if we assume that the spheres have equal density.

22. If the different parts of a particle (such as the aluminum ion discussed in Section 2-10) have volumes v_i, density ρ_i, masses m_i, particle weights M_i, then the average density of the particle is not given by (1) $\Sigma \rho_i m_i / \Sigma m_i$, ($2$) $\Sigma \rho_i v_i / \Sigma v_i$, ($3$) $\Sigma M_i / \mathbf{N} \Sigma v_i$, ($4$) $\Sigma m_i / \Sigma v_i$.

CHAPTER III
Sedimentation Rate

Having given a general description of the particles themselves, we shall now consider colloidal particles when dispersed in water. In the present chapter we shall concentrate on their behavior when the gravitational force is the only important one. Under its influence our system of colloidal particles in water will finally assume a state which is not very interesting: all the particles are tightly squashed into a thin layer at the bottom (or on top) of the pure solvent. However, if we begin with a uniform distribution of particles throughout the liquid, this final state will be reached gradually because of the viscosity of the water. It is the mechanism of this gradual change that is interesting, and we shall examine it particularly to see what information we can obtain about the nature of the particles. In order to proceed, we shall have to spend some time on the general laws of motion of particles in viscous liquids. These will be used often in the future and will therefore be presented in some detail.

3-1. Water

We are all so familiar with water that only a few properties and the effect of temperature on each need be recalled. The latter are shown graphically in Fig. 3-1.

Although the density of water varies with temperature, the effect is small around room temperature, amounting to $0.1\%/4\,°C$. Similarly, pressure has little effect on the density, which varies about $0.1\%/20$ atm. The density at room temperature is also within 0.4% of unity, so that for most computation it can safely be taken as 1.

The viscosity of water on the other hand, varies much more

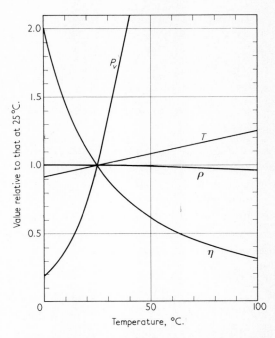

Figure 3-1. The relative changes in the density ρ, absolute temperature T, viscosity η, and the vapor pressure P_v of water between 0°C. and 100°C.

with temperature. At room temperature the change amounts to about 2.1%/°C. It is over 3% at 0 °C. and decreases to half that value at the boiling point. As a result, the viscosity of water is halved between 0 and 25 °C. and halved again when 63 °C. is reached. It is worth remembering that at 20 °C. the viscosity of water is very close to 1/100th of a poise (that is the force, in dynes per square centimeter required to pull two large planes spaced 1 cm. apart with a velocity of 1 cm./sec.). The centipose, i.e., 0.01 poise, is therefore a customary unit in dealing with aqueous systems, and approximate calculations are greatly simplified if 20 °C. is taken as a standard temperature (this is within 2% of 300 °K.). For comparison, Table 3-1 shows the viscosity of a number of other fluids.

TABLE 3-1
The Viscosity of Some Fluids in Centipoises
(Room temperature (25°C.) unless noted)

Hydrogen	0.009
Hydrogen (liquid)	0.011
Air	0.018
Diethyl ether	0.22
Water	0.89
Ethylene glycol	14
Olive oil	67
Medium engine oil	ca. 350
Castor oil	680
Glycerol	950
Sulfur (200°C.)	21,500
Asphalts, pitches	10^4–10^8 +

3-2. Dispersions

The term "dispersion," which we have used already, is a very general one. An aqueous dispersion can be the simple solution of classical chemistry, as in the case of salt or sugar; it can also be formed by relatively large chunks of matter, as in milk or mud. In the latter case the term "suspension" is often used. In the intermediate realm of colloids both terms are often used: "solution" mainly when the particles are held together by covalent bonds, as for a polystyrene solution; and "suspension," when they are relatively large, as for a clay suspension, or when one wishes to emphasize their behavior as a separate phase.

But colloid chemistry frequently deals with systems of relatively small particles where the use of either solution or suspension may be inappropriate. For example, a solution of silver iodide is normally understood to contain only Ag^+ and I^- individual ions. Hence the term solution should not be applied to a very fine dispersion of crystals of silver iodide, despite the fact that this may have many of the properties generally associated with a solution. Instead, the term "colloidal solution" or briefly "sol" is generally used. In the same way we speak of a gold or sulfur sol to indicate a colloidal dispersion of these substances.   The term "hydrosol" is used to specify that the solvent is water, and "aerosol" to mean a colloidal dispersion in air or other gases.

When the particles are known to be liquid droplets, and especially when they are relatively large, we may speak of "emulsions."

3-3. The Driving Force

It is well known that in general there is some contraction or expansion during solution so that the density of dissolved particles is not exactly equal to the density of the solute.   For the sake of simplicity we shall neglect these effects and ascribe to the particles of solute their original density ρ_2.   If the solution or suspension is rather dilute, its density ρ will be close to that of the solvent ρ_1; in the case of water, close to 1.

In a gravitational field, the particle will be subject to the force of gravity and to the buoyant effect of the surrounding solution. Both are proportional to the volume, v, of the particle and to the local acceleration, $\mathbf{g}$ (about 980 cm./sec.^{2}, i.e., within 2% of 10^3 cm./sec.^{2}).   Gravity is also proportional to the density ρ_2 of the particle, and buoyancy to the density ρ of the solution. Hence the net resultant, which we may call the driving force f_d will be given by

$$f_d = v(\rho_2 - \rho)\mathbf{g} \qquad (3\text{-}3.1)$$

This can be rewritten

$$f_d = v\rho_2(1 - \rho/\rho_2)\mathbf{g} \qquad (3\text{-}3.2)$$

and since $v\rho_2$ is the mass m of the particle, we can also write

$$f_d = m(1 - \rho/\rho_2)\mathbf{g} \qquad (3\text{-}3.3)$$

In case of a spherical particle, the volume v can be expressed in terms of the radius r since $v = (^4/_3)\pi r^3 \approx 4.2r^3$ so that

$$f_d = (^4/_3)\pi r^3(\rho_2 - \rho)\mathbf{g} \qquad (3\text{-}3.4)$$

The force thus calculated is given in dynes (a dyne is roughly the force exerted by a 1-mg. weight) and is seen to change very rapidly with the radius of the particle.   If r doubles, f_d increases eight-fold.   Since it increases with the difference between ρ_2 and ρ, this driving force is very sensitive to both densities when their difference is small but not when it becomes large.   Depending on whether the particle is denser or less dense than the solution, the driving force will be exerted downwards or upwards;   the particle will tend to "sediment" or to "cream." If the two densities are equal, there will be no net force exerted on the particle.   For simplicity, we will speak only of sedimenting particles.

Let us now consider the effect of hydration.   The molecules of water attached to the particle of course add to its weight. However, they are also buoyed by the surrounding liquid. Since the density of the solution is substantially that of the water, the two effects cancel and hydration has no appreciable effect on the driving force f_d.

3-4. Terminal Velocity

Under the influence of the driving force, the particle will accelerate according to Newton's law and begin moving through the liquid with a finite velocity.   This causes the appearance of a new factor, the resistance of the liquid.   Let us summarize this resistance by a force f_r, applied to the particle and counteracting f_d.   Hence, as soon as the particle begins moving, it becomes subject to a smaller net force.   In fact, the resistance increases with the velocity, so that the faster the particle moves the less the net force acting upon it and the less its acceleration. Finally, the particle reaches a velocity, the "terminal velocity," at which the two forces just balance

$$f_d = -f_r \qquad (3\text{-}4.1)$$

and there is no further acceleration.

This statement is a simplification, for in principle the two forces can never become equal and there should always be a residual acceleration.   For small particles, however, this residual acceleration becomes negligible in a surprisingly short time, so that the terminal velocity is reached almost instantaneously. The last column of Table 3-2 compares the radius of the particle to the calculated distance in which it would approach the terminal velocity within 1% after starting from rest.   For colloidal particles, the distance is so small as to be meaningless. We need therefore concern ourselves only with terminal velocities and not with accelerations.

3-5. Forms of Flow

The distinction between the "quiet" flow of a slow stream and the turbulence of a fast one is very familiar.   It is also of fundamental importance in hydrodynamics, where the former is called laminar flow and the latter turbulent flow.   In the former, the flow follows smooth paths or streamlines, whereas in the latter the flow is unsteady and leads to the formation of many irregular and shifting vortices.   Whenever it occurs, turbulent flow causes a higher resistance than would be calculated for laminar flow. At sufficiently low speed, the flow is always laminar, and it is turbulent at sufficiently high ones.   In addition, small size, high viscosity, and low density of the liquid favor laminar flow.   These variables are generally summarized in the so-called Reynolds number of the system $\Re = lu\rho/\eta$, where l is a characteristic dimension of the system (such as the radius of a sphere), u the velocity, ρ the density of the liquid, and η its viscosity.   Flow is generally laminar for $\Re$ less than about 2000.   (These ideas are developed in books on fluid flow, such as that given in reference 1.)

In our considerations, the velocities will be so small and the size of the particles so minute that the flow will be always laminar.

3-6. Motion of Solids

The motion of a solid, for example of a sphere, through a liquid can be looked upon from two different points of view: one is that of an observer attached to the solid, to whom the liquid seems to move by in streamlines roughly paralleling the outlines of the

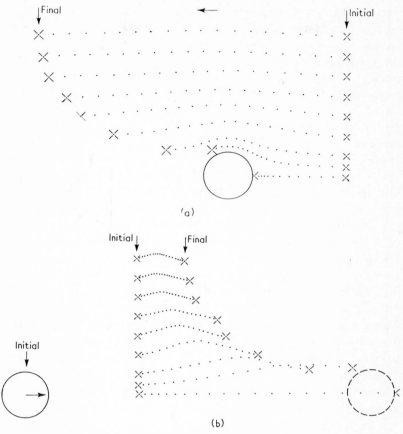

Figure 3-2. The flow of a liquid with respect to a sphere, as seen from the point of view of the sphere in (a) and from the point of view of the liquid at infinity in (b). The initial and final positions of selected particles of the liquid are indicated by crosses. Each dot corresponds to its position after an equal time interval. Note that the same particles and the same positions are represented in both parts of the figure.

solid as shown in Fig. 3-2a; the other is that of an observer stationary with respect to the liquid, who sees particles of liquid having to get out of the way of the solid and then returning to rest, as indicated in Fig. 3-2b. Hence particles of the liquid have to be accelerated and decelerated continuously while the solid moves at a uniform velocity. The work expended in moving the solid is all finally transformed into heat by friction due to the unequal speed of neighboring streamlines. Some of that work, however, is first transformed into kinetic energy of the accelerated liquid, and as such becomes proportional to the square of the velocity u of the solid. To dissipate this energy proportional to u^2, the shape of the streamlines has to change with the velocity and gradually leads to the formation of vortices at higher speeds.

For other shapes the situation is more complicated, of course, but part of the resistance encountered will, like all viscous resistance, increase directly with the velocity, and, in addition, the part due to kinetic energy will increase with the square of the velocity. We can therefore write quite generally, leaving open the possibility of still higher terms:

$$-f_r = \varphi u + \varphi' u^2 + \ldots \tag{3-6.1}$$

where φ and φ' are constants. Because the last term depends on u^2, it must become negligibly small compared to φu, provided that u is taken small enough. The same must be true of any higher terms. Fortunately, the motion of colloidal particles is always slow enough for this condition to prevail, and for our purposes we can simplify the preceding equation to

$$-f_r = \varphi u \tag{3-6.2}$$

It is customary to call φ the "friction factor" of the particle in a given solution.

Under these conditions of very low velocity, f_r is therefore due only to viscous forces, and we may call it the viscous resistance. The expression obtained for it in Eq. 3-6.2 is very simple, but it is also useless unless we have means of estimating the value of the friction factor φ. We shall therefore discuss this evaluation next.

3-7. Stokes' Law

Principles of hydrodynamics permit one to set up the exact equations describing the motion of a solid, such as a sphere, in a viscous liquid, but even in the simplest cases exact solution of these equations presents unsurmountable difficulties and only approximate solutions have been obtained.   The most important approximations have been introduced in the last century by the English physicist G. G. Stokes: namely, that the liquid extends indefinitely and that the motion is slow enough to neglect terms in u^2.   Under these conditions Stokes solved the basic equation for a sphere by a rather lengthy calculation (which may be found in advanced physics texts[2]) and obtained the remarkably simple result that

$$\varphi_{(sphere)} = 6\pi\eta r \quad \text{or} \quad -f_{r(sphere)} = 6\pi\eta r u \qquad (3\text{-}7.1)$$

Because of the simplification introduced in the derivation, this equation holds strictly only at extremely slow motions and should be corrected by terms in higher power of u, which become gradually more important as u increases.   Estimates[3] of these terms as well as experimental evaluations indicate that the error is less than 1% up to Reynolds numbers of about 0.1.   This is a value which colloidal particles do not exceed normally.

The limitation that the liquid should extend to infinity as compared to the dimensions of the sphere means that Stokes' law is strictly valid only in very dilute solutions.

Another limitation of Stokes' law stems from the general assumption of hydrodynamics that the liquid is continuous, whereas we know that in fact it is an assembly of discrete molecules. This limitation becomes important only when the discontinuity of the liquid is on a scale comparable to that of the sphere.   The numerical coefficient then decreases from 6 in Stokes' expression to 4 as the medium becomes completely discontinuous, as does a gas at low pressure.   For colloidal particles, which are always large compared to the discontinuities of water, this limitation is not important, but it becomes so for small molecules and ions.

Liquid spheres such as droplets of an emulsion, because of

their ability to flow internally, encounter somewhat smaller resistance than solid spheres of same radius,[3] but the difference can be generally neglected.

Thus Stokes' law is a simple limiting law from which deviations are to be expected for most real situations.   These deviations need not be important, however, and we shall neglect them both now and later when dealing with diffusion and with electrophoresis.

3-8. Other Shapes

Since Stokes' time, solutions have been obtained under the same approximations for a few other shapes, such as the ellipsoids, but the expressions[4] are far from simple and of course differ greatly, depending on the orientation of the ellipsoid with respect to the direction of motion.   An interesting by-product of these calculations is that, contrary to intuitive expectation, there is no torque on these bodies at sufficiently low velocities no matter what their orientation.   Hence, no orientation is made preferred by the flow itself.[3]   The small particles with which we are concerned can be expected to change orientation continuously under the influence of accidental disturbances and of thermal motion, so that the resistance they encounter may simply be averaged over all possible orientations and a single value of φ assigned even to unsymmetrical shapes.[4]

When φ cannot be calculated exactly, one has to depend on empirical determinations.

An important general result of a study of friction factors for nonspherical particles is that for solids of same total volume (and hence same mass if they have the same density), the friction factor is the smallest for spheres and increases with the dissymmetry of the shape.   In other words, although the resistance can be reduced in one direction by elongating the shape, this leads to a much greater increase in other directions so that after averaging there is always a net increase in resistance.

3-9. Hydration

Stokes' law deals with the sphere which moves through the liquid and cares nothing about how this sphere was formed. Hence, to the extent that the water of hydration is entrained by the particle, it is part of the sphere whose radius should be used in Stokes' law.   In general, the friction factor φ always refers to the hydrated particle.

3-10. The Frictional Ratio

The unhydrated particle, being smaller, will of course have a smaller friction factor than the hydrated one, and the unhydrated sphere will have the smallest friction factor of all possible particles containing the same amount of "dry" material.   This is given the symbol φ_0, and the so-called frictional ratio φ/φ_0, of the real friction factor to this ideal one, is often used as measure of dissymmetry and hydration.   Although φ/φ_0 of unity corresponds to a spherical and unhydrated particle, any increase above unity may be caused either by hydration or by dissymmetry or by both, and unless other information is available no decision as to the actual state of the particle can be made.   On the other hand, if the shape and hydration of the particle is given or assumed, one can compute the φ/φ_0 ratio.   This has been done by J. L. Oncley[5] for a wide range of conditions and is summarized in Fig. 3-3.   This graph shows by inspection the axial ratios and hydrations of ellipsoids which are compatible with a given frictional ratio.

3-11. Motion in a Gravitational Field

Having arrived at the value of the driving force of gravity f_d and at the viscous resistance f_r, we can now calculate the terminal velocity at which these two are equal and opposite, i.e. according to eqs. 3-3.1 and 3-6.2.

$$v(\rho_2 - \rho)\mathbf{g} = \varphi u \qquad (3\text{-}11.1)$$

or in terms of mass rather than volume, according to eq. 3-3.3

$$m(1 - \rho/\rho_2)\mathbf{g} = \varphi u \qquad\qquad (3\text{-}11.2)$$

This general relation is not very useful because v, m, and φ depend upon the size, and φ also on the shape, of the particle.   In case

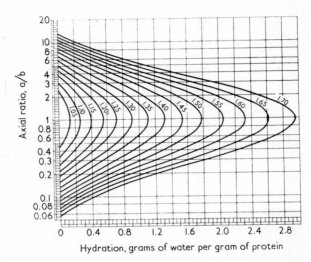

Figure 3-3. The relation between shape, hydration, and the frictional ratio for ellipsoidal proteins.   The contours correspond to the indicated frictional ratio, φ/φ_0, and delineate the combinations of hydration and axial ratio which can account for it.   (*From J. L. Oncley in E. J. Cohn and J. T. Edsall, Proteins, Amino Acids and Peptides, Reinhold Publishing Co., New York, 1943.*)

of a sphere we can write, however, according to eqs. 3-3.4 and 3-7.1

$$(4/3)\pi r^3(\rho_2 - \rho)\mathbf{g} = 6\pi\eta r u \qquad\qquad (3\text{-}11.3)$$

which gives

$$u = (2/9)r^2(\rho_2 - \rho)\mathbf{g}/\eta \qquad\qquad (3\text{-}11.4)$$

and

$$r = [(9/2)\eta u/(\rho_2 - \rho)\mathbf{g}]^{1/2} \qquad\qquad (3\text{-}11.5)$$

These are much used relations.   In the so-called falling ball viscometers (Fig. 12-3), they serve to determine the viscosity from the measured rate of fall of a sphere of known density and radius. They can be used to determine very precisely small differences in density of spheres and are thus used on small droplets of water to determine their deuterium content.[6] For us the main application of these relations will be in the determination of the radius of a sphere of known density from the measured rate of fall in water whose density and viscosity are known.

3-12. Behavior of Dispersions

The above discussion deals with the behavior of individual particles which is frequently important, especially when the particle is at the upper end of the colloidal range or above it. Millikan's oil drop experiment which led to the determination of the electronic charge is probably the most noteworthy work of this

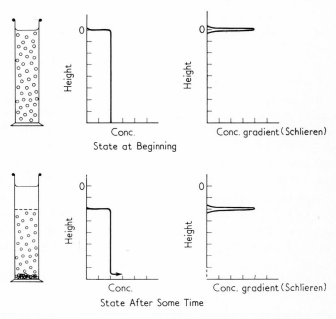

Figure 3-4. Three schematic representations of the sedimentation of a monodisperse system. Note that the concentration below the boundary remains constant.

kind.   When the particles are smaller, however, it is generally
impractical to observe their individual motion, and the collective
behavior becomes important.   We will consider it now, first for
monodisperse systems then for polydisperse ones.

If we begin with a uniform monodisperse suspension or solution
in a cylinder (Fig. 3-4) and allow the particles to settle, each
particle will settle at exactly the same rate since there is no reason
for one to behave differently from another.   The velocity of
each and all is given by the equations of the preceding section.
After a while, all particles which were originally at the upper
surface will have sedimented a certain distance, leaving a clear
solution above them.   Concurrently, all particles which were
originally this same distance above the bottom will have come to
rest there.   All particles which were originally below these will
have suffered the same fate earlier.   Thus, an upper boundary
and a lower boundary are established for the particles, but
between these boundaries their concentration remains completely
unchanged, since particles which have left any intermediate
level are replaced by others descending into it.   The net effect
is that of a falling curtain of particles.

Although this type of behavior is very simple, we shall represent it in several ways which will soon prove very useful.   Figure
3-4 shows the "before and after" state of the dispersion (i) as a
schematic drawing, (ii) as a plot of concentrations versus height
such as could be obtained by measuring the color or the refractive index of the system along different levels, and (iii) as a plot
of the slope of the previous graph or the concentration gradient
versus height.   This last type of plot is obtained directly if the
system is viewed by means of an assembly of lenses and slits which
we shall discuss later (Chapter 18) and which is called generally
a "schlieren" method of observation.

3-13. The Flux

The rate of settling of particles of a dispersion can be measured
either in terms of their velocity (which, as we have seen, is the
velocity of each and also that of the upper boundary), or in terms

of the amount crossing any given level and in particular reaching the bottom. This amount will of course be proportional to the cross section of the cylinder and to the time. If we eliminate these two trivial variables by considering the amount traversing unit cross section in unit time, we obtained the so-called flux. This is a quantity we shall be using several times in discussing the transport of solute and we shall generally indicate it by J. The flux can be measured in terms of macroscopic quantities such as grams or moles (per cm.²-sec.), or microscopic quantities such as the number of particles (per cm.²-sec.). If we wish to emphasize the use of the latter units we can denote the flux by j.

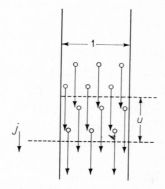

Figure 3-5. The meaning of flux. A unit cross-section is traversed in unit time by all the particles originally within a distance equal to the velocity with which they are approaching it.

As shown in Figure 3-5, the flux is simply the product of the velocity u of the particles (or of the boundary) and of the concentration, since all material within a cylinder of unit cross section and a height equal to the distance covered in unit time, i.e., u, will cross the base of the cylinder. This gives

$$J = u\mathfrak{C} \qquad (3\text{-}13.1)$$

which holds true as long as $\mathfrak{C}$ denotes the amount of solute per unit volume of solution. The units of J must correspond to those of $\mathfrak{C}$.   Thus if we measure the concentration by $\mathfrak{W}$, the weight of solute per unit volume

$$J = u\mathfrak{W} \tag{3-13.2}$$

will give us the flux in the same weight units.   If we measure the concentration by $\mathfrak{n}$, the number of particles per unit volume

$$j = u\mathfrak{n} \tag{3-13.3}$$

will give us the flux in the number of such particles.

Since a boundary corresponds to an abrupt change of concentration, it will also correspond to a sudden change in flux. Hence measurement of flux can give us knowledge of the velocity if the concentration is known, and measurements of changes in flux a knowledge of the boundaries.

3-14. Polydisperse Systems

If we now look at a dilute dispersion of spheres of two sizes, each fraction will behave independently of the other, and the effect is that of two curtains dropping at different rates.   Hence two upper boundaries will be formed, one between the clear liquid and the finer particles, the other between the finer ones and the mixture of the two.   The corresponding graphical presentations are given in Fig. 3-6.   It may be noted that the gradient (schlieren) plot shows a separate peak for each fraction, and that the areas under the peaks measure the amounts of each fraction.

In a sedimenting system of two kinds of particles, the total flux is the sum of the fluxes of each kind.   This total flux changes abruptly at each boundary by an amount determined by the concentration and velocity of one of the fractions.

As the number of fractions increases, so does the number of boundaries.   As the difference between neighboring fractions becomes smaller, so does the separation of their boundaries. Soon one obtains a smooth gradation corresponding to the line of Fig. 2-12.   The flux changes correspondingly in a smooth manner.   Since the individual boundaries can no longer be distinguished, their velocities cannot be determined and in-

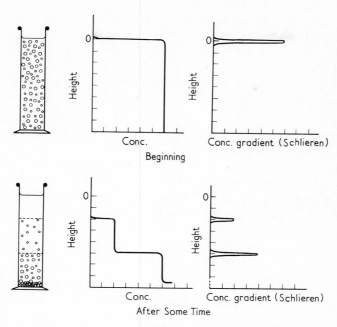

Figure 3-6. Three representations of the sedimentation of a system formed by particles of two sizes.   Note that below the boundaries the concentration is constant.

terpreted.   However, measurements of the flux and of its changes with time can still be made and can be interpreted in terms of the distribution of particle sizes.

3-15. Experimental Methods

Thus in the experimental study of sedimentation rates, the purpose is to obtain information either about the rate of motion of boundaries or about the flux and its changes.   There are many experimental methods available.[7]   The choice depends on convenience, on the properties of the particular system, and on the precision and accuracy desired.   Some of the principles involved are outlined below.

A complete picture of the concentration or of the concentration

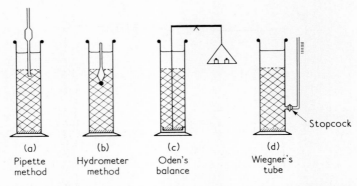

Figure 3-7. The principle of four sedimentation-rate methods of determining particle size distribution in coarse suspensions.

Figure 3-8. An Andreasen pipette.   The sampling tube is rigidly connected to the sedimentation vessel.   The measuring bulb at the top is filled and emptied through the three-way stopcock.   (*Courtesy of Fisher Scientific Company, Pittsburgh, Pa.*)

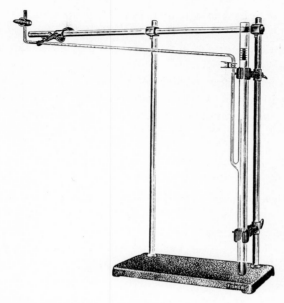

Figure 3-9. An apparatus for the Wiegner method. The long, almost horizontal capillary facilitates measurements of small level differences.   (*Courtesy of
Fisher Scientific Company, Pittsburgh, Pa.*)

gradient in a sedimenting system can be obtained periodically
by visual observation or by light absorption methods or by the
schlieren method.   These give essentially the kind of information
shown in Figs. 3-4 and 3-6 (see also Fig. 18-9).

One can also note how concentration changes with time at a
given level by measuring this concentration periodically.   This
can be done by observing changes in a narrow beam of light,
or by withdrawing periodically with a pipette (the Andreasen
pipette) a small sample of the solution from this level (Figs.
3-7a and 3-8), or by observing the indications of a hydrometer
which is inserted periodically into the system and whose bulb is
near the desired level (Fig. 3-7b).

The flux itself can be measured by intercepting it at the desired
level with the pan of a balance (the Oden balance) which col-

lects and weighs the sedimenting material (Fig. 3-7c).   This method, however, almost always leads to a disturbance of the normal settling pattern by the rise of the clear liquid formed below the pan.   A better, though less precise, method is to measure the average density of the liquid above the plane by balancing it against a column of clear solvent;   as sedimentation proceeds, the balancing column decreases slightly in height. This, the so-called Wiegner method, is shown in Figs. 3-7d and 3-9.

3-16. Frontal and Zonal Analysis

As a mixture of two fractions sediments, the fractions become separated—up to a point.   As may be seen in Fig. 3-6, a portion of the slower fraction becomes completely free of the faster one, but the faster one never becomes disentangled from the slower. Thus, by allowing the sedimentation to proceed until the coarse particles have all reached the bottom and then pouring off the supernatant, one could obtain a suspension of the finer particles alone.   The sediment would contain all the coarser ones mixed with that portion of the finer ones which has also settled.   By repeating the process a large number of times on the sediment, one could finally reach an almost complete separation.   If an intermediate fraction were present, part of it could become completely free of the fastest, but not of the slowest, in one operation.

This separation of fractions as they settle is quite useful for analytical purposes when we wish to learn about the existence of the fractions and perhaps about their amounts.   It is a special case of a quite general method, the so-called frontal analysis, where successive fractions appear (or disappear) one after the other in addition to all the preceding ones, and only a part of the first (or the last) one is free of the others.

Another very general class of method is the so-called zonal analysis, in which each fraction appears separated from the preceding and from the following ones.   This permits the preparation of individual fractions and a more precise estimate of their individual amounts or properties.   Zonal methods can be used in sedimentation experiments, and we will also encounter them later, along with frontal methods, in connection with electrophoresis and chromatography.

3-17. Zonal Methods

If a thin layer of a dispersion of two fractions is deposited on top of a high column of solvent, again each fraction will move through the solvent like a curtain, but now as a very short curtain whose

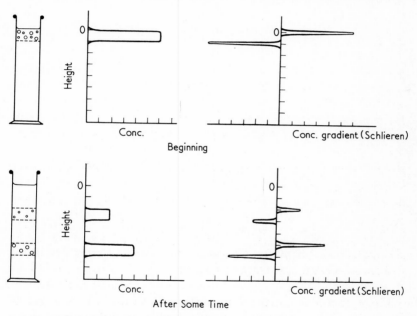

Figure 3-10. Three representations of the sedimentation of a suspension of particles of two sizes, deposited as a thin layer on top of a column of solvent (zonal method).

length is determined by the height of the original layer.   In other words, there will be two narrow layers of particles each keeping its height and each moving with a different velocity.   Before long, therefore, the layer of larger particles will completely outrun that of the smaller ones, and an increasing layer of clear solvent will appear between them as shown in Fig. 3-10. The two fractions are now segregated, and their sedimentation rates and amounts may be determined, for example, by measuring the height or weight of the deposit as each arrives at the bottom. The fractions can be also separated, e.g., by means of an appropriate slide at the bottom.

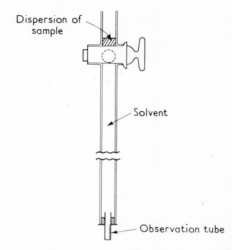

Figure 3-11. A simple apparatus for zonal sedimentation. By turning the stopcock, the sample is allowed to sediment through the column of solvent. The volume of the sediment is measured as a function of time. (*After D. Werner, Trans. Farad. Soc.*, **21**, *381* (*1925*).)

These methods have an important limitation; the layer of suspension, being denser, is not in stable equilibrium above a layer of solvent; hence there is always a tendency for bulk flow of this whole layer to the bottom of the column. This effect can be minimized if the dispersion is very dilute so that the difference in density is slight, if the particles are not too small so that sedimentation is rapid, and if the container is narrow so that the bulk flow is slow. Figure 3-11 shows a simple apparatus using this approach, and several commercial instruments are also available (Fig. 3-12).

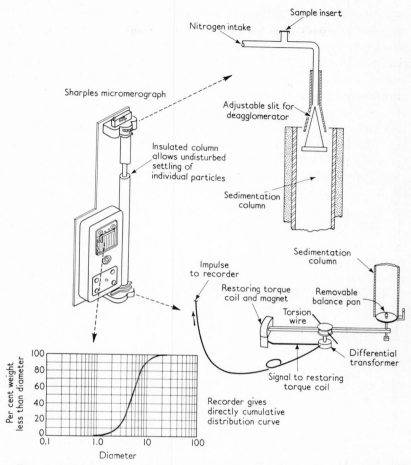

Figure 3-12. A commercial instrument for the zonal sedimentation rate analysis of particle size distribution, the Sharpless Micromerograph. The sample is injected through a deagglomerator at the top of a column of air through which it settles onto the pan of a recording balance. (*Based on material courtesy of the Sharpless Corporation, Bridgeport, Pa.*)

3-18. Density Gradient Methods

A complete stabilization of the column used in a zonal method is possible if the clear solvent is given a density gradient which is greater than that produced by the suspension.   Graded mixtures of brine and water or of water and alcohol have been used for this purpose, and temperature gradients (such as used in continuous cloud chambers[8]) could presumably also be utilized.

A somewhat related and very valuable group of methods uses a continuous gradient of densities bracketing that of the particle. Hence, there is within the gradient one level at which there is no driving force on the particle—here it comes to rest.   When it is above the level it tends to sediment; when it is below, it tends to cream.   One application of this method is to separate particles which differ in density, since they come to rest at different levels.[9]   If the gradient is made very small, a large separation of levels can correspond to very small differences in density. Another application lies in the determination of the density of particles—and of larger objects as well—from the level they assume in a known density gradient.   The method can be made sensitive enough to determine small differences in isotopic composition of droplets of water[10] or other particles.

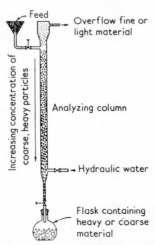

Figure 3-13. Elutriation.   Water flowing upwards through the analyzing column entrains the particles having a lower sedimentation velocity into the overflow, while the remainder settles to the bottom.   (*From G. G. Brown, Unit Operations, John Wiley and Sons, N. Y., 1950.*)

3-19. Elutriation

Another method of zonal analysis is so-called elutriation. Here the solvent is made to flow upward at a rate which is intermediate between the terminal velocities of the two fractions. Hence the faster one will sediment downwards, while the slower

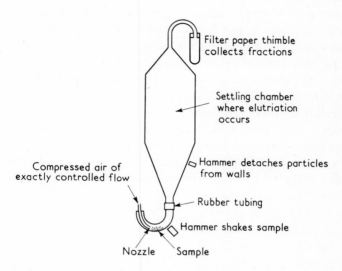

Figure 3-14. The principle of the Roller Analyzer. (*Adapted from T. S. Roller, Proc. A.S.T.M. (1932), p. 607.*)

one will be carried upwards and may be collected from the overflow (Fig. 3-13). Here again the question of density differences and stability, as well as that of uniform velocity of the solvent, enter as a limitation, but the method is otherwise very useful. Figure 3-14 shows the principle of the so-called Roller Analyser in which an air stream elutriates fine fractions from a violently agitated sample. Successive fractions may be collected and weighed. Their size is controlled by the speed of the air stream and the cross section of the settling chamber.

3-20. Meaning of the Results

We can now determine the sedimentation velocity in a gravitational field and even separate fractions according to it. With the aid of Stokes' law, this velocity can be translated into a radius according to Eq. 3-11.5. The question then arises as to the meaning of this radius.

In the first place, the measurement of the rate of sedimentation does not by itself give us any information as to the shape of the particle. Hence if we apply Stokes' law, we shall obtain an equivalent spherical radius which may be only vaguely related to the actual dimensions of the particles.

Secondly, the measurement pertains to the particles actually present in the solution. These may, of course, be aggregates rather than primary particles.

Thirdly, derivation of Eq. 3-11.5 assumed that the same radius is used in estimating the driving force and the viscous resistance so that they may cancel each other when these are equated (Eq. 3-11.3). For this assumption to be correct, all quantities, especially the density, must pertain to the hydrated particle, and this requires a knowledge of its hydration. In the absence of such information one generally assumes zero hydration, but this may lead to grossly erroneous radii.

However, if the unhydrated particle weight is known from other work (and we will study several ways of obtaining it), then terminal velocity gives us, according to Eq. 3-11.2, a method of determining the friction factor φ and hence the friction ratio φ/φ_0, which then provides information about the shape and hydration. Conversely, if φ is known from other work (particularly diffusion measurements), the terminal velocity gives us the driving force and hence m and φ_0.

3-21. Orders of Magnitude

Let us now consider basic Eq. 3-11.4

$$u = (2/9)r^2(\rho_2 - \rho)\mathbf{g}/\eta$$

from a more quantitative point of view. The velocity is inversely proportional to the viscosity, which varies but little in

TABLE 3-2

Rate of Fall in Water of Spheres of Varying Radii and Constant Density of 2^a as Calculated by Stokes' Law[b]

Radius			Terminal velocity, u						Reynolds number	Distance[c] radii
mm.	μ	A	cm./sec.	cm./min.	cm./hr.	cm./day	cm./year	cm./century		
10	10^4	10^8	(2.2×10^4)						2×10^6	(4×10^6)
1	1000	10^7	(220)						2000	(4000)
0.1	100	10^6	(2.2)						2	(4)
0.01	10	10^5	2.2×10^{-2}	1.3					2×10^{-3}	4×10^{-3}
10^{-3}	1	10^4	2.2×10^{-4}	0.013	0.8	19			2×10^{-6}	(4×10^{-6})
10^{-4}	0.1	10^3	2.2×10^{-6}	1.3×10^{-4}	8×10^{-3}	19×10^{-2}	70		2×10^{-9}	( )
10^{-5}	0.01	100	2.2×10^{-8}	1.3×10^{-6}	8×10^{-5}	19×10^{-4}	0.7	70	2×10^{-12}	( )
10^{-6}	10^{-3}	10	2.2×10^{-10}	1.3×10^{-8}	8×10^{-7}	19×10^{-6}	7×10^{-3}	0.7	2×10^{-15}	( )
10^{-7}	10^{-4}	1	(2.2×10^{-12})					(7×10^{-3})	2×10^{-18}	

[a] To apply to other conditions, multiply the u value by the pertinent density difference and divide it by the pertinent viscosity in centipoises.

[b] Values in parentheses are calculated by Stokes' law under conditions where this law is not applicable.

[c] The distance traveled before terminal velocity is reached within 1%.

the case of water but could be changed a great deal by using air or an oil.   The rate of motion is proportional to the difference of density, which in the case of water cannot be less than -1 for a gas bubble nor more than 21.5 for osmium.   It can, however, be zero or close to it for many organic compounds.   For simplicity, since adjustment to other systems is readily made, let us continue with a density difference of 1, which would be the case of sulfur.

Table 3-2 shows velocities calculated for spheres of different radii having a density of 2 in water at 20 °C.   Since doubling the radius quadruples the velocity, the range of speeds is very extended.   For particles that are visible to the naked eye (above about 0.1 mm.) the velocities calculated by Stokes' law are meaningless because of the high Reynolds numbers.   Below this range, Stokes' law may, however, be safely applied until solvent discontinuities introduce uncertainties below 10 A. The rate of sedimentation also becomes too large for convenient measurement when the particles become visible.   Then it decreases rapidly, becoming inconveniently slow (less than 1 cm./hr.) as the upper range of colloidal dimensions (10^4 A.) is reached.   Finally, the rates of sedimentation become ridiculously slow, with times in centuries, as molecular dimensions are approached.

Thus our previous discussion of sedimentation rates may seem pertinent only in the realm of particles which are small but much above colloidal dimensions.   Indeed, as far as actual determination of particle size and fractionation is concerned, gravitational sedimentation rate methods are used almost exclusively in the "subsieve" range of particles, passing the finest practical sieves (200 mesh $=$ 0.07 mm., 300 mesh $=$ 0.05 mm.) yet above the colloidal range limit of about 0.001 mm. $= 10^4$ A.   This type of work is of particular importance in the study of soils, pigments, cements, powdered metals, etc.   On the other hand, application of these same principles to colloidal particles becomes very fruitful once the special problems involved in extremely slow sedimentation rates are understood and means of accelerating these rates are devised.

3-22. Convection Currents and Stability

Thus far we have thought of the solvent as a stationary medium through which the particles move downward.   Only in elutriation was our attention called to the fact that motion of the liquid can greatly influence this pattern, and that when the flow of liquid becomes fast enough sedimentation can be completely prevented.

Under ordinary laboratory conditions, water in a bottle or cylinder appears to be immobile, any temporary disturbances being rapidly quenched by viscous resistance.   Viscous forces are, however, proportional to the velocity of flow and inversely proportional to the width of the moving layers.   Hence, when we consider rates of flow comparable to the extremely slow sedimentation of colloids, we are dealing with currents which are not easily visible and which will be quenched only very slowly in this type of apparatus.   Yet this is also the type of current which is being continually generated by temperature differences (and the corresponding density differences) between the sides and the center of the container as room temperature varies.

The disturbing effect of these thermal convection currents has been often overlooked and has led to many erroneous statements in the past, yet the only reason why colloids, particularly the denser and coarser ones, do not show any sedimentation under ordinary conditions is that convection currents keep them uniformly distributed.

In order to overcome the effect of convection currents one must either greatly reduce the cross section of the sedimentation liquid or carefully control its temperature.   We will return soon to this type of apparatus (Section 7-6), but we can note now that elaborate thermostating and thermal lagging of relatively large cells[11] or only good insulation of capillary tubing,[12] have been shown to cause sedimentation of colloids which otherwise stay uniformly dispersed.   These experiments, although important in demonstrating the principle involved, are seldom performed because of the long time required to obtain results and of the difficulty of completely eliminating the sources of error.   They have shown, conclusively, however, that, as far as sedimentation is concerned, the stability of colloids is primarily due to thermal convection currents.   Later we will examine the contribution made by thermal motion and also other aspects of stability.

The only practical way to use sedimentation rate methods for colloids is to increase the rate of sedimentation by increasing the driving force.   This is done by subjecting the system to centrifugal force in a centrifuge, instead of the gravitational force of the earth.

3-23. Centrifugation

It is well known that centrifugal force, like gravity, is proportional to the mass, but the coefficient instead of being g is $x\omega^2$ where x is the distance from the center of rotation, and ω, the rate of rotation in *radians* per second, is $2\pi = 6.28$ times the revolutions per second or 0.105 times the revolutions per minute. Hence the acceleration is no longer constant throughout the system but varies with the distance from the center.   As we shall see, the actual distance from top to bottom of the sedimenting column is generally small compared to the distance from the center, so that the variation is small and we can simplify the problem by considering only the average acceleration in the system.   Under these conditions everything we have said about gravitational behavior applies to centrifugation, except that g is replaced by the much larger $x\omega^2$.   Further simplification is introduced by the customary expression of $x\omega^2$ as a multiple of g.   Thus we speak of the number of g's which a centrifuge can create.

3-24. Ultracentrifuges

Centrifuges are used for many purposes both in industrial production and in the laboratory.   The main types are the preparative ones, used to separate a sediment from the supernatant liquid, and the analytical ones, used for sedimentation rate determinations.   We shall later discuss those used for sedimentation equilibrium measurements.   The last two types,

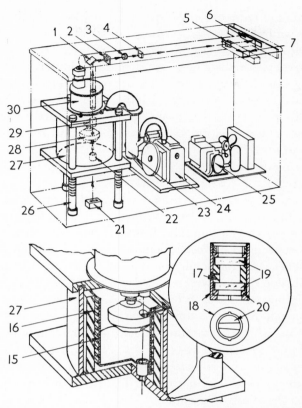

Figure 3-15. The structure of an ultracentrifuge. Above: overall view showing refrigerating compressor *25;* high vacuum pumps *23, 24;* motor and gear
train *30;* rotor *28* in vacuum chamber *27;* optical system from lamp *21* via
mirror *1* to photographic plate *6* with visual observation at *7.* Below: detail
of rotor in refrigerated (*15*) and armor protected (*16*) vacuum chamber. Insert shows cross-section and top view of cell which is placed in rotor. Quartz
windows *19* and centerpiece *17* are compressed in housing *18.* Note the sector
shaped space which holds the solution under study. (*Courtesy Spinco Division,
Beckman Instruments, Palo Alto, Calif.*)

in which disturbing convection currents and vibrations are
carefully eliminated, are generally called ultracentrifuges to
distinguish them from other types of centrifuges which do not
satisfy these requirements.

An average student centrifuge as used in qualitative analysis develops about 1000 **g**. Other laboratory and commercial centrifuges operating in air develop up to about 25,000 **g**, but air resistance then becomes a limiting factor. Very small centrifuges spun in air may reach up to a million **g**'s, and large ones spun in vacuum reach several hundred thousands **g**'s.[13] The limiting factor in the latter case is the ultimate strength of the rotor. Tiny steel balls, 0.25 mm. in radius, have been spun in vacuum until they exploded at some 600,000 r.p.s. corresponding to fields of 400,000,000 **g**'s at the periphery.[14] In the past, several types of analytical ultracentrifuges and of methods of observation were important,[15] and in the future others may rise to prominence. At present there is only one type which is widely used—the commercial instrument manufactured by the Spinco (Specialized Instruments Co.) division of Beckman Instruments, and the schlieren method is the main one used for sedimentation rate studies.

The Spinco, as shown in Figs. 3-15, is composed essentially of a driving mechanism, a rotor holding the cell which contains the system studied, a thermostated vacuum chamber within which it spins, and an optical system for schlieren (or absorption) observation. The cell is formed by a sector shaped trough some 8 mm. deep, closed at both ends by quartz windows through which observations are made. The whole is held securely in a cylindrical barrel fitting into a hole in the rotor some 7 cm. from the center. The rotor is suspended and driven by a thin steel wire and is surrounded by an armored steel safety shield. This wire enters the chamber through a vacuum-tight oil gland and is connected on the outside to an ingenious gear train capable of increasing the 12,000 r.p.m. of an electric motor to 60,000 r.p.m.[16] The rotor spins around its own center of gravity, and the wire bends slightly if this does not correspond to the geometrical center. Any vibrations of the rotor are transmitted by the wire to the gear train and motor and are damped out by their mountings.

A good ultracentrifuge, with its elimination of convection

currents and its tremendous increase in driving force, lowers the limit of applicability of sedimentation rate methods to the smallest colloids, provided that the density difference is reasonable. By layering pure solvent over the solution during centrifugation so as to obtain a very sharp "synthetic" boundary, sedimentation rates could be determined even for sugars.[17]

3-25. Centrifugal Comminuters

A machine whose description properly belongs at this point is the so-called colloid mill.   It is a comminuting instrument used for reducing the size of emulsion droplets and for the break-

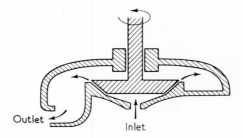

Outlet

Inlet

Figure 3-16. Principle of one form of colloid mill.   Comminution and centrifugation occur simultaneously in the slit between the stator and the rotor.

ing up of aggregates by subjecting them to the high shearing force of a liquid.   In this respect it is similar to a homogenizer. In the latter, however, the shear is produced by forcing the liquid through a narrow slit by high pressures, whereas in the colloid mill the shear is produced by the rotation of one surface of a radial slit through which the liquid flows (Fig. 3-16).   Thus in addition to the shear there is also produced a centrifugal field, and, with particles which are less dense than the liquid, the radial flow of liquid serves to elutriate the smaller particles in the rotating gap until they become small enough to be entrained.   The effect of the mill is therefore greatest when the liquid has a low viscosity and the comminuted material a low density.

Another machine operating on essentially the same principle

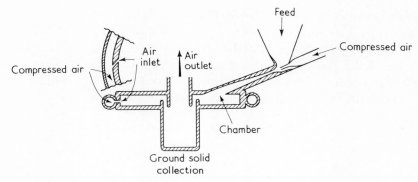

Figure 3-17. Principle of the "Micronizer" grinding machine. Compressed air from the annular conduit enters the main chamber through several oblique air inlets, thus imparting a rapid swirling motion to particles of the feed which become comminuted by impact against each other. The particles remain in the chamber until small enough to be entrained by the air into the enlarged outlet where they settle. (*From materials courtesy of the Sturtevant Mill Company, Boston, Mass.*)

is the Micronizer, in which a rotating air mass produces the grinding and centrifugal effects, and only sufficiently small particles are elutriated and discharged at the center (Fig. 3-17).

Summary

The rate of sedimentation of a particle is the result of a balance of two forces: (*1*) the driving one, dependent primarily on the mass of the unhydrated particle and the ratio of its density to that of the solvent, and (*2*) the viscous resistance proportional to the velocity and to the friction factor.   The latter depends on the size of the hydrated particle and the viscosity of the solvent. It is $6\pi\eta r$ for a sphere and increases with hydration and with dissymmetry.   Colloidal particles sediment normally at rates so low that minute convection currents are sufficient to keep them dispersed indefinitely. However, their sedimentation rates can be measured in ultracentrifuges, while a variety of related methods are available for the study of suspensions of larger particles.

References

1. H. Rouse, *Elementary Mechanics of Fluids*, John Wiley & Sons, Inc. New York, 1946, Chap. VI.
2. L. Page, *Introduction to Theoretical Physics*, D. Van Nostrand Co., Inc., New York, 1935, pp. 268–73.
3. G. Barr, *A Monograph of Viscometry*, Oxford University Press, London, 1931, Chap. VIII, also ref. 1, Fig. 125.
4. A. E. Alexander and P. Johnson, *Colloid Science*, Oxford University Press, London, 1949, pp. 259–61; also ref. 3.
5. J. L. Oncley, *Ann. N. Y. Acad. Sci.*, **41**, 121 (1941).
6. A. S. Keston, D. Rittenberg, and R. Schoenheimer, *J. Biol. Chem.*, **122**, 227 (1937–8).
7. R. D. Cadle, *Particle Size Determination*, Interscience Publishers, Inc., New York, 1955, Chap. VII, or American Society for Testing Materials, *Symposium on New Methods for Particle Size Determination in the Subsieve Range*, Philadelphia, Pa., 1941.
8. A. Langsdorf, *Ind. Eng. Chem.*, **44**, 1298 (1952); A. L. Kuehner, *J. Chem. Educ.*, **29**, 511 (1952); T. S. Needels and C. E. Nielsen, *Rev. Sci. Instr.*, **21**, 976 (1950): E. W. Cowan, *Rev. Sci. Instr.*, **21**, 991 (1950).
9. S. Tessler, N. T. Woodberry, and H. Mark, *J. Polymer Sci.*, **1**, 439 (1946); M. Meselson, F. W. Stahl, and J. Vinograd, *Proc. Natl. Acad. Sci.*, **43**, 581 (1957).
10. K. Linderstrom-Lang, O. Jacobsen, and G. Johansen, *Compt. rend. trav. lab. Carlsberg, Ser. chim.*, **23**, 17 (1938); also K. Linderstrom-Lang and H. Lanz, *Compt. rend trav. lab. Carlsberg, Ser. chim.*, **21**, 315 (1938); *Mikrochim. Acta*, **3**, 210 (1938).
11. N. Johnston and L. G. Howell, *Phys. Rev.*, **35**, 276 (1930); C. M. McDowell and F. L. Usher, *Proc. Roy. Soc. (London)*, **A138**, 133 (1932).
12. H. H. Paine, *S. African J. Sci.*, **35**, 170 (1938).
13. J. W. McBain, *Colloid Science*, D. C. Heath and Co., Boston, 1950, Chap. 16.
14. J. W. Beams, *Scientific Monthly*, **66**, 255 (1948).
15. T. Svedberg, and K. O. Pedersen, *The Ultracentrifuge*, The Clarendon Press, Oxford, 1940.
16. E. G. Pickels, *Machine Design*, **22**, 102 (Sept. 1950).
17. H. K. Schachman and W. F. Harrington, *J. Polymer Sci.*, **12**, 379 (1954).

Problems

23. The driving force f_d on a sedimenting particle does not change when only (1) the density of the liquid is decreased, (2) the shape of the particle is modified, (3) the system is transported to the moon, (4) the volume of the particle is reduced while its mass remains the same.

1. If a spherical particle falls in water with a terminal velocity of 1 cm./sec., one can be quite sure that a similar particle having a 10 times larger radius will fall with a terminal velocity of (1) 10 cm./sec.; (2) less than 100 cm./sec.; (3) 100 cm./sec.; (4) over 100 cm./sec.

35. If a represents a concentration versus height diagram, the corresponding schlieren pattern is _____.

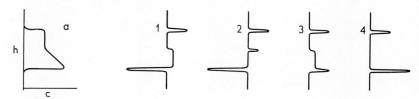

11. If the conventional scheme of qualitative inorganic analyses had to be classified as either (1) frontal or (2) zonal, it should be classified as _____.

13. A very dilute uniform dispersion contains spherical particles of same density having radii in the ratio of 1:2. It is allowed to settle, and as soon as all the larger particles have settled all the supernatant is separated. The per cent of smaller particles recovered in the supernatant is (1) 100, (2) 75, (3) 50, (4) 25, (5) none of these, (6) insufficient information.

31. If an originally uniform dispersion containing equal numbers of large and small particles is allowed to settle, the weight concentration versus height diagram after some time will have the approximate shape of _____.

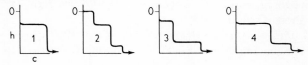

37. The terminal velocity in water of an oil droplet having a density 0.9 and a radius of 5×10^3 A. is of the order of 1 cm. per _____ sec.

40. Stokes' law is based on a number of approximations. The one which is least likely to hold for a sol is that (1) the fluid is continuous, (2) it extends indefinitely, (3) terms in u^2 can be neglected, (4) the terminal velocity has been reached.

34. Two particles sediment at the same velocity under the same conditions and are formed of the same material. A is a compact sphere and B is a random coil. Therefore the unhydrated weight of A is (compared to B) (1) equal, (2) larger, (3) smaller, (4) no way of telling.

27. A centrifuge rotating at 1.8×10^3 r.p.m. produces, at a point 10 cm. from center, a field which is higher than gravity by a factor of about (1) 3.2×10^6, (2) 3.8×10^5, (3) 3.2×10^3, (4) 9×10^2, (5) 3.8×10^2, (6) 9×10^{-1}, (7) nowhere near any of these.

 2. A spherical particle has a dry radius, when placed in water it swells to a hydrated radius. From its sedimentation rate in water and its dry density one computes an effective radius. One can be sure that the order of increasing radii is (1) dry, hydrated, effective; (2) dry, effective, hydrated; (3) effective, dry, hydrated; (4) effective, hydrated, dry; (5) hydrated, effective, dry; (6) depends on other factors.

CHAPTER IV

Some Aspects of Flocculation

In the previous chapter we saw that sedimentation of colloidal particles is so slow that it is normally prevented by small convection currents, whereas larger particles sediment quite rapidly. Yet, frequently, a colloidal system will sediment rapidly, either after a while or upon addition of small amounts of a salt. This proves that its particle size has increased, and it is said to have flocculated or coagulated. Sometimes a proper change in the solvent may reverse this effect, and we speak of deflocculation or peptization. In the present chapter we will consider briefly these phenomena, noting some of their manifestations, reviewing the underlying forces (again under conditions when these forces are the only ones that are important), and making some general observations about the rates and equilibria involved. We will return to the subject of flocculation later, especially in connection with protective action (Chapter 9), rheology (Chapter 13), and electrical interactions (Chapter 17).

4-1. Sedimentation Rate and Sedimentation Volume

Aggregation will generally cause a faster sedimentation rate because the driving force will increase proportionately to the number of particles in the aggregate, whereas the resistance will increase only with its radius and therefore with the cube root of the number of particles. Hence, if the system is partially flocculated before sedimentation, its behavior will indicate particles coarser than the primary ones. Therefore, when one wishes to study the primary particles, steps must be taken to insure deflocculation before the beginning of an experiment. Thorough mixing and agitation may sometimes be sufficient, but often the

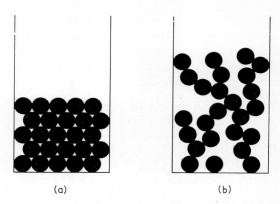

(a)   (b)

Figure 4-1. The sedimentation volume depends upon interparticle forces: (a) perfectly deflocculated particles can slip past each other and settle into a compact layer. (b) particles which stick on contact form a voluminous sediment. (*See also* M. J. Vold, *J. Colloid Sci.*, **14,** *168 (1959)*.)

use of mild grinding and the addition of "deflocculating agents" is required. These agents seldom serve to deflocculate but rather prevent immediate reflocculation after the aggregates have been broken up mechanically. Phosphates are thus often used in soil or clay studies. Of course, care must be taken not to break the primary particles by excessive mechanical treatment, and often the definition of primary particle becomes quite dependent on the grinding procedure.

If flocculation occurs during sedimentation, the interpretation based on the falling curtain concept breaks down, since the curtain now sheds faster moving layers as it is falling. Thus, for example, the flux of a solute across a plane, which is constant for monodisperse systems and can only decrease with time for polydisperse ones, may actually increase with time for a flocculating system.

In a system in which there is no tendency to flocculate, the particles as they approach the bottom of the vessel settle down next to each other, each seeking the lowest possible point and all together forming a compact layer, as indicated in Fig. 4-1a. The volume of this layer, or "sedimentation volume," will therefore be relatively small.   If, on the other hand, the particles tend to stick to each other as they come in contact, they will be stopped before they can find the lowest point, bridging will readily occur, and a loose, thick layer will be formed, as shown in Fig. 4-1b.   The sedimentation volume will be relatively large.

Sometimes a paradoxical behavior is observed, particularly with not very dilute systems.   Addition of a small amount of a flocculating agent causes obvious sedimentation but addition of a larger amount does not, unless the system is stirred after a while. The reason is that in the latter case the sedimentation volume is large enough to occupy the whole of the solution.   In other words, the particles form a continuous, very loose structure from bottom to top.   This structure is, however, easily broken up by stirring, which also forces the particles closer together so that they form compact flocs which then settle rapidly to a much smaller volume.

There are many practical examples of the importance of flocculation and of sedimentation volumes.   For example, the hardpan which forms upon settling and drying of deflocculated soil suspensions can be converted into agriculturally desirable loose, crumbly aggregates by the addition of small amounts of flocculating agents such as calcium salts.   In the very different system of pigmented paints, the primary particles are so large that they sediment readily even if completely deflocculated. Considerable flocculation which gives a loose, easily dispersed sediment is much more desirable than the compact and hard to disperse layer obtained when the particles do not readily stick to each other.

4-2. Equilibrium

Thus flocculation is a widespread and important phenomenon among colloids, yet it is still far from being fully understood. One of the great difficulties of reaching a clear picture lies in the problem of differentiating clearly between rate and equilibrium effects.   This problem is not peculiar to this field but becomes particularly troublesome here as we shall see.

An equilibrium system may be defined as one of least free energy or as one which undergoes no net spontaneous change. The two definitions are roughly equivalent but both require amplification in order to become unambiguous. As given, the definitions say nothing about the possible changes which are being considered. Thus let us consider a mixture of O_2 and H_2 gases at about room temperature. Their volume changes readily with pressure or temperature and, if the original concentration was not uniform, it will tend to equalize by diffusion. After some time at any temperature and pressure, the system will reach a state where its volume and concentration seem to suffer no further change and to correspond to least free energy. Should this be called an equilibrium state? We know that introduction of a catalyst at room temperature or a short heating to 500–600 °C. may cause the rapid change to a very different state, and there are good reasons to believe that even in the absence of any catalyst and at room temperature the formation of water proceeds, though at an imperceptible rate. In addition, there may be other changes such as nuclear ones, which may occur in this system under some conditions. Hence, there can be no useful statement whether the system is or is not at equilibrium until we specify with respect to what changes. Thus our system may be in equilibrium with respect to rapid temperature and pressure changes over a limited range and to other rapid changes, but not with respect to slow water formation, to water formation if a catalyst is introduced, or to exposure to high temperature.

4-3. Rate

A decision whether a system is in a state of equilibrium can only be based on a consideration of the alternative states that are permissible and of the rates of the processes involved. Schematic diagrams of the most important categories of rates are given in Fig. 4-2. As shown in this figure, the scale by which the rate has to be measured is the time during which the system can be observed in an experiment. If this time is long, rates may

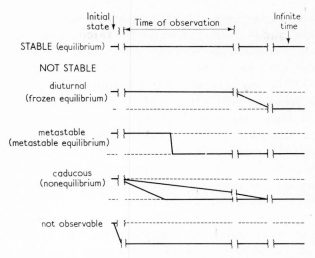

Figure 4-2. Rate phenomena determine the characteristics of systems which are not stable. A subdivision into diuturnal, metastable, caducous, and not observable is therefore useful.

become important which are too slow to affect a shorter experiment. If the change is completed before observation can begin, it becomes unobservable. Another important scale is given by the precision of the observations themselves. If this precision is high, it may render important a change which would escape cruder measurements of the same duration.

Thus there can be nothing absolute about our categories; they must be taken in the context of the experiment or observation on which they are based.

4-4. Diuturnity and Caducity

If the system is in true equilibrium (with respect to a given change) we call it stable. If not, it is not stable or unstable. A well known special category of the latter are the metastable systems whose rate of change is not perceptible but for which it is known that, once started, change continues at a rapid rate. As the $H_2 + O_2$ example shows, it is also particularly important to distinguish between unstable systems which change at an observable rate and those in which the rate escapes observation. The former are clearly not in equilibrium, the latter are in "frozen" equilibrium.   There seem to be no accepted adjectives to characterize these two cases and to differentiate them clearly.   Yet there are two seldom used words which have exactly the required scope: "diuturnal," meaning of long duration, and "caducous," signifying falling off, transitory.   We shall therefore avail ourselves of these for the purpose.

These distinctions between stable, metastable, diuturnal, and caducous are not always made nor are they always clear cut, but they must be kept in mind whenever discussing equilibrium and rate.   The difficulty of clear-cut differentiation may be illustrated by an emulsion of tiny droplets of supercooled tin.[1] As the tin solidifies, the volume of the system decreases.   Each droplet is in a metastable state while liquid, because once crystallization begins the complete transformation of this droplet is practically instantaneous.   Yet this crystallization begins randomly in each droplet and, because of their large number, it occurs almost continuously at some point or another of the system.   The total volume therefore decreases continuously as far as direct observation is concerned.   Hence we would say that the system as a whole is caducous, or if the rate is slow enough that it is diuturnal, although it consists of metastable droplets.

If we apply these considerations to colloids, the situation is sometimes perfectly clear, but at other times it is very obscure, even if we limit ourselves for the time being to the problem involving equilibrium with respect to the formation of larger particles, such as occurs in flocculation and precipitation.

4-5. Stable Colloids

There are colloidal systems which are clearly stable with respect to aggregation.   Among these are many association colloids such as soaps and detergents, e.g., sodium dodecyl (lauryl) sulfate (NaLS).   Thus crystals of NaLS when placed in water at room temperature dissolve copiously and freely to give a solution containing some simple LS^- ions, a considerable amount of Na^+ ions, and a major proportion of particles (the micelles) formed by some 60 LS^- ions and some 40 Na^+ ions.[2] Upon cooling or adding enough common Na^+ ions, the crystals reprecipitate, and for each temperature there is a definite concentration of NaLS which can exist in equilibrium with excess solid. The properties of the solution are constant and reach the same value within less than a few seconds[3] under a given set of conditions independently of the previous history of the sample, as long as chemical changes, such as formation of lauryl alcohol and sulfate ion, do not occur.

Other examples of stable colloids are given by many proteins, although here the ruggedness of the particle is much lower, and irreversible changes, known as denaturation, occur readily if the material is exposed to high temperatures, to air-water interfaces, extreme pH's, etc.[4]

Many natural and synthetic high polymers, such as rubber, polystyrene, and polymethyl methacrylate (plexiglass), dissolve in appropriate nonaqueous solvents to give solutions having properties independent of the previous history (i.e., showing no hysteresis) and from which the material may be recovered unchanged and the cycle repeated. The solubility behavior is here much more complicated because of two factors: (1) the usual polydispersity of the material which leads to fractionation in two phase equilibrium systems and (2) the great swelling of the saturating phase. Here too, since the particles are of the long, string-of-pearls type, their intertwining and entangling may slow down considerably the reaching of equilibrium.

4-6. Caducous Colloids

These are, of course, short lived systems since, by definition, they must flocculate or precipitate perceptibly during the period of observation. Any system to which a flocculating amount of an additive has been added will be unstable until it has flocculated and thus reached its new equilibrium state. In the common blood sedimentation test for the presence of infections, red blood corpuscles flocculate forming stacks, the so-called rouleaux, and even larger aggregates, which then sediment rapidly. The corpuscles themselves, although above colloidal dimensions, are small enough to make their rate of sedimentation extremely slow. Hence it is really the rate and extent of flocculation which is measured in this test on a caducous system.[5]

4-7. Metastable Colloids

A rather trivial case of the metastability of colloids is presented by supersaturated solutions of the stable ones. Thus, if a solution of NaLS is slowly cooled, crystals do not appear till several degrees below the saturation temperature and, once the first crystal has appeared, equilibrium is promptly reached.

No other cases of metastability of colloids seem to exist.

4-8. Diuturnal Colloids

In this class belong systems which flocculate so slowly that the change is imperceptible in the time considered yet have a lower free energy in the flocculated state. A simple example may be produced by any caducous system if observed for a short enough time. More interesting and much more difficult is, however, the case of systems which really do not show any change in experiments which can be practically performed. In order to decide whether such a system is stable or diuturnal, two main methods are available.

1. One approach is to produce the flocculated or precipitated state. If dispersion proceeds spontaneously, the disperse system is stable. This was the criterion we applied above to some stable systems. If dispersion does not occur spontaneously, the experiment is inconclusive because either the rate of dispersion may be too slow to be observed, or the system may now be stable and have no tendency to disperse. In this type of experiment the "spontaneity" of dispersion is of critical importance. Thus dispersion produced by agitation, however gentle, is not spontaneous although it may persist indefinitely—since the dispersed state may be diuturnal and show no reversion. In other words,

a test for the difference of free energy levels of the two states must avoid introducing into the system any energy which may supply this difference. Since in many colloids this difference is probably extremely small, even very mild mechanical treatment may cause errors.

2. The other approach is to introduce a true catalyst for the flocculation process so that it becomes rapid enough to be observed. For many diuturnal aqueous systems a trace of simple salt can be such a catalyst. One must make sure, of course, that what is supposed to be a catalyst does not alter the system sufficiently to shift the equilibrium from one state to the other, and if no such catalyst is found the question remains unanswered.

Later when we study electrical effects, and particularly the flocculating effect of electrolytes in Chapter 17, we will have a better basis for applying these thoughts to particular cases, but we shall now consider only a relatively simple and clear-cut case.

Carbon black is formed by minute particles of soot obtained under controlled conditions of incomplete combustion of hydrocarbons. Since there are many kinds of carbon black, the behavior to be described[6] may not be general but applies to some of them at least.

When placed in water, carbon black forms poorly wetted clumps. Under very vigorous agitation, such as obtained in a blender operating at high speed, it forms a highly dispersed and intensely black suspension. If left alone, this suspension remains essentially unchanged for days and shows no settling. Gentle agitation with a stirring rod, however, causes a rapid decrease in color intensity, formation of visible flocks, and settling. If the original vigorous agitation is then applied, the intensely black persistent suspension is re-formed and the process may be repeated many times.

Since there seems to be no conceivable way in which mechanical agitation could make particles stick together if they have no tendency to do so, whereas it is obvious that agitation can tear apart particles that tend to stick together, the above behavior shows that the highly disperse suspension is diuturnal while the flocculated state is stable.   Gentle agitation serves to bring together the individual particles and gives them a chance to flocculate.   Vigorous agitation on the other hand tears the flocks apart and transforms the system into a diuturnal one.

4-9. Reversibility and Revertibility

The carbon black system discussed above shows a relatively easy change from a well dispersed to a flocculated state and vice versa.   There are other systems, for example red colloidal gold, which cannot be redispersed in any simple way once they have been flocculated.   These different behaviors are quite generally called reversible and irreversible flocculations.   "Reversible" and "irreversible" are words, however, which have a very definite and widely accepted meaning in thermodynamics, referring to processes which proceed (or not) in either direction upon an infinitesimal change of conditions, i.e., in which entropy does not (or does) increase.   The so-called reversible colloidal phenomena, on the other hand, generally require large changes of conditions to revert to the original state and hence involve considerable increases of entropy.   It might therefore be wiser to call them "revertible and "irrevertible" instead.   The terms "flocculation" and "coagulation" are generally used interchangeably, but if a distinction is to be made flocculation refers to revertible processes and coagulation to irrevertible ones.

4-10. Reasons for Stability

The above discussion of stability and its lack was concerned with the question of how a given system can be classified and not with what makes it stable or not.   If we knew the answer to the latter question, however, we might be able to predict, and control stability and flocculation.   The problem is essentially very similar to that of solubility in classical chemistry and involves the question: Why do some particles prefer to stick to similar ones while others prefer to intermingle?

If two gases form a gaseous solution, they are always completely miscible.   This is because thermal agitation tends to

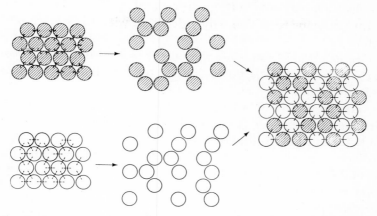

Figure 4-3. In going from pure solute and solvent (left) to a solution (right) some solute-solute and solvent-solvent bonds must be broken and some solute-solvent bonds must be formed, as indicated.

disperse each throughout the space available, and any forces between the particles are small. In condensed phases, however, there must always be strong forces acting between particles to keep them condensed and prevent them from vaporizing. During solution or dispersion, as shown in Fig. 4-3, these forces between similar particles of *both* solute and solvent have to be overcome, while forces between dissimilar particles enter into effect. If the latter are much larger than the former, solution is favored, whereas in the opposite case it will be hindered, leading to insolubility, precipitation, or flocculation, as the case may be. If the effect of these forces just cancels, the particles behave as if they were in the gaseous state, intermingling freely and forming what we call ideal solutions. Thus it is the nature of interparticle forces which determines the stability of dispersions and should be considered in some detail.

4-11. Interparticle Forces

The principal forces between particles can be broadly classified into coulombic and van der Waals'. The former are due to net electric charges of both particles, and, as is well known, may be attractive or repulsive; they decrease with the square of the distance.

Van der Waals' forces, on the other hand, although also based on electric interactions, do not involve two net charges, are always attractive, and decrease more rapidly with distance. They are due to the interaction of dipoles which may be either the permanent dipoles of polar particles or the induced dipoles of nonpolar but polarizable ones.

When a dipole interacts with an ion, one of its ends is attracted and the other repelled. The force is greater on the end closer to the ion. As a result, the attracted end tends to stay closer to the ion and the repelled one further away, so that the net result is an attraction. In an extreme case, such as the hydration of a small ion, the dipole may become immobilized in this position. If we assume this extreme position, we can calculate how the force decreases with distance. Let us take all charges equal to unity and call a the distance between the ion and the nearest charge, and b that between the charges of the dipole. The force between the two particles is then

$$F = 1/a^2 - 1/(a + b)^2 = (2ab + b^2)/(a^4 + 2a^3b + a^2b^2)$$
$$= [2b + (b^2/a)]/(a^3 + 2a^2b + ab^2) \approx 2b/a^3 \quad (4\text{-}11.1)$$

The last approximation assumes that b is small and that it is small compared to a. Thus, the force resulting from an ion-dipole interaction decreases, roughly, with the cube of the distance.

Two dipoles will interact somewhat similarly, attracting when the opposite ends are closer and repelling when the similar ones are closer. Thus, again, the attracting position is favored, a net attraction results, and it decreases rapidly with distance.

A nonpolar particle is composed of positive and negative parts, nuclei and electrons, which become slightly displaced with respect to each other when in an electric field, so that a dipole is produced which is always in an attracting position. Its magnitude will depend on the ease of displacement of the charges (i.e., the polarizability of the molecule) and on the applied field.   Hence, the magnitude of the induced dipole will decrease rapidly with distance, and the attractive force decreases even more rapidly.

The electric field inducing a dipole in a nonpolar particle may be due to an ion, or to a permanent dipole, or even to any accidental slight displacement of charges in another nonpolar particle.   This last effect is sometimes said to lead to London forces, named after Fritz London who first computed their magnitude using the quantum theory and showed that they decrease with the seventh power of the distance.[7]

There are two other types of forces which we can neglect at present: one is gravitational forces, which are negligibly small between particles of colloidal dimensions; the other is the force due to exchange of electrons between atoms, or covalent bonding, which is a force of extremely short range exerted really within a particle rather than between particles.

The quantitative application of these considerations to any individual system, particularly a colloidal one, is seldom if ever possible at present, but their qualitative aspects give considerable insight into many phenomena.

4-12. Lyophilic and Lyophobic Colloids

The terms "lyophilic," or solvent loving, and "lyophobic," or solvent fearing, and "hydrophilic" and "hydrophobic" when referring to water are frequently used to describe the tendency of a surface, particle, or functional group to become wetted, to combine or intermingle with the solvent.   With respect to colloidal systems, stable colloids are always classed as lyophilic, a term sometimes extended to the easily revertible ones.   The irrevertible ones are always classed as lyophobic, and this term is sometimes extended to all the diuturnal ones and to those that are readily flocculated by small amounts of electrolytes.

Roughly speaking, the separation into lyophilic and lyophobic corresponds to that into stable and unstable colloids, but different authors give it slightly different meaning.   Since, as we have seen, stability depends not only on the love between particle and solvent molecules, this application to colloids while very widespread is not so clearly understandable as it is to surfaces and groups.

4-13. Reasons for Irrevertibility

Not much seems to be known about the interesting subject of irrevertibility, and the following presents only some general considerations. When two particles stick together during flocculation, one might perhaps expect them to lose their identity and coalesce into a new single particle of the material. This may occur sometimes with liquid or semiliquid particles, as in the clean "breaking" of some emulsions, but is rarely if ever encountered otherwise. One reason is that the surface of the particle may be quite different from its bulk, and upon flocculation only the outer layers may touch and stick to each other while still separating the two bulks. A more important reason is that solid particles are rigid and hence touch only at points unless they possess flat faces, and their crystal structures are unlikely to fit smoothly together unless flocculation occurs in special alignment. Hence, the floc formed by their aggregation is generally weak and can be broken up into the original particles with a minimum of effort, so that the system is revertible.

The loose, initial contact may be transformed into a firm one with time, if the particles can sinter or recrystallize, thus gradually coalescing. Because of the minute size of the particles, these processes, which we generally consider to be negligibly slow, may become quite important.

Another reason for easy revertibility is encountered in association colloids, where the transition from massive solid to micelle occurs, presumably, by way of the small particles such as the Na^+ and LS^- ions of NaLS, which behave like any small particle of classical chemistry.

4-14. Reasons for Diuturnity

As we have seen, for a system which is diuturnal with respect to flocculation, the flocculated state is the stable one but the rate

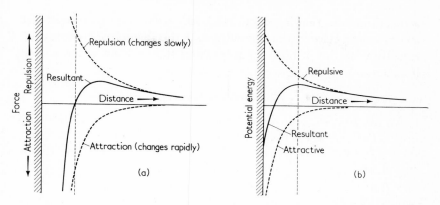

Figure 4-4. The effect of interparticle distance upon (a) the forces acting between particles in a diuturnal system, (b) the resulting potential energy of the particles. Note that at the distance indicated by the vertical dashed line the attractive and the repulsive forces are equal, so that the resultant force is zero and the potential energy passes through a maximum. Note also that the potential energies change less rapidly with distance than the corresponding forces.

of flocculation is negligibly slow. Stability of the flocculated state implies that there are net attractive forces between the particles when close together. Slowness of flocculation means that the particles do not often get close enough together for these forces to become effective.

This differentiates the diuturnal system from the caducous one and involves two factors. One is the rate of motion of the particles. This is primarily due to thermal agitation and, as we shall shortley see, would by itself cause frequent collisions except for extremely dilute systems or very large particles. In the latter case hydrodynamic forces of stirring, convection, etc. can become important. Since these rates of motion are all the same whether a system is stable, caducous, or diuturnal, they cannot be responsible for diuturnity. The other factor, and this is the important one, is that there may be net attractive forces acting when the particles are close together, but net repulsive forces acting when they are further apart, as shown by the solid line in Fig. 4-4a. Such a change from repulsion to attraction can readily occur if both attractive and repulsive forces exist between the particles, but the former decrease more rapidly with the distance of separation than do the latter. This is also shown in the figure by the dotted lines.

4-15. Potential Energy

An alternative, and often more significant, presentation of the interaction between two particles may be obtained by plotting their potential energy instead of their relative forces, as shown in Fig. 4-4b. The superiority of this second plot stems from the fact that the magnitude of a force, which can be read directly from the upper part of the figure, is not sufficient alone to explain its effects. The distance over which this force extends and especially the total work which it can perform must also be considered, since the real question is whether energy is gained in moving the particle from one position to another. In the potential energy graph, the height above the zero level measures the amount of work required to bring the particle to that point from infinity, and therefore the work of shifting the position is represented directly by the difference of corresponding levels, as shown in the lower part of the figure. One can note that the maximum of potential energy corresponds to the point where no net force is exerted on the particle and that work can be gained by moving the particle to either side of this hump.

Figure 4-5 shows several typical potential energy curves for different types of systems. If the particles are to tend to stick together rather than to separate spontaneously, i.e., for the system to be unstable, there must be a trough below the zero level of potential energy when the interparticle distance is small. Furthermore, this trough must be deep enough to resist the effects of thermal agitation. If the particles are to be able to get close enough together for this trough to become effective, i.e., for the system to be caducous, they have to be able to get over any hump in potential energy which lies between. Hence the height of this hump—the activation energy—cannot be too large compared to thermal agitation or whatever else drives the particles

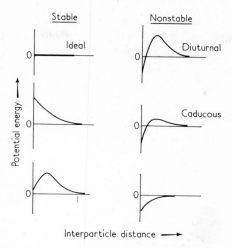

Figure 4-5. Typical potential energy diagrams for colloidal dispersions. It is the potential energy upon close approach which determined the stability or nonstability of the system. The presence and height of the hump determine the rate at which equilibrium is attained. Changes in potential energy become important as they become commensurate with kT.

towards each other. If the hump is too high to be overcome, the system is diuturnal.

Thus the question of whether a dispersion is stable or not depends on the existence and absolute depth of the trough, whereas for an unstable one it is the height of the hump that determines whether it is diuturnal or caducous.

4-16. The Repulsive Forces

The behavior of a system, as far as flocculation is concerned, depends therefore on the balance between attractive and repulsive forces. We have already seen that the attractive forces are mainly van der Waals', but we have not yet looked into the reason for the repulsion between colloidal particles. At this point we can only briefly assign its principal cause to a combination of coulombic and thermal agitation effects. It is due mainly to the presence of a layer of ions held close to each particle by electrostatic attraction yet prevented by thermal agitation from sticking to it.   When two particles approach each other, these layers must be pushed out of the way, and this requires energy. An understanding of this behavior thus requires some knowledge of the effect of both electric forces and, again, of thermal agitation.   We will therefore return to it in Chapter 17 after first discussing thermal agitation in several manifestations and then electrical effects in general.

Summary

Equilibrium and stability should always be considered in the light of the alternative states and of the rates of reaching them. Depending on rate, an unstable system may be caducous, meta-stable, or diuturnal.   Colloidal dispersions which do not floc-culate may be stable with respect to flocculation if the particles have no tendency to stick together, and they may be diuturnal if long range repulsive forces prevent stronger attractive forces of shorter range from becoming effective.   Attractive forces may be coulombic or van der Waals', which include the London forces decreasing with the seventh power of the distance.

References

1. G. M. Pound and V. K. LaMer, *J. Am. Chem. Soc.*, **74,** 2323 (1952).
2. D. Stigter and K. J. Mysels, *J. Phys. Chem.*, **59,** 45 (1955).   K. J. Mysels and L. H. Princen, *J. Phys. Chem.* **63** (1959).
3. P. Mukerjee and K. J. Mysels, *J. Am. Chem. Soc.*, **77,** 2937 (1955).
4. F. W. Putnam, in *The Proteins*, H. Neurath and K. Bailey, eds., Academic Press, Inc., New York, 1953, Vol. IB, Chap. 9.
5. R. Fåhreus, *Acta Med. Scand.*, **55,** 1 (1921), especially pp. 95–105 and 51–53;   or, sketchily, M. M. Wintrobe, *Clinical Hematology*, Lea & Febiger, Philadelphia, Pa., 1946, p. 228.
6. I. Reich and R. D. Vold, *Abstracts of Papers, 130th Meeting of the American Chemical Society, September 1956;* I. Reich, Ph.D. Dissertation, University of Southern California, Los Angeles 1956.
7. R. Eisenchitz and F. London, *Z. Physik*, **60,** 491 (1930); F. London, *Z. Physik*, **63,** 245 (1930);   B. V. Derjaguin, I. I. Abrikosova, and E. M. Lifshitz, *Quart. Revs.* (*London*), **10,** 295 (1956).

Problems

2. Two sols of the same material are both monodisperse and have the same particle weight but different sedimentation velocities, A sedimenting faster than B. This could be due to (*1*) a higher viscosity of the solvent in A, (*2*) flocculation occurring in B, (*3*) the particles being more symmetrical in A, (*4*) hydration being more pronounced in A.

20. The AgCl obtained in a well-conducted gravimetric determination of chloride is (*1*) irrevertibly flocculated, (*2*) stable with respect to growth of larger crystals, (*3*) well deflocculated, (*4*) unstable when dispersed in the beaker for washing.

12. Two magnetic compasses are to be placed with their centers along the periphery of a fixed horizontal circle. How should they be located so that the force between them is minimized?

16. How should the two compasses in problem 12 be located so that their indication is most correct?

39. A maximum on a force-distance diagram corresponds on a potential energy diagram to a (*1*) maximum, (*2*) minimum, (*3*) zero, (*4*) inflection.

CHAPTER V

Diffusion and Brownian Motion

The existence of thermal motion is a basic postulate of the kinetic-molecular theory and is amply supported by all that we learn in physics and classical chemistry. It provides the driving force spreading a gas spontaneously throughout its container and tends to equalize spontaneously the concentration throughout any one-phase system. Thus it manifests itself by diffusion when we consider macroscopic amounts of materials. When the behavior of a single particle is considered, thermal motion gives it a velocity which decreases as its mass increases, so that at any temperature (and in the absence of force fields) the kinetic energy is the same for all particles. If we measure the average velocity u along a given direction, it is given by $mu^2 = \mathbf{k}T$ where $\mathbf{k}$, the Boltzmann constant, is equal to $\mathbf{R}/\mathbf{N}$, the gas constant per molecule. Though having this average velocity, the individual particle must very frequently change direction and velocity because of collisions with other particles and with the walls of the vessel. Hence each particle pursues an indescribably complicated and irregular zig-zag path whose nature is determined entirely by the random collisions. When the particles become large enough to be microscopically perceptible, we speak of their motion as Brownian motion in memory of the botanist who first observed it.

These two manifestations of thermal agitation, diffusion at the macroscopic level and Brownian motion at the particle level, must be intimately interrelated and must both depend on the nature of the particle. In this chapter we shall therefore consider the effects of thermal motion alone, as reflected in diffusion, in Brownian motion, and in their interpretation.

5-1. Fick's First Law

In its simplest form, diffusion manifests itself in a dilute solution of uniform cross section A, whose concentration $\mathfrak{C}$ varies only along a direction x perpendicular to that cross section. At any point x there is therefore a concentration gradient $\partial\mathfrak{C}/\partial x$. As time passes, the concentration becomes more uniform, due to diffusion. This means that some of the solute moves from the region of higher concentration to that of lower, and furthermore that the concentration, at least in some parts of the system, changes with time.

A quantitative formulation of what happens in diffusion may therefore deal either with the quantity Q of solute which crosses a given cross section (this is the so-called permeation) or with the change of concentration with time, i.e., $\partial\mathfrak{C}/\partial t$, at a given point. We shall begin with the former aspect.

The solute will move in the direction of decreasing concentration so that the permeation Q will be positive when $\partial\mathfrak{C}/\partial x$ is negative. One may also confidently expect that Q will be proportional to the cross section A, since any part of it is identical with any other part, and also that it will be proportional to the time t as long as other factors remain the same, since there is no reason for its rate to change under this restriction. Thus we are brought again to the concept of transport through unit cross section in unit time, i.e., to the flux J. We can write

$$Q = AJt \tag{5-1.1}$$

and then concern ourselves only with what causes variations of J. Since there is no flux when the concentration gradient is zero, one would expect J to increase with $-\partial\mathfrak{C}/\partial x$. In fact, it is found experimentally that the two are directly proportional for any system under constant conditions. By introducing a proportionality constant D, which is called the diffusion coefficient, we can write

$$J = -D\partial\mathfrak{C}/\partial x \tag{5-1.2}$$

and by combining it with the previous equation we obtain for the permeation

$$Q = -DA(\partial \mathfrak{C}/\partial x)t \qquad (5\text{-}1.3)$$

This is called Fick's[1] first law. D is a constant independent of the gradient but affected by most other changes of the system. Its variation with concentration is generally definite but rather slight, and for the sake of simplicity we will neglect it. This is particularly justified when we deal with highly dilute solutions. D is also affected by temperature and pressure and by the solvent, for which we shall shortly consider the reasons. It is especially dependent on the solute and thus gives us a way of learning something about its nature.

Fick's first law gives us a way to determine the permeation or the flux through any cross section if we know the value of $\mathfrak{C}$ throughout the system. It can also serve as a basis for estimating how the system changes with time as a result of this flux.

5-2. Fick's Second Law

The concentration within a small volume can change with time only as the result of a net flow of solute into or out of it. This net difference will generally be the result of a difference between the inflow and the outflow. Let us consider, for example, a small region limited by unit cross sections, separated by a small distance dx, and perpendicular to the direction of the flux. The volume is therefore also dx.

The flux throughout this region and its neighborhood will not in general be constant but will change and have a gradient $\partial J/\partial x$. Hence the flux through the two limiting cross sections of our region will differ. If J corresponds to one, $J + (\partial J/\partial x)dx$ will correspond to the other. During a very short time (during which $\partial J/\partial x$ does not change appreciably), the amount flowing into the region will be Jdt, and the amount leaving, $[J + (\partial J/\partial x)dx]dt$. Hence the net increase in the amount of solute contained in the region will be the difference, $-(\partial J/\partial x)dx\,dt$.

To obtain corresponding change $d(\mathfrak{C})$ in concentration we must divide this amount by the volume, dx, which gives

$$d\mathfrak{C} = -(\partial J/\partial x)dt \qquad (5\text{-}2.1)$$

This change of concentration is also given, however, by the rate at which the concentration changes and the time involved, i.e., by $(\partial\mathfrak{C}/\partial t)dt$. By equating these two expressions for $d\mathfrak{C}$ and cancelling the dt factor in both we obtain

$$\partial\mathfrak{C}/\partial t = -\partial J/\partial x \qquad (5\text{-}2.2)$$

In other words, the concentration changes with time as the flux changes with distance at any given point.   We have already seen how the flux is related to the diffusion coefficient and the concentration gradient by Eq. 5-1.2. Differentiating both sides of this equation we obtain $\partial J/\partial x = -\partial(D\partial\mathfrak{C}/\partial x)/\partial x$ or, if D is constant as we have assumed,

$$\partial J/\partial x = -D\partial^2\mathfrak{C}/\partial x^2 \qquad (5\text{-}2.3)$$

Combining with the previous equation gives

$$\partial\mathfrak{C}/\partial t = D\partial^2\mathfrak{C}/\partial x^2 \qquad (5\text{-}2.4)$$

This is known as Fick's second law and gives us a way to determine the rate of change of concentration if we know its values throughout the system at any moment.

5-3. Simple Cases

To illustrate the meaning of Fick's law let us consider the behavior of the three simple systems of Fig. 5-1.   The figure shows for each system how $\mathfrak{C}$ varies with x and also how $\partial\mathfrak{C}/\partial x$ and $\partial^2\mathfrak{C}/\partial x^2$ vary.   The flux across certain cross sections is indicated by horizontal arrows, whose lengths indicate its magnitude.

Figure 5-1a shows a system of constant concentration.   Both derivatives are zero so that the flux is also zero.   There is no change in concentration, and no diffusion is observable.

Figure 5-1b shows a system whose concentration increases uniformly so that $\partial\mathfrak{C}/\partial x$ is constant and $\partial^2\mathfrak{C}/\partial x^2$ is zero.   Diffusion

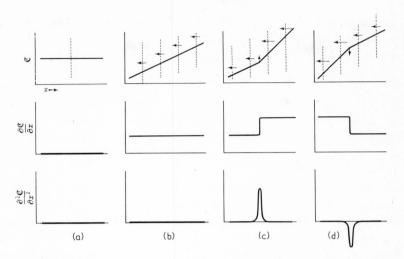

Figure 5-1. The application of Fick's laws to simple cases. Top: change of concentration with distance for four cases; middle: the derivative of this concentration; and bottom: its second derivative. The length of the horizontal arrows indicates the permeation through the dotted planes; the vertical arrows give the resultant change in concentration.

occurs; the flux is negative and of constant magnitude across each cross section indicated because the slope of c is constant. Hence, as much material diffuses into any volume between two cross sections as diffuses out of it, and the concentration within it must remain unchanged.

Figure 5-1c shows a system in which the slope of concentration changes. Here $\partial c/\partial x$ has two positive values, and $\partial^2 c/\partial x^2$ is zero except in the region of changing slope where it rises to a sharp maximum. Diffusion occurs; the flux is negative and its magnitude has one of two values, depending on the region considered. As before, concentration remains unchanged where the slope is constant. In the region where the slope changes, it is clear that more solute diffuses into than diffuses out of it. Hence the concentration increases here as indicated by the vertical arrow, and this change makes the slope of concentration more uniform.

Figure 5-1d shows the same situation as Fig. 5-1c but with a reversal of the relative position of the slopes and corresponding reversal in $\partial^2\mathbb{C}/\partial x^2$ and in the sign of the change in concentration.

5-4. Measurement of Diffusion

Fick's laws tell us only what happens in very short times (while $\partial\mathbb{C}/\partial x$ or $\partial^2\mathbb{C}/\partial x^2$ remain constant) and in very thin layers of solution of uniform cross section which correspond to very small permeations.   Experimentally, on the other hand, we can measure only macroscopic amounts of permeation over reasonably extended times in necessarily changing systems.   To tell us what happens under these conditions, Fick's laws must be integrated, which is never very easy and is feasible only for rather simple systems.   This is true despite the fact that results of heat-flow calculations are generally applicable to diffusion problems because of the similarity of the basic laws involved—temperature taking place of concentration—and heat flow has long been of great theoretical and practical interest.[2]   The basic problem of measuring diffusion is to determine the transport of matter under conditions where it can also be calculated and to make sure that all this transport is due to diffusion.   Diffusion being a rather slow process, transport by flow or convection must be very carefully excluded.   Without going into the detailed interpretation of the results we can examine some aspects of the experimental methods.[3]

In principle, the simplest diffusion system is formed by layering the solvent (or a more dilute solution) over a solution.   The initial situation of such a system is shown by the line of zero time in Fig. 5-2, while later stages are correspondingly numbered. The concentration at the initial boundary remains constant at the average of the two extremes, and the gradient becomes smaller and smaller as diffusion proceeds.   The diffusion co-efficient can be calculated either from the shape of the gradient or from the amount transported after a given time.

The development of the gradient is generally followed by optical methods, particularly refractometric ones such as the

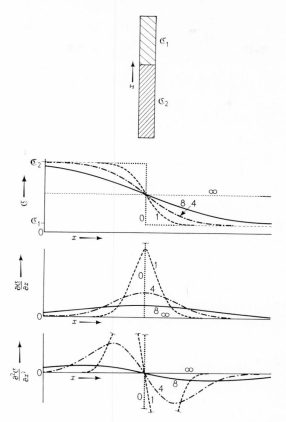

Figure 5-2. Unlimited free diffusion. The diagram at the top shows the original position of the two solutions layered on top of each other. The lower diagrams show the progress of diffusion with time. The numbers indicate the relative lengths of time from beginning.

schlieren method (already mentioned), or the so-called Gouy method, which is more precise. We will describe these later in connection with optical phenomena in Chapters 18 and 19. Since optical measurements naturally require that diffusion be conducted in a transparent and relatively wide vessel, there is some problem in preventing convection currents if there is little difference in the density of the two solutions.

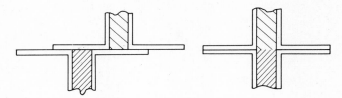

Figure 5-3. The shearing method of producing a boundary between two liquids.

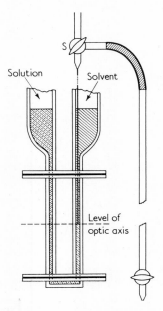

Figure 5-4. Producing a sharp boundary.   The boundary is first formed by shearing along the horizontal plates.   It is then shifted to the desired level and sharpened by sucking away any mixed layers through the thin capillary which is then slowly removed.   (*From L. J. Gostlin, E. M. Hansong, G. Kegeles, and M. S. Morris, Rev. Sci. Instr.*, **20,** *209 (1949)*.)

The calculations involved in these methods are also greatly simplified if the initial boundary is very sharp, approaching an ideal plane.   This cannot be realized by simple layering with a pipette or the like, but is much better done by sliding the two

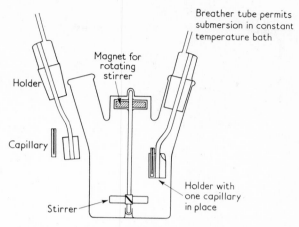

Figure 5-5. An apparatus for measuring diffusion coefficients by the open capillary method.   Diffusion occurs out of the capillary into the large volume of stirred solution in the flask.   (*Based on apparatus of R. Mills and A. W. Adamson, J. Am. Chem. Soc., 77, 3454 (1955).*)

solutions on top of each other as shown in Fig. 5-3.   Figure 16-10*b* shows a cell suitable for this operation.   A still better way, which gives completely satisfactory sharp boundaries, is to flow away, under laminar flow conditions, any mixed layers formed during initial layering.   Since pure liquids must replace the removed streamlines, the final boundary is formed by neighboring streamlines of the flowing system, and these streamlines are formed by the pure liquids.   The flow may be produced quite simply by a fine tube inserted from above to the boundary level, as shown in Fig. 5-4.   Once the boundary is properly formed, the tube is gently withdrawn.

Instead of observing the shape of the gradient, as in the optical methods, one can separate the two parts of the solution after some time and analytically determine the amount that has crossed the boundary.   Since the relatively wide vessel is no longer needed for optical measurements, it can be replaced by a porous medium such as fritted glass, in whose capillaries the liquid is effectively immobilized.   This has the advantage that

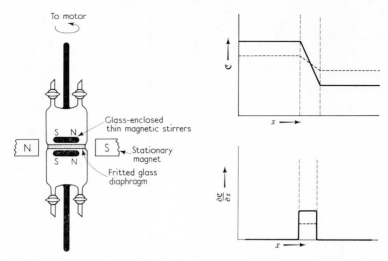

Figure 5-6. An apparatus for the measurement of diffusion coefficients by the porous diaphragm method (left), and the changes produced in the course of diffusion (right). The two thin magnets are maintained in fixed position and homogenize the contents of the two compartments when the cell rotates. (*Based on apparatus of J. M. Nielsen, A. W. Adamson and J. W. Cobble, J. Am. Chem. Soc.*, **74,** *446 (1952)*.)

convection currents, whose occurrence limits the previous method, are suppressed, even in long experiments or for solutions of small density difference. Another approach, shown in Fig. 5-5, uses a capillary closed at one end and completely immersed in an agitated flask. Under these conditions the concentration in the flask may be assumed to be constant throughout the experiment, and the agitation is believed to extend exactly to the open end of the capillary. The material contained in the capillary is allowed to diffuse out for a given time, and that remaining is then determined analytically. This method also is successful with little or no density difference.

In this last method, the concentration at one end of the boundary—in the flask—is kept constant while it develops freely the other end. In the previous ones both ends were allowed this free development. A method which depends on constraining both ends of the gradient is the so-called porous diaphragm method.   Here, the two solutions are in compartments separated by a porous disk of fritted glass, and the concentration in each compartment is kept uniform by convection currents or even by stirring.   As shown in Fig. 5-6, a constant concentration gradient is rapidly established within the thin diaphragm and remains unchanged as long as the two end concentrations are constant (compare Fig. 5-1b).   However, as diffusion proceeds through the diaphragm, the concentrations of the two compartments change, though very slowly, and the gradient adjusts itself accordingly.   The amount crossing the diaphragm after some time is determined analytically and serves to compute the diffusion coefficient.

5-5. Brownian Motion

Having briefly reviewed diffusion as a macroscopic phenomenon, we may now look at its microscopic aspect, the motion of the individual particle, or in its observable aspect, Brownian motion.   As already mentioned, this motion is the purely mechanical result of the innumerable collisions between all the particles in the system.   Each of these collisions produces a change in the direction of motion and a change in velocity, and there are billions of them per second.   Obviously a motion changing so rapidly cannot be followed in detail.   One may, however, observe microscopically[4] the position of the particle at reasonably spaced time intervals.   If these positions are connected by straight lines, one obtains a picture of a completely irregular zig-zag, as would be expected from the random character of the collisions.   Fig. 5-7a shows an experimentally obtained zig-zag of Brownian motion.

If one connects, say, every tenth observed position, one obtains of course a much smoother zig-zag, as shown in Fig. 5-7b. Hence, if the observations were made at ten times shorter intervals, then each segment of the original zig-zag would have been replaced by a ten-membered zig-zag, and the over-all appearance would have been much more irregular.   Any such picture of the

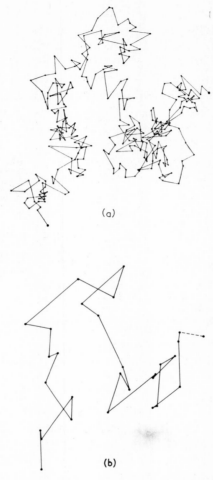

(a)

(b)

Figure 5-7. Above: an observed Brownian motion path of a gamboge particle. Below: the same path, but with only every tenth position shown and connected by straight lines. (*Top part from J. Perrin, The Atoms, Constable and Co., London, 1923.*)

trajectory of a particle can give only a great oversimplification of its actual path.

5-6. Random Walks—One Dimension

One way of approaching the study of Brownian motion is to start with the fact that neither the direction nor the length of any one segment of the simplified zig-zag trajectory is influenced by that of the previous one.   The directions are completely random and the lengths vary irregularly around an average.   This kind of motion is called a "random flight."   It can be simplified

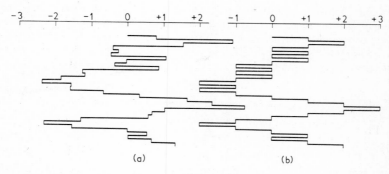

(a)   (b)

Figure 5-8. A one-dimensional random flight on the left and a corresponding one-dimensional random walk on the right.   For clarity, each successive flight or step begins slightly below the end of the preceding one.

somewhat by assuming that the lengths are always equal to the average; this is a "random walk" of equal steps taken in random directions.   If the directions of the steps of a random walk are restricted to a plane, we have a two-dimensional random walk, and, if they are restricted to a line, i.e., to just back and forth, it is a one-dimensional random walk.   Figure 5-8 shows schematically such a one-dimensional random flight on the left and the corresponding random walk on the right.

Although the quantitative treatment of such random motions is not excessively complicated,[5] it is too long for this book and we shall only present some results which are quite apparent intuitively.   We shall use these not only in the study of diffusion and Brownian motion but also later when we consider the shape

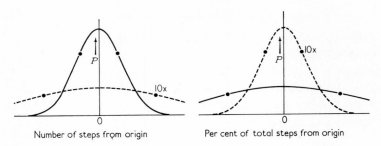

Number of steps from origin   Per cent of total steps from origin

Figure 5-9. The probability of reaching a certain final position in a one-dimensional random walk; solid line: after a given number of steps; broken line: after a tenfold larger number of steps. The distance of this position from the center is measured on an absolute scale on the left and on a relative scale on the right. The dots indicate the average distance in each direction.

of high polymers, their osmotic pressure, chromatography, light scattering, the growth of particles, etc.

The results of a one-dimensional random walk, i.e., the position reached at its end, is the same as the result of pitching pennies and counting the excess of heads (forward steps) over tails (backward steps).

The most probable position after any large number of steps is always the origin, just as an equal number of heads and tails is most probable. The extreme positions, obtained if all steps are taken in one direction, are highly improbable, and intermediate positions have intermediate probabilities, as shown by the curves of Fig. 5-9. The curves are symmetrical since the chances of a forward or backward net motion—of excess heads or excess tails—are, of course, the same. To each position corresponds a distance from the origin. Hence a zero net distance is the most probable, but there are many nonzero distances which have a finite probability.

The average net distance travelled in a random walk or, more precisely, the average of the net distances travelled in each of a large number of such walks, is of course zero since these distances are just as likely to be positive as negative. On the other hand, the average of their absolute values, or their root mean square average, or the average of excursions in one direction only, has an appreciable value.   For brevity this is what we will mean by "the average distance" in the following.

An important question for us, and one to which the layman's answer is frequently wrong, is about the effect of increasing the number of steps N upon the probability of reaching a given point in a random walk.

If we first consider the probability of returning to the origin, we can see that it will decrease as N increases: for two steps the probability of ending where one started is clearly 0.5 since the only possibilities are to end at -2 (by -1 and -1), at $+2$ ($+1$, $+1$), and at 0 (-1, $+1$ or $+1$, -1), so that two out of the four equally probable combinations lead to the origin.   On the other hand, the probability of taking exactly 50 forward steps and exactly 50 backward steps out of 100 completely random steps is certainly less than 0.5.   Exact calculation shows that this probability decreases with $1/\sqrt{N}$ when N is large.

The situation must be quite the opposite if we consider a position that is far removed.   This is best shown by the fact that the probability of ending somewhere must be 1 no matter what N is, and since the probability of ending at or near the center is reduced, that of ending elsewhere, i.e., at a more distance point, must be increased.   Figure 5-9a shows these relations for a tenfold increase in the number of steps.

As the number of steps increases, the average distance reached in a large number of random walks, each having N steps, must also increase since the chances of ending any of them close are decreased and those of ending it far are increased.   Again it turns out that the increase is proportional to $1/\sqrt{N}$.   We will shortly demonstrate this point (Sections 5-8 and 5-9) and use it frequently afterwards.

It is the absolute distances travelled in a random walk, the net number of excess steps in one direction, that vary in the above way.   Frequently, however, it is the relative excess of such steps which is of greater interest.   Thus we may ask what is the probability of ending within say 1% of the total number of steps away from the origin, i.e., between -1 and $+1$ when $N = 100$ or between -10 and $+10$ when $N = 1000$. Here the number of individual positions within the region of interest increases directly with N, whereas the probability of reaching each decreases more slowly, with $1/\sqrt{N}$ as we have stated. Hence the probability of ending within the same relative interval near the origin increases with $N/\sqrt{N} = \sqrt{N}$. Conversely, the probability of ending within the same relative interval far from the origin must decrease as N increases to keep the total probability equal to 1.

The average distance, which increases with $\sqrt{N}$ on an absolute scale, must therefore decrease with $\sqrt{N}/N = 1/\sqrt{N}$ on the relative scale. Figure 5-9*b* shows these relations for a tenfold change in the number of steps; it is the exact inverse of the *a* part of this figure.

5-7. Two- and Three-Dimensional Walks

A simple type of random walk in three dimensions is shown, in Fig. 5-10. Here steps are taken along one of the three axes, but the choice between the six possible directions is random. Thus certain definite points can be reached by the walk. Each point can also be reached by a certain minimum number of steps from the origin which is its distance therefrom. The same was true in one dimension. There is, however, an important difference; in one dimension only two points corresponded to any distance, whereas in two or three dimensions the number of points situated at a given distance increases rapidly with that distance. Thus in three dimensions, as shown in Fig. 5-11, 6 points can be reached in one step, 18 by two steps, etc.

A random walk in three dimensions can be regarded as the superimposition of three one-dimensional walks, so that the probability here is the product of three one-dimensional probabilities. Hence the probability of reaching any particular point has to be highest for the origin and to decrease rapidly away from it. But when it comes to the probability of travelling a certain dis-

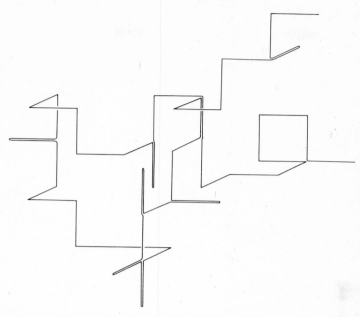

Figure 5-10. A form of three-dimensional random walk. The direction of each
successive step is chosen at random, but along a cubic lattice.

tance, the situation is different, because the number of points
corresponding to that distance increases rapidly.   The answer is
given by the product of the probability for each point times
their number.   The former decrease with distance first slowly
then more and more rapidly, the latter increase but more uniformly.   As a result, the product first increases then decreases as
shown in Fig. 5-12 for two and three dimensions along with,
again, the one-dimension case.

Returning now to Brownian motion, if we could observe it
fully we would see a three-dimensional random walk under the
influence of thermal agitation.   Through a microscope it is a
two-dimensional projection thereof that is seen, as illustrated in
Fig. 5-7.   And if we record only the right and left or only the
up and down components, it is a one-dimensional random walk
that results.   The number of steps in this walk is not only tre-

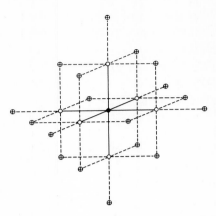

Figure 5-11. If steps in a three-dimensional random walk are taken along three mutually perpendicular axes, six different points (O) are reached by one step from the origin, and eighteen ($\oplus$) by two such steps.

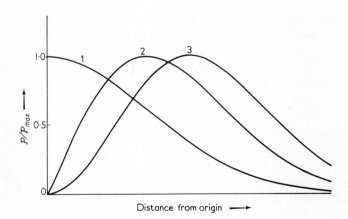

Figure 5-12. The probability of reaching a certain distance as a result of a random walk in one, two, and three dimensions. This probability decreases continuously in one dimension, and passes through a maximum in two and three dimensions because of the increasing number of points located at an increasing distance in the latter two cases. Note that the curves have been normalized so that the maximum probability is the same in every case.

mendous, it is also unknown, but it must be proportional to the time. The average distance travelled should therefore increase with time, but proportionately only to its square root. This has indeed been verified experimentally, and the two parts of Fig. 5-7 show it qualitatively; the average length of the straight lines in b is clearly greater than in a, but it also is not ten times greater although each corresponds to a ten times longer random walk.

5-8. Brownian Motion and Diffusion

Another and very useful approach to the study of Brownian motion concentrates on the fact that diffusion and the Fick's laws which it obeys must be the resultants of Brownian motion. Hence, a relation between the two must give information about the microscopic one in terms of what is known about the macroscopic one.

Let us consider the system illustrated in Fig. 5-13a. In a vessel of unit cross section are present particles subject to Brownian motion. Their initial distribution has a uniform concentra-

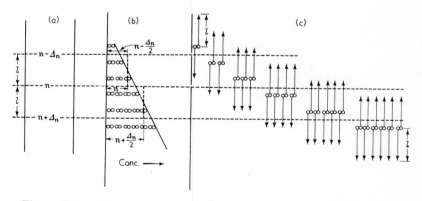

Figure 5-13. Schematic diagrams for the derivation of Einstein's law of Brownian motion. (a) The concentrations and distances involved. (b) The average concentrations and the position of particles at the beginning. (c) The fate of the individual particles after each has travelled the same distance in one of the two opposite directions. A net permeation in the direction of decreasing concentration is the result.

tion gradient, as shown schematically in Fig. 5-13b so that $\mathfrak{n}$
particles are present at the zero level, $\mathfrak{n} + \Delta\mathfrak{n}$ a distance l below
this level, and $\mathfrak{n} - \Delta\mathfrak{n}$ a distance l above.   The concentration
gradient is therefore $[\mathfrak{n} - \Delta\mathfrak{n} - (\mathfrak{n} + \Delta\mathfrak{n})]/2l = -\Delta\mathfrak{n}/l$.
According to Fick's first law, the permeation q expressed in
number of particles crossing the zero level upward is given by

$$q = -D(-\Delta\mathfrak{n}/l)t = Dt\Delta\mathfrak{n}/l \qquad (5\text{-}8.1)$$

Now let us calculate q from the point of view of Brownian
motion.   To simplify, we shall look only at the vertical component of this motion and assume that it is equal for all particles
so that each travels the average distance either up or down.
Furthermore, we can choose the time interval t so that the distance thus travelled by the particle in either direction is equal to
l.   Because of the random character of the motion, half of the
particles at any one level moves up by l and the other half
moves down by l, as indicated in the c part of the figure.   As a
result, half of all the particles originally within l of the zero level
cross it, and no other particles reach it.   The number of particles below and within l of this level is given by the total volume
$(l \times 1)$ times the average concentration $[\mathfrak{n} + (\Delta\mathfrak{n}/2)]$.   Hence
the number crossing upwards is half of this or $l[\mathfrak{n} + (\Delta\mathfrak{n}/2)]/2$.
Similarly, the number crossing downward is $l[\mathfrak{n} - (\Delta\mathfrak{n}/2)]2$.
The net result, the difference of these two quantities, is of course
our permeation q, so that

$$q = l[\mathfrak{n} + (\Delta\mathfrak{n}/2)]/2 - l[\mathfrak{n} - (\Delta\mathfrak{n}/2)]/2 = l\Delta\mathfrak{n}/2 \quad (5\text{-}8.2)$$

Thus we have two expressions for g over the same time t in the
same system.   One is based on Fick's law, the other on consideration of random Brownian motion.   The two must be equal, so
that

$$Dt\Delta\mathfrak{n}/l = l\Delta\mathfrak{n}/2 \qquad (5\text{-}8.3)$$

or simplifying

$$D = l^2/2t \qquad (5\text{-}8.4)$$

This is Einstein's law of Brownian motion, named after the man who first derived it rigorously[6] and later gave a simplified demonstration[7] like the one above.

5-9. The Meaning of Einstein's Law

The expression $D = l^2/2t$ is not only very simple but also very important.

In the first place, we may note that since D is constant, l^2 must be proportional to t, or l proportional to $\sqrt{t}$, which demonstrates that the average displacement in Brownian motion or in a random walk is proportional to the square root of time and hence to the square root of number of steps, as we have anticipated earlier (Section 5-6).

In the second place, Einstein's law shows that by measuring average displacements of Brownian motion we can determine diffusion coefficients. This gives us a method of determining D for particles which diffuse too slowly for other methods.

Thirdly, this derivation shows clearly how Fick's law, which describes an orderly macroscopic movement of matter, is the result of the random motion of individual particles. It is just because this motion is random that it results in the transport of matter from a region of higher to a region of lower concentration.

5-10. Self-Diffusion

Although diffusion slows down as the concentration gradients decrease, Brownian motion continues unchanged. Hence, even when the concentration is uniform and no net transport of matter occurs, the motion of the individual particles remains unchanged, and we may properly ask about the value of the diffusion coefficient under these conditions. In other words, although diffusion stops in such a system because the gradient is zero, D should still have a definite value. Observation of Brownian motion gives one way of measuring the diffusion coefficient corresponding to this state of affairs and appropriately called the "self-diffusion coefficient." Another way tags some of the particles, for example by using isotopic atoms, and then measures their diffusion by one of the standard methods suitable for systems of uniform density.

5-11. The Speed of Brownian Motion

Since in Brownian motion it is l^2/t that is constant, if we compute an average velocity between any two points, i.e., l/t, the value will vary inversely with the distance, and according to Einstein's law it is given by

$$l/t = 2D/l \qquad (5\text{-}11.1)$$

Over large distances the average velocity will be very slow and will increase as the distance gets smaller until it reaches the value given by $mu^2 = \mathbf{k}T$ when the distance is travelled in essentially a straight line. However, if we consider any given macroscopic distance, the average velocity over that distance has a definite meaning and value and is directly proportional to the diffusion coefficient. In particular, if we consider a distance of 1 cm., $l/t = 2D$. Hence the diffusion coefficient which is expressed in square centimeters per second is equal numerically to half the average velocity of Brownian motion over a distance of 1 cm.

5-12. Einstein's Law of Diffusion

Diffusion is caused by thermal agitation, which imparts to each particle a kinetic energy proportional to $\mathbf{k}T$. This term may be considered as the product of the distance travelled times a force proportional to $\mathbf{k}T$, acting on the particle. During this travel, the viscous resistance produces a force proportional to the friction factor φ of the particle and to its velocity. As we have seen, this average velocity over a given distance is proportional to D. Under terminal velocity conditions, these two forces balance so that $\mathbf{k}T$ should be proportional to φD. In Section 7-4 we will show rigorously that this is so and that the proportionality constant is unity

$$\varphi D = \mathbf{k}T \qquad (5\text{-}12.1)$$

or, as it is customarily written

$$D = \mathbf{k}T/\varphi \qquad (5\text{-}12.2)$$

This is Einstein's law of diffusion which connects the macroscopic diffusion coefficient to the microscopic friction factor of the particle, which is related to its size and shape.

It may seem strange that shape and size of the particle thus enter this expression through φ, whereas its mass and density do not.   This may be rationalized as follows: for particles of same size and shape, if the density increases, the average velocity decreases since $mu^2 = \mathbf{k}T$; at the same time, however, the velocity and direction of motion is less affected by each collision because of greater inertia.   As a result, the motion of a denser particle is slower but less random, and the two effects cancel. In terms of random walk, there are fewer steps per unit time, but each is longer.

5-13. Structural Significance of D

We have encountered the friction factor φ previously in sedimentation rate processes (Chapter 3) and have seen how it is related to the size and shape of the particle.   To determine it there, we needed a knowledge of the driving force, and this was often unavailable.   In diffusion, however, Einstein's law shows that we can consider the driving force to be $\mathbf{k}T$, which is the same for all particles and, in addition, is known from other measurements.   Therefore, from a measurement of D we can calculate φ directly and then use it either alone or in connection with other information about the particle.

1.   If no other information is available one can assume that the particle is spherical and calculate an equivalent radius from Stokes' law.

2.   If the weight of the particle m and its density ρ_2 are known from any other source, we can calculate the radius r_0 that it would have if it were an unhydrated sphere

$$r_0 = (3m/4\pi\rho_2)^{1/3} \qquad (5\text{-}13.1)$$

The friction factor, φ_0, that it would have as such an unhydrated sphere is then given by Stokes' law

$$\varphi_0 = 6\pi\eta r_0 \qquad (5\text{-}13.2)$$

This combined with the actual friction factor, φ, given by the diffusion measurements, yields directly the frictional ratio, φ/φ_0, which can be interpreted in terms of dissymmetry and hydration as indicated by Fig. 3-3.

3. If sedimentation rate measurements are available, they can be combined with diffusion measurements to give the weight of the particle, m, needed for the above calculation. In Chapter 3 we have seen (Eq. 3-3.7) that the sedimentation rate u is given by

$$m(1 - \rho/\rho_2)\mathbf{g} = \varphi u \qquad (5\text{-}13.3)$$

now we have obtained an independent expression for φ in terms of D (Eq. 5-12.2). Combining these two gives

$$m(1 - \rho/\rho_2)\mathbf{g} = \mathbf{k}Tu/D \qquad (5\text{-}13.4)$$

$$m = \mathbf{k}Tu/D(1 - \rho/\rho_2)\mathbf{g} \qquad (5\text{-}13.5)$$

which gives the weight of the particle in terms of directly measurable quantities.

5-14. Serum Albumin

As an example we may consider horse serum albumin.[8] For its dilute solutions in water at 20 °C., careful measurements have given a diffusion coefficient of 6.1×10^{-7} cm.^{2}/sec., a sedimentation rate of 4.46×10^{-13} for a field of 1 cm./sec.^{2}, and a density of 1.34. This gives all the data required to apply Eq. 5-13.5 and yields directly the weight of the particle as equal to 1.16×10^{-19} g., i.e., a particle weight of 70,000. This is in close agreement ($\pm 5\%$) with values obtained by other methods which we are going to study later, such as sedimentation equilibrium (Chapter 7) and light scattering (Chapter 20).

A particle weighing 1.16×10^{-19} g. and having a density of 1.34 corresponds to an unhydrated sphere of a radius of 27.5 A., and therefore to $\varphi_0 = 5.15 \times 10^{-8}$. The diffusion coefficient of 6.1×10^{-7} gives, by Eq. 5-12.2, $\varphi = 6.6 \times 10^{-8}$, Hence, the friction ratio, φ/φ_0 is about 1.28. This could correspond to a sphere having a hydration of 0.8 g./g. of dry substance, or to an anhydrous ellipsoid having an axial ratio of about 5.5, or to an intermediate combination of hydration and dissymmetry. By considering other measurements, such as those of intrinsic viscosity which we will discuss in Chapter 13, an axial ratio of 5 as shown in Fig. 2-3, and hydration of 0.2 are considered most likely.[9]

5-15. The Determination of Avogadro's Number

Thus, nowadays, measurements of diffusion are used to provide information about the nature of the particles. There was a time (1905–15), however, when particles of known size and shape, such as microscopically visible spherules of the gum gamboge, were used to determine Avogadro's number **N** and to verify the basis of the kinetic molecular theory.[10] For this purpose, Einstein's two laws are combined to give

$$l^2/2t = \mathbf{k}T/\varphi \qquad (5\text{-}15.1)$$

Now, if φ is replaced by Stokes' value of $6\pi\eta r$, and **k** by $\mathbf{R}/\mathbf{N}$ one obtains

$$l^2/2t = \mathbf{R}T/6\mathbf{N}\pi\eta r \qquad \text{or} \qquad l = (\mathbf{R}Tt/3\mathbf{N}\pi\eta r)^{1/2} \qquad (5\text{-}15.2)$$

which relates the observable average Brownian displacement to **N** if the other quantities were known. Of these r is most difficult to determine, but it was obtained by microscopic and sedimentation-rate measurements. Variations of r, t, and T over the accessible range gave only small variations in **N** around a mean value, which was close to values determined by other independent methods, thus confirming the theory.

5-16. Orders of Magnitude

From Einstein's laws we can calculate the diffusion coefficients and also the rates of Brownian motion for particles of known

TABLE 5-1
Some Rates of Diffusion and of Brownian Motion[a]

Radius			D,	Time for average Brownian displacement in one direction by				
mm.	μ	A.	$cm.^2/sec.$	1 cm.	1 mm.	1μ	100 radii	1 radius
A. Calculated for spheres in water at 20°C.								
1	10^3	10^7	2.15×10^{-12}	7300 yr.	73 yr.	40 min.	7×10^5 yr.	73 yr.
0.1	100	10^6	2.15×10^{-11}	730 yr.	7.3 yr.	4 min.	730 yr.	27 days
0.01	10	10^5	2.15×10^{-10}	73 yr.	9 mo.	23 sec.	9 mo.	40 min.
10^{-3}	1	10^4	2.15×10^{-9}	7.3 yr.	27 days	2.3 sec.	6.5 hrs.	2.3 sec.
10^{-4}	0.1	10^3	2.15×10^{-8}	9 mo.	2.7 days	0.23 sec.	23 sec.	2.3×10^{-3} sec.
10^{-5}	0.01	100	2.15×10^{-7}	27 days	6.5 hr.	2.3×10^{-2} sec.	2.3×10^{-2} sec.	2.3×10^{-6} sec.
10^{-6}	10^{-3}	10	2.15×10^{-6}	2.7 days	40 min.	2.3×10^{-3} sec.	2.3×10^{-5} sec.	2.3×10^{-9} sec.
10^{-7}	10^{-4}	1	(2.15×10^{-5})	(6.5 hr.)	(4 min.)	$(2.3\times10^{-4}$ sec.)	$(2.3\times10^{-8}$ sec.)	
B. Measured values for some particles in water at 20°C.								
H_2 (gas at S.T.P.)			1.3					
H_2			4×10^{-5}					
Cs^+			1.9×10^{-5}					
Na^+			1.2×10^{-5}					
Li^+			9.4×10^{-6}					
Sucrose			4.7×10^{-6}					
NaLS micelle			9.0×10^{-7}					
Serum albumin			6.1×10^{-7}					
Hemocyanin of *Helix Pomatia*			1.4×10^{-7}					
Gamboge ($r = 0.5\mu$)						1.6 sec.		
Gamboge ($r = 2.1\mu$)						6 sec.		

[a] Parentheses indicate values based on Stokes' law under conditions where it is not valid.

friction factor, especially for spheres.   The value of **k** is 1.38 $\times$ 10^{-16} ergs/degree so that for 20 °C. **k**T is 4.047 $\times$ 10^{-14} (which is within about 1% of 4 $\times$ 10^{-14}) ergs.   Hence, for spheres in water

$$D \approx 2.15 \times 10^{-13}/r \qquad (5\text{-}16.1)$$

where c.g.s. units are used throughout.   Table 5-1 tabulates some values thus calculated along with some experimental ones. According to Einstein's law D is directly related to the average time required to cover any given distance by Brownian motion. Such values for several typical distances are also included in the table.

The whole of the above discussion shows that the rate of diffusion changes gradually with the size of the particle, and in fact changes only as the first power of the radius.   Thus, diffusion rate changes much less than either the mass or the surface area of the particle.   Yet, because of the great range of sizes between the classical molecules and the larger colloids, the rates of diffusion cover a great range too, varying by a factor of some 10^4. This explains why early investigators, unable to detect or measure the slower rates of diffusion and lacking any good theory of this phenomenon, thought that colloids were characterized by a complete lack of diffusion and thus contrasted sharply with classical particles.   Now we know that the difference is one of degree only.

5-17. Maximum Flocculation Rate

In considering colloidal systems, one is often interested in the average time that it takes for one particle to encounter another as they all drift randomly by Brownian motion.   For example, this gives an idea of the minimum time required for spontaneous flocculation when there are no other forces affecting the mutual approach of the particles.   We can now estimate at least the order of magnitude of ths time.

We will assume that the particles are monodisperse spheres of radius r, and that they are originally spaced regularly at the

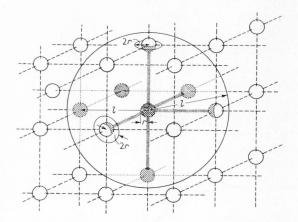

Figure 5-14. If all the particles are located on the corners of a cubic lattice there are six of them on a sphere of radius l around the central particle. If the radius of each particle is r, contact occurs if the centers approach to within $2r$.

corners of a cubic lattice, so that each particle has six nearest neighbors, each at a distance l as indicated in Fig. 5-14.   If one of them now diffuses this distance l it has a probability $\wp$ of encountering one of these neighbors.   This diffusion will take a time t'.   If we also assume that the process is then repeated, the average time for our particle to encounter another will be of the order of $t'/2\wp$ which is the desired result.   The factor 2 comes in because other particles diffuse, just like the one we considered.

The distance apart l of the particles will depend on their concentration, i.e., on their number $\mathfrak{n}$ per cubic centimeter, since there are $1/l$ particles/cm., so that

$$(1/l)^3 = \mathfrak{n} \tag{5-17.1}$$

Their number, in turn, depends on their size and on the total volume present per cubic centimeter.   This is called the volume fraction $\mathfrak{V}$.   We have

$$\mathfrak{n} = \mathfrak{V}/(4/3)\pi r^3 \tag{5-17.2}$$

hence

$$l = r[(4/3)\pi/\mathfrak{B}]^{1/3} = 1.6r/\mathfrak{B}^{1/3} \tag{5-17.3}$$

Thus if the system contains 0.1% by volume of particles ($\mathfrak{B} = 10^{-3}$), their average distance is about 16 times their radius.

The total area of a sphere of radius l around the particle is $4\pi l^2$. If the particle reaches it so that its center is within $2r$ of the center of one of the six neighbors, they will touch. Hence $6\pi(2r)^2$ is the "target" area and the probability of reaching it is

$$\mathcal{P} = 24\pi r^2/4\pi l^2 = 6r^2/l^2 = 6r^2\mathfrak{B}^{2/3}/(1.6)^2r^2 = 2.3\mathfrak{B}^{2/3} \tag{5-17.4}$$

and is independent of the size of the particles.

The time t' required for the particle to diffuse the distance l is given according to Einstein's laws

$$t' = l^2/2D = l^2 6\pi\eta r/2\mathbf{k}T = 24\eta r^3/\mathbf{k}T\mathfrak{B}^{2/3} \tag{5-17.5}$$

The average time for encounter is, as we have seen above, of the order of

$$t = t'/2\mathcal{P} = 5.2\eta r^3/\mathbf{k}T\mathfrak{B}^{4/3} \tag{5-17.6}$$

For water at 20 °C. this becomes

$$t = 1.3 \times 10^{12}r^3/\mathfrak{B}^{4/3} \tag{5-17.7}$$

Hence, for 0.1% of particles 1000 A. in radius, this time is about 3 sec.

A more accurate calculation[11] which takes into account the fact that the particles are randomly distributed and that collisions can follow each other, gives a result differing mainly by changing $\mathfrak{B}^{4/3}$ into $\mathfrak{B}$ and reducing the constant in Eq. 5-17.6 from 5.2 to π. This gives for our example about 1 sec. which is even faster.

Thus the time required for particles to meet each other in the absence of any forces between them is rather short and increases rapidly with size and slowly with dilution. Hence not only the existence of diuturnal systems but even that of caducous systems shows that the repulsive forces must be quite strong in many colloidal systems.

5-18. Flexible Particles

An implicit assumption in the above discussion of diffusion and Brownian motion is that the particles are rigid and move as a whole.   The flexible, chain-like particles of linear high polymers whose segments can move with respect to each other essentially independently, except for their interconnection at ends, were neglected.   In these particles each segment is independently subject to thermal agitation and each executes its own Brownian motion.   Two problems then arise: what is the resulting configuration of the particle, and what is its behavior as a whole? We shall return to this last problem in the next chapter and consider now the first one.

As we have seen in Chapter 2, a flexible particle may be considered as a chain of segments of equal length, joined by perfectly flexible joints.   Thus the orientation of each segment with respect to the preceding and following ones is random, whereas the length is fixed, realizing the premises of a random walk. The sequence of segments of a flexible particle, therefore, should be the same as the simplified path of a small particle executing its Brownian motion and tracing a random coil.   Figures 2-10 and 2-13 were drawn on that basis.   This shape will therefore be changing constantly, but its average characteristics have a definite value.   The average distance between the two ends of the molecule, for example, will correspond to the average distance of a random walk whose number of steps equals the number of segments.   It will therefore increase with the square root of the length of the chain.

In drawing the analogy between the random coil and Brownian motion, two important differences should be kept in mind.   One is that a single particle can return to the same position (in fact this is the most probable spot for it), but a chain cannot return to the spot already occupied by one of its segments.   Thus, the volume already occupied by other segments is no longer available to any given segment.   This is called the "excluded volume."

Its effect is to distort the random coil and make it more extended than a random walk, because successive segments, unable to enter the excluded volume, tend to place themselves further away from the center.

The other difference is that a particle, especially in dilute solution, is surrounded uniformly by the solvent, whereas segments of a chain are surrounded not only by the solvent but also by other segments. If attractive forces between the two do not balance exactly, the segments will either have a tendency to stick together, giving a coil which is tighter than a truly random one, or, on the contrary, the segments may avoid each other, thus giving a looser, more spread out, coil. As we will see in more detail later (Section 8-1), the tendency of the segments to stick to each other leads to a precipitation, if it is at all pronounced. Hence, most often when flexible molecules dissolve, their segments also tend to avoid each other.

Both the excluded volume and the solvent effect tend to make real coils of flexible molecules more extended than random ones. Nevertheless, because of its simplicity, the random coil remains a good first approximation of the behavior of high polymers.

Summary

Thermal motion manifests itself macroscopically in diffusion, governed by Fick's laws, and microscopically in Brownian motion. Einstein's laws connect the two and express the diffusion coefficient as a balance between thermal agitation and the friction factor of the individual particle. The latter can thus be determined and, in combination with sedimentation rate measurements can give the particle weight. This in turn yields the frictional ratio of the particle. While diffusion is a slow process, it is nevertheless important for colloids as it is for smaller particles. Simple random processes illustrated by a random walk are helpful in understanding both Brownian motion and the shape of linear polymers.

References

1. A. Fick, (*Pogg*) *Ann. Physik*, **94,** 59 (1855); but according to S. Wroblewski, (*Wied.*) *Ann. Physik*, **13,** 606 (1881) it was Berthollet, *Essai de Statique Chimique*, Paris, 1803, who first clearly recognized the relation.

2. J. Crank, *The Mathematics of Diffusion*, The Clarendon Press, Oxford, 1956; L. R. Ingersoll, O. J. Zobel, and A. C. Ingersoll, *Heat Conduction*, McGraw-Hill Book Co., Inc., New York, 1948.

3. A. L. Geddes, in A. Weissberger, ed., *Techniques of Organic Chemistry*, Vol. 1, Part 1, Interscience Publishers, Inc., New York, 1949, p. 551.

4. J. Perrin, *The Atoms*, Constable and Co., Ltd., London, 1923, pp. 94, 114; T. Svedberg, *Colloid Chemistry*, The Chemical Catalog Co. (Reinhold), New York, 1928, p. 115.

5. W. N. Bond, *Probability and Random Errors*, Edward Arnold and Co., London, 1935, Chap. 2.

6. A. Einstein, *Ann. Physik*, **17,** 549 (1905); also in English, *Investigations on the Theory of the Brownian Movement*, Methuen and Co., London, 1926; Dover, N. Y., 1956, p. 1.

7. A. Einstein, *Z. Elektrochem.*, **14,** 235 (1908); also in English, *Investigations* (see ref. 6), p. 68.

8. E. J. Cohn and J. T. Edsall, *Proteins, Amino Acids and Peptides* (ACS Monograph No. 90), Reinhold Publishing Corp., New York, 1943, p. 428.

9. J. L. Oncley, in ref. 8, p. 562.

10. J. Perrin, *The Atoms*, Constable and Co., Ltd., London 1923, Chap. IV; T. Svedberg, *Colloid Chemistry*, Chemical Catalog Co., (Reinhold), New York, 1928, p. 114.

11. J. Th. G. Overbeek, in H. R. Kruyt, *Colloid Science*, Vol. 1; Elsevier, New York, 1952, Chap. VII.

Problems

24. The time required for 1 g. of sucrose to diffuse from a solution kept at 10 g./100 cc. into pure water across a fritted glass disk, 3 mm. thick and 2 cm. in radius is, assuming that the fritted disk is equivalent to 25% open surface, approximately (*1*) 1 min., (*2*) 30 min., (*3*) 6 hr., (*4*) 2 days, (*5*) 2 weeks, (*6*) 2 months.

3. If sucrose is replaced in problem 24 by serum albumin, the answer becomes _____.

19. In random walks the most probable distance is (*1*) 475 in 1000 steps, (*2*) between 45 and 50 in 100 steps, (*3*) 100 in 200 steps, (*4*) between 450 and 455 in 1000 steps.

6. In a three dimensional random walk of 10,000 steps the most probable is the reaching of (*1*) $x = 5, y = 5, z = 5$; (*2*) $x = 5, y = 0, z = 0$; (*3*) $x + y + z = 5$; (*4*) $x + y + z = 15$.

20. If particles move with a velocity u, and their number per milliliter is n in a solution of concentration C g./ml., the weight of material crossing per unit time a plane having an area A and forming an angle θ with the direction of the velocity, is (*1*) $nA \sin \theta$; (*2*) CnA; (*3*) $CnA \cos \theta$; (*4*) $CA \sin \theta$.

9. Using the known values of **k** and D for sucrose which are given in the text, its equivalent radius is found to be _____.

4. The time required for a sucrose molecule to diffuse 1 mm. along a given direction is about _____.

17. The time required for the sucrose molecule to diffuse 1 cm. along a given direction is about _____.

14. A helix pomatia hemocyanin molecule requires about _____ to cover 1 mm. along a given direction by diffusion.

33. In each of the diagrams below, the solid line represents the same original concentration of the system. In which one does the dotted line represent correctly the concentration after diffusion has proceeded for a short time?

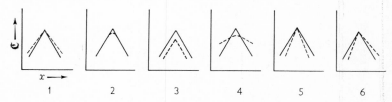

29. The Brownian motion of a particle is observed by noting its positions at regular intervals. The average distance between successive positions is found to be 3.5 μ. Then the distance between positions 1 and 5, 2 and 6, 3 and 7, etc. is measured. This should, on the average, be _____ μ.

38. If we are given the density of a solid and the weight of rigid particles which it forms, we can calculate for its diffusion coefficient

in water (*1*) the exact value, (*2*) a lower limit, (*3*) an upper limit, (*4*) an equivalent value which may be higher or lower than the actual one.

32.   The length of a segment of a polymer is 15 A.   If the average end to end distance of the particles of this polymer in an ideal solvent is about 100 A. then the number of segments in the particle is of the order of (*1*) 7, (*2*) 50, (*3*) 500, (*4*) no way of telling.

50.   A spherical particle has a dry radius and when placed in water it swells to a hydrated radius.   From its measured diffusion coefficient in water one computes its equivalent radius.   It is certain that the radii increase in the order (*1*) dry, equivalent, hydrated; (*2*) dry, hydrated, equivalent; (*3*) equivalent, dry, hydrated; (*4*) none of these.

CHAPTER VI

Colligative Properties

In the last chapter we considered thermal motion as it manifests itself in the actual spontaneous transport and movement of matter on a microscopic and on a macroscopic scale. This spontaneous tendency to spread can be prevented by an impervious wall provided that the wall is held with a force sufficient to counteract it. Determination of this force gives an independent, static method of measuring thermal motion. For gases this amounts simply to measuring their pressure.

The connection between the pressure of a gas and the thermal motion of its molecules is derived early in the study of the kinetic theory. This same pressure may also be quantitatively connected directly with the thermodynamic properties of the gas, such as its free energy and entropy. With a few additional assumptions, this same connection with thermodynamic properties may be established by statistical considerations of the probability of finding gas molecules in a certain volume. These different points of view are in principle equivalent, but their simplicity and usefulness vary.

When it comes to solutions, the corresponding measured quantity is any one of the colligative properties, i.e., the vapor pressure lowering, the freezing point lowering, the boiling point elevation, the osmotic pressure, or some derived quantity. Their interpretation is now generally given in thermodynamic terms rather than in kinetic ones, although much of the original work[1] on their meaning and significance was in the latter terms. In this book we will use the kinetic treatment because of its greater simplicity.

127

6-1. The Colligative Properties

Whenever a solution is placed in the presence of the solvent, there is always a spontaneous tendency for the solution to become more dilute until a uniform concentration (or activity) is present throughout the system.   This is one of the results of thermal agitation of all the particles.   When the solution is in direct contact with the solvent, this results, as we have seen, in diffusion.

If the solution and solvent are in contact through the vapor phase, the same process occurs through distillation, because of the lower equilibrium vapor pressure of the solvent over the solution.   In particular, if the temperature is high enough to cause boiling of the solvent, the solution (of a nonvolatile solute) will still be below its boiling point.   Equilibrium can be restored in such a system if the proper pressure is exerted on a piston separating the two vapors, or if the temperature of the solution is raised so as to increase its vapor pressure.   Thus we measure the tendency of thermal motion to equalize concentration by determining the vapor pressure lowering or the boiling point elevation.

If the frozen solvent cannot dissolve the solute, and is brought while at, or very near, its melting point in contact with the liquid solution at the same temperature, dilution occurs through melting of the solvent.   Again, equilibrium can be restored by lowering the temperature of the system so as to increase the tendency of the solvent to solidify; this gives the freezing point lowering method of measuring colligative properties.

Finally, if the solvent and the solution are separated only by a membrane which is permeable to the solvent but not to the solute, i.e., a "semipermeable" membrane, dilution can occur only by motion of the solvent into the solution across the membrane.   This occurs spontaneously and is called osmotic flow. Flow of solvent through the membrane can occur also under other conditions, in particular under the influence of a difference in hydrostatic pressure.   Hence, if a proper hydrostatic pressure is applied so that it causes a flow which just balances the osmotic flow, a state of equilibrium is observed.   This balancing pressure is the osmotic pressure.   It is of sufficient importance in the field of colloids to warrant more detailed examination.

6-2. Positive and Negative Pressures

The difference in hydrostatic pressure between a solvent and a solution can be produced in two ways.   One is to increase the pressure on the solution by simply compressing it with a piston or raising its level in a tube.   The other way is to reduce the pressure on the solvent, for example by pulling upon it with a

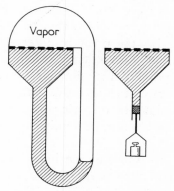

Figure 6-1. Negative pressure can prevail in a liquid having an open surface, if this surface is supported by well-wetted capillaries.

piston or allowing a column of liquid to hang from it.   The existence of such negative pressures[2] up to hundreds of atmospheres for water is possible (metastably) in closed systems because of difficulty in the formation of the first bubbles of vapor. Negative pressure is therefore closely related to the more familiar stress existing in a superheated liquid.[3]   A negative pressure is also possible, but to a much lesser extent, in systems with open surfaces if the surface is formed in fine capillaries of wetted solid.[4]   Surface forces then hold the liquid in the capillaries, and it can be stretched to some extent by a hanging column or by a well wetted and tightly fitting piston, as shown in Fig. 6-1.

It may be noted that the energy required to remove a liquid

from that state increases when it is subject to negative pressure. In other words its free energy is lowered. Hence its tendency to vaporize, its vapor pressure, is also lowered. This is exactly the opposite of what happens when the liquid is subject to a positive pressure.

6-3. Semipermeable Membranes

Although a semipermeable membrane is the basic prerequisite for defining or determining the osmotic pressure, we may note that the magnitude of the osmotic pressure cannot depend on the nature of the membrane, provided that the latter is truly semipermeable. Otherwise, the pressure difference between "equilibrium" systems using different membranes could be readily utilized to drive a perpetual motion machine. As a corollary, we need not know anything about *how* the membrane acts in order to use or calculate the osmotic pressure. Any mechanism which will make the membrane semipermeable must give the same result.

Among possible membrane mechanisms are: the simple sieve, allowing the smaller particles to pass but retaining the larger ones; the selective solvent, in which one kind of particles can dissolve and then diffuse through while the other kind cannot dissolve and is therefore retained; and the charged membrane, formed by thin capillaries having charged walls so that similarly charged ions are repelled and cannot enter the capillaries, whereas oppositely charged ions and uncharged particles travel through them freely.

Each of these types of membranes probably is known in the quite pure state. Thus, cellophane behaves as a sieve with pore size of about 30 A. Rubber dissolves benzene and permits its passage, but is impervious to water. Oxidized nitrocellulose membranes are negatively charged and are impervious to anions. In many cases, however, the actual mechanism of membrane action is unknown and, as we have seen, often unimportant. Thus, there seems to be no adequate explanation of the perfect semipermeability[5] of copper ferrocyanide membranes towards sugar solutions.

6-4. Colligative Character of Osmotic Pressure

The fact that osmotic pressure is equivalent to vapor pressure lowering can be shown in two very simple ways. One is to consider a special case of a semipermeable membrane formed by narrow capillaries having unwettable walls. Surface tension prevents the liquid from entering the capillaries, but the vapor can pass freely from one surface to the other (Fig. 6-2). If the

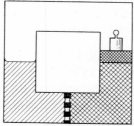

Figure 6-2. Osmotic equilibrium through the vapor phase in case of a non-wetted membrane. Note that an air space within each pore separates the two liquids and that equilibrium requires that the solution be under an osmotic pressure.

solute is nonvolatile, only the solvent can cross the membrane. Osmotic flow is therefore clearly the result of vapor pressure difference between solvent and solution. It stops when sufficient hydrostatic pressure difference is applied to bring the two vapor pressures to equality. In view of what was just said about the unimportance of the mechanism, the same correlation between these two colligative properties must hold for any semipermeable membrane.

The other way is to consider the idealized system[6] shown in Fig. 6-3. Semipermeable membrane S separates a solution in the tall tube T from the surrounding solvent. In this system the solvent can reach the solution (or escape from it) either through the semipermeable membrane or through the vapor phase sepa-

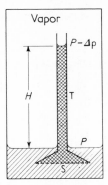

Figure 6-3. At the height H to which the osmotic column rises at equilibrium, the vapor pressure lowering Δ_p due to the weight of the vapor, is equal to that produced by the concentration of the solute.

rating the open surfaces of both liquids.   If the system is in equilibrium (with respect to the distribution of the solvent) there can be no tendency for the solvent to take either path.   For suppose that there is osmotic equilibrium but that some solvent distills into the tube through the vapor phase.   This would raise the level of the liquid in the tube, thus increasing the hydrostatic pressure so that solvent would escape through the membrane restoring exactly the original state;   then more distillation would take place, and the process would repeat itself indefinitely. The resulting contonous flow in the tube could be harnessed to produce work and we would have a perpetual motion machine. Since the same kind of reasoning shows that the reverse flow is impossible, we must conclude that when there is equilibrium as far as osmosis is concerned there has to be also equilibrium as far as vapor pressure is concerned.

The tendency of the solvent to enter the solution through the semipermeable membrane is counterbalanced by the osmotic pressure, π, exerted by the height of the solution in tube T.   The tendency to distill is due to the vapor pressure difference between the pure solvent and the solution.   This difference is counterbalanced by the weight of the vapor itself between the two levels.   If the pressure of the vapor at the lower level is equal to P, the pressure of the vapor will decrease with height until it reaches a value $P - \Delta_P$ at the height H.   For equilibrium to prevail this must also be the vapor pressure of the solution.

Qualitatively this shows again that the two—vapor pressure lowering and osmotic pressure—must measure the same property of the solution, since to every height there must correspond an osmotic pressure and a vapor pressure lowering for dilute solutions in the same solvent.   It also shows that both must increase together.

6-5. Van't Hoff's Law

The same system of Fig. 6-3 can be used to connect quantitatively the osmotic pressure of dilute systems with their vapor pressure lowering and also with their concentration.   For this purpose we relate the height H first to the osmotic pressure, π, of the solution and to its density, ρ, which can be taken as equal to the density of the solvent.   This gives

$$\pi = H\rho\mathbf{g} \qquad (6\text{-}5.1)$$

Then we relate this same height H to the vapor pressure lowering Δ_P and to the average density ρ_v of the vapor.   Since H and Δ_P are both small for dilute solutions, we can consider the vapor in the system to have the density which corresponds to the pressure P.   Applying the laws of ideal gases to the vapor gives $\rho_v = M_1 P / \mathbf{R} T$ where M_1 is the molecular weight of the vapor. This gives

$$\Delta_P = H\rho_v\mathbf{g} = H\mathbf{g}M_1 P / \mathbf{R} T \qquad (6\text{-}5.2)$$

Eliminating H between these two equations gives

$$\pi = \mathbf{R} T(\Delta_P / P)(\rho / M_1) \qquad (6\text{-}5.3)$$

which gives the osmotic pressure in terms of the vapor pressure lowering, the density of the liquid, and the molecular weight of the vapor of the solvent.

The vapor pressure lowering of dilute ideal solutions is given by Raoult's law as $\Delta_P / P = \mathfrak{x}_2$ where $\mathfrak{x}_2$ is the mole fraction of solute.   If we consider a volume V of the dilute solution containing N_1 and N_2 moles of the two components, where N_2 is negligible compared to N_1, and if we denote by W_1 the weight of the solvent in that volume, we can transform Raoult's law as follows

$$\Delta_P/P = \mathfrak{x}_2 = N_2/(N_1 + N_2) = N_2/N_1$$
$$= N_2/(W_1/M_1) = N_2/(\rho V/M_1) \quad (6\text{-}5.4)$$

It may be worth noting that in relating the mole fraction to the directly determinable weight of the solvent we are using the molecular weight M_1 of the vapor as is necessary[13] for Raoult's law to hold.   If now we insert this result into the previous relation and simplify, we obtain

$$\pi = N_2 \mathbf{R} T/V \qquad (6\text{-}5.5)$$

This is van't Hoff's law of osmotic pressure.   We can immediately notice that it has the same form and involves the same constant $\mathbf{R}$ as the law of ideal gases $P = N\mathbf{R}T/V$.   If we wish to consider individual particles rather than moles we can notice that $n_2 = \mathbf{N}N_2$ while $\mathbf{R} = \mathbf{N}k$, hence $N_2\mathbf{R} = n_2 k$ and

$$\pi = n_2 \mathbf{k} T/V \qquad (6\text{-}5.6)$$

A convenient form of van't Hoff's equation is

$$\pi = \mathbf{R} T \mathfrak{M}_2 \qquad (6\text{-}5.7)$$

where $\mathfrak{M}_2 = M_2/V$ is the molarity of the solute.

6-6. Meaning of Osmotic Pressure

Although the above reasoning does give us a value for the osmotic pressure, it does not tell us anything about its cause. A very simple kinetic picture is, however, consistent with these results.   It is that particles of the solute move in the total volume of the solution as gas molecules move through their container. Whenever the particles encounter an impervious wall, they have to reverse direction and give up twice their momentum mu, just as gas molecules do at the walls of the container.   When this reversal occurs at the limits of the solvent (be it an open

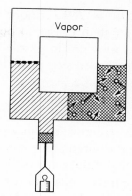

Figure 6-4. An equilibrium system showing the equivalence of negative pressure and of the action of solute molecules.

surface or the wall of the vessel), it is the cohesive forces of the solvent that prevent the further travel of the solute particle and counteract the change of momentum. Thus the solvent is "stretched" or subject to an internally generated and negative pressure. As a result, the pressure exerted by the thermal motion of solute particles is not ordinarily perceived as such at the walls of a container of the solution, but the vapor pressure of the solvent is lowered because of negative internal pressure to which it is subject.

When a semipermeable membrane is encountered through which the solvent passes freely, it is no longer the solvent which limits the travel of the particles but only the membrane. Hence, it is the membrane that must take up their change of momentum and is subject to a pressure. Figure 6-4 represents an equilibrium system of solvent, solution, and vapor, showing how the osmotic pressure of the solute is equivalent to a negative hydrostatic pressure exerted on the solvent both in maintaining osmotic equilibrium and in lowering the vapor pressure.

Quantitatively, the osmotic pressure π should be equal to the pressure P exerted by the same number of gas moles $N = N_2$ in the same volume V at the same temperature T. This is indeed born out by the identity of van't Hoff's Law $\pi V = N_2 \mathbf{R} T$ and of the ideal gas law $PV = N\mathbf{R}T$ under these conditions. Of course, as soon as the system ceases to be ideal, deviations are to be expected, just as they are in gases. As the concentration becomes larger and forces between particles increase, deviations from these ideal laws become greater. However, in the limit at infinite dilution, they hold exactly.

Another aspect of this picture which is in good agreement with reality is that the structure of the solvent plays no role. It may be continuous or discrete, polymerized or dissociated, it may solvate the particles of the solute or it may not interact with them—none of this matters. Nor did it matter in our quantitative calculation. We used the molecular weight of the solvent in the vapor phase, M_1, and its total weight. What happened upon liquefaction—reaction with the solute, or association, or polymerization—did not enter the calculation, at least not for dilute solutions.

6-7. The Particle Weights

The great value of colligative properties lies in the information they give about the particle weights of solutes. All these properties are equivalent, as we have seen, so they must all furnish us with the same information and this is simply N_2, the number of moles of solute. Thus, we have already written Raoult's law as $\Delta_P/P = N_2/(\rho V/M_1)$, which gives us N_2 as a function of the vapor pressure lowering and of other known quantities. Similarly van't Hoff's law can be written as

$$N_2 = \pi V/\mathbf{R}T \tag{6-7.1}$$

which relates N_2 to the measured osmotic pressure and to other easily determined values.

To utilize this number of moles we need also the weight W_2 of solute present in the solution, and this is in general easily available. Then simple division gives the desired result

$$W_2/N_2 = M_2 \tag{6-7.2}$$

The two equations can be combined into one

$$W_2 \mathbf{R} T / \pi V = M_2 \qquad (6\text{-}7.3)$$

If we desire information about the individual particles, we can note that $W_2/n_2 = m_2$ and, using Eq. 6-5.6, write

$$W_2 \mathbf{k} T / \pi V = m_2 \qquad (6\text{-}7.4)$$

which is also the same as the above equation divided by $\mathbf{N}$.

This somewhat detailed discussion of the meaning and utilization of the measurement permits us immediately to interpret the result in terms of hydration and polydispersity. The number of particles formed by the solute, N_2, is not influenced by their hydration. If the solute was weighed anhydrous, the resulting particle weight refers therefore to the dry weight of the particle. If for any reason W_2 was obtained on wet material, M_2 refers to correspondingly hydrated particles.

Similarly, the osmotic pressure does not depend on the size or on the equality of the particles which cause it. It is only their number which matters. When we divide the total weight by this total number in Eq. 6-7.2 above, we perform exactly the operation leading to M_n, the number-average particle weight as we defined it in Section 2-8.

6-8. The Importance of Osmotic Measurements

The above reasoning about the utilization of colligative properties is based on the assumption that the solution is ideal so that Raoult's or van't Hoff's laws hold. This assumption becomes truer as the weight concentration becomes lower. Since $\mathfrak{W} = N_2 M_2 / V$ we can rewrite van't Hoff's law as

$$\pi = \mathfrak{W} \mathbf{R} T / M_2 \qquad (6\text{-}8.1)$$

Thus lower concentrations mean lower osmotic pressures and correspondingly lower other colligative properties. In our case there is an additional factor: as the particle weight M_2 increases, and it can increase a great deal for colloids, the colligative properties decrease again. Hence, in practice, a very sensitive method is desired to make possible the precise determination on solutions containing as few moles as possible per unit volume.

The sensitivity of the methods for measuring colligative properties varies enormously.   Thus a 0.1 M solution in water has a freezing point lowering of about 0.18 °C. but a boiling point elevation of only 0.052 °C., and the latter is much more difficult to measure because of local superheating.   The vapor pressure lowering of such a solution at 25 °C. is about 0.05 mm. Hg or 0.7 cm. H_2O, whereas its osmotic pressure amounts to about 2.4 atm. or 1830 mm. Hg.   Although the former pressure is rather too small for convenient measurement, the latter is uncomfortably large.   Table 6-1 further illustrates these differences as a function of particle weight for solutions of constant concentration of 1%.

6-9. Measurement of Osmotic Pressure

As shown by Table 6-1 osmotic pressure is the most promising colligative property for the determination of particle weights of colloids, but even so, the upper limit of accessible weight seems to be of the order of ten millions.   A great deal of work has therefore been spent on perfecting sensitive methods of measuring osmotic pressure.[7]   We will review only some of the difficulties and ways of overcoming them.

The preparation of suitable membranes is one of the big obstacles when dealing with small particles, but as their size increases, sieve type membranes such as cellophane become available and solve the problem.   Still, in the case of association colloids the small particles pass readily through all available membranes even when their micelles are retained.   Hence, very sensitive vapor pressure lowering methods are generally used in this case.

If the volume of osmotic flow is large, the concentration of the solution becomes uncertain and the time required for the experiment very long.   Hence, one seldom allows the solution simply to rise and seek its own level in the capillary but generally introduces from the beginning a pressure almost equal to the equilib-

TABLE 6-1

Colligative Properties Produced by 1 g. of Ideal Solutes of Different Particle Weight per 100 ml. of water

(Values in parenthesis are not measurable at present by most precise methods[b-f] even under favorable conditions. Hence determinations to 1% stop at 100–1000 times lower particle weights.)

Particle weight	Particle radius[a], A.	Conc., $\mathfrak{M}_2$	Vapor pressure lowering[b], mm. Hg	Boiling point elevation 100°C.[c] °C.	Boiling point elevation 25°C.[d] °C.	Freezing point depression[e], °C.	Osmotic pressure[f] 20°C. Hg	Osmotic pressure[f] 20°C. H_2O
1	0.58	10	4.3	5.2	3	18.6	176 m.	2.4 km.
10	1.25	1	0.43	0.52	0.3	1.86	18 m.	240 m.
100	2.7	0.1	4.3×10^{-2}	0.05	0.03	0.19	1.8 m.	24 m.
10^3	5.85	10^{-2}	4.3×10^{-3}	5×10^{-3}	3×10^{-3}	0.02	18 cm.	2.4 m.
10^4	12.5	10^{-3}	(4.3×10^{-4})	5×10^{-4}	3×10^{-4}	2×10^{-3}	1.8 cm.	24 cm.
10^5	27	10^{-4}	(4.3×10^{-5})	(5×10^{-5})	(3×10^{-5})	2×10^{-4}	1.8 mm.	2.4 cm.
10^6	58.5	10^{-5}	(4.3×10^{-6})	(5×10^{-6})	(3×10^{-6})	2×10^{-5}	0.18 mm.	2.4 mm.
10^7	125	10^{-6}	(4.3×10^{-7})	(5×10^{-7})	(3×10^{-7})	(2×10^{-6})	0.018 mm.	0.24 mm.
10^8	270	10^{-7}	(4.3×10^{-8})	(5×10^{-8})	(3×10^{-8})	(2×10^{-7})	1.8×10^{-3} mm.	0.024 mm.
10^9	585	10^{-8}	(4.3×10^{-9})	(5×10^{-9})	(3×10^{-9})	(2×10^{-8})	$(1.8 \times 10^{-4}$ mm.)	$(2.4 \times 10^{-3}$ mm.)

[a] Assuming spheres of density 2 g./cc.

[b] G. Scatchard, W. J. Hamer, and S. E. Wood, J. Am. Chem. Soc., 60, 3061 (1938).

[c] E. Plake, Z. physik. Chem., A172, 105 (1935).

[d] A. P. Brady, H. Huff, and J. W. McBain, J. Phys. and Colloid Chem., 55, 304 (1950) (indirect determination).

[e] G. Scatchard, P. T. Jones, and S. S. Prentiss, J. Am. Chem. Soc., 54, 2676 (1932).

[f] S. Claesson, and G. Jacobson, Acta Chem. Scand., 8, 1835 (1954).

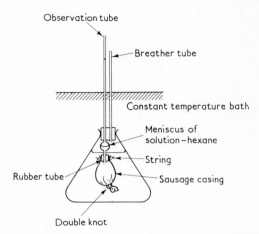

Figure 6-5. A simple osmometer in which the osmotic pressure of the solution contained in the sausage casing is measured by means of a column of hexane. Equilibrium is reached very slowly and temperature constancy is very important.

rium one. Often, the equilibrium pressure is not reached at all, but is calculated from the rates at which slightly higher and lower pressures change with time. This rate of change is proportional to the distance from the equilibrium value.

If the level of the liquid is observed in tubes of large diameter, it takes a relatively large volume of osmotic flow to produce a visible change. If the tube is very fine, capillary forces cause a large level difference and the meniscus of water often tends to stick to a position because of imperfect wetting. Hence a liquid of low surface tension and good wetting properties such as hexane is often used in fine capillaries. It stays above the water because of its lower density. The meniscus separating the two is kept in an enlargement where surface forces become unimportant. To further reduce the effects of flow and of surface forces, the height of the liquid in the capillary is often kept almost constant, and it is the pressure of the air above the liquid that is varied and measured separately.

A dilemma arises if one observes the level of the solution, as

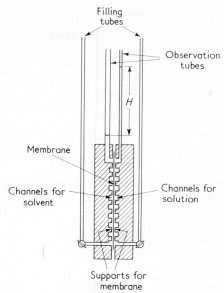

Figure 6-6. Schematic cross-section through the Fuoss-Mead osmometer, in which the semipermeable membrane is clamped between two stainless steel blocks provided with channels into which small volumes of solvent and solution are introduced.   The membrane is firmly supported by ridges between the channels and the approach to equilibrium is rapid because of the high surface-to-volume ratio.   (*Based on R. M. Fuoss and D. J. Mead, J. Phys. Chem.,* **47,** *59,* (*1943*).)

is frequently done.   If the volume of the solution is small, large changes of concentration are produced by even small osmotic flows.   If the volume is large, the osmometer acts like a thermometer, since variations in total volume of the solution due to fluctuations in temperature cause large changes in the observed level.   The way out of this dilemma is to observe instead the level of the solvent.   Its volume can be kept small since osmotic flow does not affect its concentration, and so the effect of temperature fluctuations is reduced.   Good thermostating nevertheless is still indicated.

In order to speed up the experiment it is always desirable to increase the area of the membrane, but this also increases volume

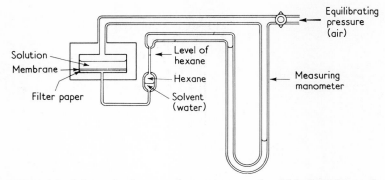

Figure 6-7. Schematic diagram of an osmometer in which the volume of solvent is greatly reduced and kept constant by applying an air pressure differential which is measured on a separate manometer.   Equilibration is very rapid, and temperature variations have little effect.   (*Based on G. Scatchard, American Scientist* **40,** 61 (1952); *G. Scatchard, A. Gee, and J. Weeks, J. Phys. Chem.,* **58,** 783 (1954).)

changes due to any deformation of the membrane.   Hence the membrane is often supported by a rigid network.

Figures 6-5 through 6-7 show schematically three popular types of osmometers ranging from a very simple one to very efficient but much more complicated ones.

6-10. Results of Colligative Measurements

If we neglect charge effects (which will come later as "Donnan effects," Sections 14-11 and 14-12), the results of osmotic and related measurements fall into roughly three classes as shown in Fig. 6-8.   The osmotic pressure in each case goes necessarily to zero at zero concentration as required by van't Hoff's law

$$\pi = N_2 \mathbf{R} T/V = (W_2/M_2)\mathbf{R} T/V = \mathfrak{W} \mathbf{R} T/M_2 \qquad (6\text{-}10.1)$$

where $\mathfrak{W} = W_2/V$ is the concentration of solute by weight per unit volume of solution.   (The actual units used determine the value of $\mathbf{R}$.   If $\mathfrak{W}$ is in grams per liter and π in millimeters of mercury, then $\mathbf{R} = 62.37$.)   A more useful form of this equation is

$$\pi/\mathbf{R} T \mathfrak{W} = 1/M_2 \qquad (6\text{-}10.2)$$

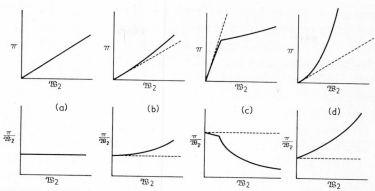

Figure 6-8. Schematic variation of osmotic pressure π and of the reduced osmotic pressure $\pi/\mathfrak{W}$ in typical systems: (a) ideal; (b) simple nonideal; (c) association colloid; (d) linear high polymer.

which means that, for ideal solutions, the ratio $\pi/\mathfrak{W}$ is constant and inversely proportional to the particle weight. Hence a plot of $\pi/\mathfrak{W}$ versus $\mathfrak{W}$ should be a horizontal line (Fig. 6-8a). In nonideal solutions, a different shape is obtained, but extrapolation to infinite dilution ($\mathfrak{W} = 0$) gives the value of $\pi/\mathbf{R}T\mathfrak{W}$ under conditions where Eq. 6-10.2 is strictly valid and hence gives the molecular weight.

The deviations from horizontality may be upward or downward. In some cases they are small, showing that the solution is almost ideal (Fig. 6-8b). This is, for example, the case of some proteins such as serum albumin, if precautions are taken to eliminate charge effects. In other cases large deviations from ideality are encountered; we shall consider two particular cases.

6-11. Association Colloids

The typical result of a colligative property measurement on an association colloid[8] such as sodium lauryl sulfate is shown in Fig. 6-8c. The osmotic pressure (computed from other colligative properties actually measured)[9] at first increases rapidly and almost ideally, extrapolating to a particle weight of 144 which is half of the empirical formula weight. This agrees with the presence of simple ions Na^+ and LS^- in the solution.   Soon, however, a concentration is reached above which osmotic pressure increases almost linearly but much more slowly, while the $\pi/\mathfrak{W}_2$ plot shows a corresponding rapid drop to a much lower level.   This indicates that now larger particles are formed in agreement with the idea that these must be the micelles of colloidal dimensions resulting from the association of many ions, as we have already stated in Section 4-5.   The concentration at which the sharp change in osmotic properties occurs is called the critical micelle concentration or, briefly, the c.m.c.   (Note that the same abbreviation is often used for carboxy methyl cellulose.)   Since the presence of the micelles should have little effect on the behavior of the monomers present, it is only the solute in excess of the C.M.C. that forms micelles.

6-12. Long Flexible Chains

The typical results obtained with long flexible chains[10] are shown in Fig. 6-8d.   Here osmotic pressure increases much more rapidly than in an ideal solution so that the $\pi/\mathfrak{W}$ plot rises rapidly.   The extrapolated low value of $\pi/\mathfrak{W}$ at infinite dilution corresponds to the true weight of the whole particle.   At very high concentrations it tends to a high value which would correspond to a low particle weight of the order of that of one segment of the chain.

Another anomaly of these results is that, if the same material is measured in a good and in a poor solvent, the behavior seems more ideal, i.e., the $\pi/\mathfrak{W}$ plot is closer to horizontal, in the poor solvent.

To account qualitatively for this behavior we can return to the picture of particles moving like gas molecules through the solvent and consider what happens if the particle is composed of n_s segments capable of almost independent thermal motion. Let us first consider only one such particle, of total mass m. Each segment having a mass m_s moves with an average velocity u_s such that along one direction $m_s u_s^2 = \mathbf{k}T$.   These velocities are randomly directed forwards and backwards, and each contributes $1/n_s$ to the movement of the center of gravity. Thus we have again a random walk situation in which the average resultant velocity will be proportional to $u_s\sqrt{n_s}$. Since this average velocity of a segment contributes $1/n_s$, the center of gravity will have a velocity u proportional to $u_s/\sqrt{n_s}$. As $m = n_s m_s$, we have $mu^2 \propto n_s m_s(u_s/\sqrt{n_s})^2 = m_s u_s^2$. Since we have set $m_s u_s^2 = \mathbf{k}T$ this means also that $mu \propto \mathbf{k}T$. This is as it should be; the particle as a whole, i.e., its center of gravity, also obeys the equipartition principle.

When a particle of this sort approaches the semipermeable membrane and is reflected by it, the momentum given up is mu which corresponds to the particle as a whole, so that the osmotic pressure at infinite dilution corresponds to the true particle weight. In other words, in very dilute solutions the particle moves as a whole, and mild contact of a few segments with a membrane or another particle suffices to deflect it, but this still transmits the momentum of the whole particle to the membrane.

In more concentrated solutions, however, the particle is subject to the crowding pressure of the segments of its neighbors as well as to the deflecting action of the membrane, so that the simple effect of the motion of the center of gravity tends to disappear, and the pressure exerted by the individual segments becomes important. In the extreme case of very concentrated solution, the segments of different particles are so interwoven that their interaction eclipses their occasional interconnection, hence each is deflected individually by the membrane with a momentum corresponding to $m_s u_s$. This gives a much higher osmotic pressure and an apparent particle weight of the order of that of a segment.

In a poor solvent the segments of the individual particle tend to stick together, the coil is tighter and behaves more as a unit, thus giving more ideal behavior. Consequently, in a good solvent expansion is favored and the interaction of segments of different molecules occurs at lower concentrations, thus giving less ideal behavior.

6-13. Dialysis and Ultrafiltration

A subject which should be mentioned at this point, although it does not relate to colligative properties but only to semipermeable membranes, is that of dialysis and ultrafiltration.

In dialysis[11] a semipermeable membrane is used to permit the spontaneous separation of small particles from larger ones by diffusion of the former through the membrane.   This is a frequently used method of purification of various colloids, serving

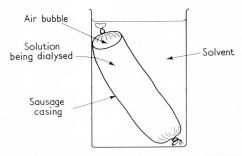

Air bubble

Solution being dialysed

Solvent

Sausage casing

Figure 6-9. A simple dialysis set-up using a sausage casing as a semipermeable membrane.

especially to separate them from simple salts.   This can often be done very simply by placing the solution in a sausage casing dipping in water, as shown in Fig. 6-9.   Dialysis is hastened by increasing the area of the membrane and by maintaining a high concentration gradient across the membrane through stirring the two liquids and renewing the outer one continuously, or at least frequently.   A variety of devices is available for this purpose.[11]

In ultrafiltration,[12] as shown in Fig. 6-10, hydrostatic pressure is applied to force the solvent and small particles across a membrane, while the large particles are retained.   This yields a more concentrated solution of the colloid and some interparticle liquid, the ultrafiltrate, whose composition may be studied.   Membranes can be prepared so as to have all pores of a uniform size which changes in a controlled manner from membrane to membrane.

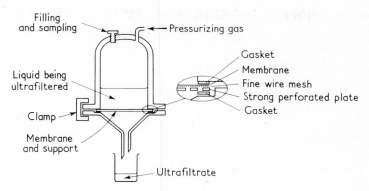

Figure 6-10. Principle of an ultrafiltration apparatus. Pressure forces the ultrafiltrate through the membrane which has to be elaborately supported to prevent its rupture.

Some of them are now available commercially. By using a set of such graded membranes and noting which one allows the particles to pass and which retains them, it is possible sometimes to draw conclusions about the size of the particles. The difficulty involved in this method of particle size determination lies in preparing and calibrating the membranes and also in the tendency of many particles to stick to the pores and obstruct them. Ultrafiltration is therefore not used widely for determining particle sizes.

Summary

Among the colligative properties osmotic pressure is outstanding in its applicability to dilute solutions of large particles. Like all colligative properties, it generally requires extrapolation to infinite dilution in order to be readily interpreted in terms of particle weight of an ideal solute. The particle weight thus determined refers to the same composition of the particle as that used in establishing its concentration in the solution. For polydisperse systems a number-average is measured. The osmotic pressure of linear high polymers in good solvents increases much faster with concentration than for ideal solutions because of the increasing effect of individual segments. Association colloids show almost ideal behavior below the critical micelle concentration, whereas above this the osmotic pressure measures the average of micelles and monomers.

References

1. J. H. van't Hoff, *Arch. Neerl.*, **20,** 239 (1886); *Z. physik. Chem.* **1,** 481 (1887); (accounts: *Ber.*, **27,** 1 (1894); A. Findley, *Osmotic Pressure*, Longmans, Green and Co., London, 1919, Dover Publications, New York, 1956, Chap. 2); W. Nernst, *Z. physik. Chem.*, **2,** 613 (1888); **4,** 129 (1889), *Theoretical Chemistry*, many editions; A. Einstein, ref. 6, of Chap. 5.
2. L. J. Briggs, *J. Appl. Phys.*, **21,** 721 (1950); **24,** 488 (1953); *J. Chem. Phys.*, **19,** 970 (1951).
3. L. J. Briggs, *J. Appl. Phys.*, **26,** 1001 (1955).
4. R. V. Townend, *J. Am. Chem. Soc.*, **50,** 2958 (1928); also (according to W. Nernst, *Theoretische Chemie*, Ferdinand Enke, Stuttgart, 1926, p. 163) Magnus, 1827, and Askenasy, *Verh. naturh.-med. Vereins, Heidelberg*, **5** (1896).
5. H. N. Morse, *Am. Chem. J.*, **45,** 91, 558 (1911); through Findley, see ref. 1, p. 5.
6. S. Arrhenius, *Z. physik. Chem.*, **3,** 115 (1889).
7. R. H. Wagner, in A. Weissberger, ed., *Techniques of Organic Chemistry*, Vol. I, Part 1, Interscience Publishers, Inc., New York, 1949, p. 487. R. Bonnar, M. Dimbat, F. Stross, *Number Average Molecular Weights*, Interscience Publishers, Inc., New York, 1958.
8. J. W. McBain, *Colloid Science*, D. C. Heath and Co., Boston, 1950, Chap. 17; or Chap. 5 in R. E. Burk and O. Grummit, ed., *Frontiers in Chemistry* Vol. VIII, Interscience Publishers, Inc., New York, Dover, New York, 1950.
9. A. P. Brady, H. Huff, and J. W. McBain, *J. Phys. and Colloid Sci.*, **55,** 304 (1950).
10. K. H. Meyer, *Natural and Synthetic High Polymers*, Vol. IV of *High Polymers*, Interscience Publishers, Inc., New York, 1950, Sect. H-III.
11. E. Staufer, in A. Weissberger, ed., *Techniques of Organic Chemistry*, Vol. III, Part 1, Interscience Publishers, Inc., New York, 1956, p. 65.

12. J. D. Ferry, *Chem. Revs.*, **18,** 373 (1936).
13. J. M. Bijvoet and A. F. Peerdeman, *J. Chem. Educ.*, **35,** 240 (1958).

Problems

41. According to the adjoining graph, the particle weights can be arranged as (*1*) $b > c > a$, (*2*) $c > b > a$, (*3*) $c > a = b$, (*4*) $b > c = a$.

59. If both a and c on the adjoining graph are the same linear polymers, then the solvent is (*1*) better in a, (*2*) better in c, (*3*) no way of telling.

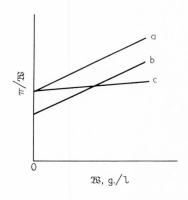

79. An aqueous solution contains two solutes A and B, both forming compact molecules. Their respective concentrations are 1 and 10 g./liter, mol. wt. 2×10^2 and 2×10^5. The freezing point of this solution is likely to be about (*1*) $-1.5°C.$, (*2*) $-0.5°C.$, (*3*) $-0.1°C.$, (*4*) $-0.05°C.$, (*5*) $-0.01°C.$, (*6*) $-0.005°C.$, (*7*) nowhere near any of these.

55. If the equilibrium osmotic pressure of the solution described in question 50 is measured with a cellophane membrane at room temperature, it is likely to be about (in cm. H_2O) (*1*) 2500, (*2*) 125, (*3*) 25, (*4*) 1.25, (*5*) 0.25 (*6*) nowhere near any of these.

62. Other things being equal, the osmotic pressure under ideal conditions (infinite dilution) will depend on (*1*) the molecular weight of the solvent, (*2*) the temperature, (*3*) the extent of solvation of the solute, (*4*) the vapor pressure of the solvent.

CHAPTER VII

Sedimentation Equilibrium

In the previous chapter we reviewed the interaction of thermal agitation with an immovable obstacle, such as an interface or semipermeable membrane, and the colligative properties which result from this interaction. We shall now consider what happens when a particle is subject to both thermal agitation and some other influence of the same order of magnitude. In the present chapter gravity will be this other influence; in the next one, van der Waals forces. Earlier, in Chapter 3 under the heading of sedimentation rate we covered the effect of gravitational forces when they are overwhelming, and we saw that the final state is then formed by all the particles settled to a more or less compact layer at the bottom, with pure solvent as the supernatant phase. On the other hand, thermal agitation always tends to distribute the particles uniformly throughout the solvent, and does achieve this result when other forces are negligible. We saw this in Chapter 5 which dealt with diffusion. When both effects are commensurate, we can expect an intermediate distribution of particles, neither uniform nor all at the bottom. This final equilibrium state will not be reached instantaneously but at a rate determined by the driving and resistant forces involved. In this case, consideration of the equilibrium state is very instructive and useful, whereas that of the rate is much more complicated[1] and of less general interest. We shall therefore confine ourselves to the former.

7-1. The Barometric Formula

The simplest case of such an equilibrium is presented by a gas in the gravitational field. To understand its behavior let us per-

151

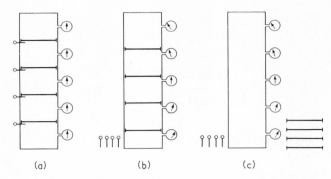

Figure 7-1. The formation of an equilibrium concentration and pressure gradient in a column of gas by the mutual compression of its layers in a gravitational field.   Weightless and frictionless pistons are supported by pins in (*a*), are free to move in (*b*) and are removed in (*c*).

form an idealized experiment.   The gas is confined in a tall tube divided into compartments by ideal pistons having no weight and moving without friction (Fig. 7-1).   At first, let the pistons be held rigidly at equal intervals and equal amounts of the gas be in each of the small compartments thus formed throughout the height of the tube.   As a result, the pressures and concentrations of gas in each compartment are the same (Fig. 7-1*a*).

Now, let us free the weightless and frictionless pistons.   In the absence of gravity, this would cause no change because all the pressures are equal.   Because of the presence of this force, however, each layer of gas has a certain weight, and this is transmitted through the piston to the layer below.   Thus, the bottom layer is compressed by the weight of all the layers above it, whereas the top layer is free of such forces.   As a result, the bottom layer will assume a smaller volume and will have a higher pressure and concentration, whereas the top layer will expand to a larger volume with lower concentration and pressure (Fig. 7-1*b*).

After the new state of equilibrium has been reached, we can remove the weightless and frictionless pistons without causing any change in the system, since the pistons did not exert any net force

(Fig. 7-1c).   Hence, at equilibrium the column of gas will have a pressure and concentration which gradually decreases from bottom to top.   We shall now calculate this decrease.

The density ρ of a very thin horizontal layer may be considered constant and equal to its average, because any relative variation decreases with the thickness ΔH of the layer while the average itself remains unchanged.   The pressure difference ΔP between the top and bottom of this layer is given by its weight per unit cross section.

$$-\Delta P = \rho \mathbf{g} \Delta H \qquad (7\text{-}1.1)$$

The sign is negative since pressure decreases as height increases. Hence

$$\Delta P/\Delta H = -\rho \mathbf{g} \qquad (7\text{-}1.2)$$

and as the layer becomes thinner

$$\partial P/\partial H = -\rho \mathbf{g} \qquad (7\text{-}1.3)$$

This applies to any fluid.   In the case of gases we know from Boyle's law that the density is directly proportional to the pressure

$$\rho = KP \qquad (7\text{-}1.4)$$

where $K = \mathbf{M}/\mathbf{R}T$ according to the ideal gas law and the definition of molecular weight.   Combining Eqs. 1.3 and 1.4 we obtain

$$\partial P/P = K\mathbf{g}\partial H \qquad (7\text{-}1.5)$$

From this equation the barometric formula (Eq. 7-1.10) follows by purely mathematical operations.   Integrating Eq. 7-1.5 gives

$$\ln P = -K\mathbf{g}H + \text{Constant} \qquad (7\text{-}1.6)$$

If the pressure P_0, at a height H_0 is known, the constant can be calculated since the above equation must apply there too

$$\ln P_0 = -K\mathbf{g}H_0 + \text{Constant} \qquad (7\text{-}1.7)$$

This gives

$$\text{Constant} = \ln P_0 + K\mathbf{g}H_0 \tag{7-1.8}$$

Introducing this into 7-1.6 gives

$$\ln P = -K\mathbf{g}(H - H_0) + \ln P_0 \tag{7-1.9}$$

or

$$\ln P/P_0 = -K\mathbf{g}(H - H_0) \tag{7-1.0}$$

This is Laplace's barometric formula, which was derived by him without any knowledge of the kinetic theory. As we have seen, it requires only Boyle's law. If we now introduce the formal def-

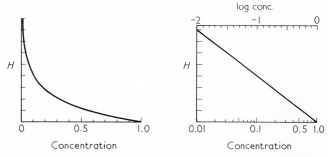

Figure 7-2. The relation of concentration to height in sedimentation equilibrium (barometric formula) as plotted on a linear scale (left) and on a semilogarithmic one (right).

inition of the molecular weight of a gas by replacing K with its explicit value, we obtain

$$\ln P/P_0 = -(M/\mathbf{R}T)\mathbf{g}(H - H_0) \tag{7-1.11}$$

Since the concentration of an ideal gas is proportional to its pressure, exactly the same expressions apply to the change in concentration with height

$$\ln \mathfrak{C}/\mathfrak{C}_0 = -(M/\mathbf{R}T)\mathbf{g}(H - H_0) \tag{7-1.12}$$

Figure 7-2 shows how concentration varies with height according to this formula on a linear and on a semilogarithmic plot.

These equations mean that as we go up by equal heights in a given system the logarithm of the pressure ratio, and therefore the pressure ratio P/P_0, is constant. Hence, pressure decreases in the same proportion for equal heights, and both pressure and the absolute change in pressure decrease with total height. The magnitude of the change of pressure with height depends on the molecular weight of the gas. The greater the molecular weight the greater the density at any given pressure and the greater the pressure change with height. Higher temperatures, on the other hand, tend to equalize the distribution of gas throughout the column.

If the numerical constants and common logarithms are introduced, the expression becomes for 20 °C.

$$\log P/P_0 = \log \mathfrak{C}/\mathfrak{C}_0 = -1.75 \times 10^{-8} M(H - H_0) \quad (7\text{-}1.13)$$

where H is in centimeters and the pressure, or concentration, in arbitrary units. Hence, the effect is small for gases over small heights but becomes significant if it is applied to gases over large heights or, alternatively, to large particles over small heights. Since we have already seen that particles of solute behave in some ways like gas molecules, this points to interesting applications in colloids. Before pursuing this topic we will first establish a very generally useful interpretation of the barometric formula in terms of the kinetic theory.

7-2. The Boltzmann Distribution

Let us now consider our equilibrium column of gas from the kinetic molecular point of view. The molecules of the gas keep an average velocity given by $mu^2 = \mathbf{k}T$, and this tends to carry them to great heights. They are also subject to the force of gravity, which tends to pull them down. As a result, if collisions were absent, only the fastest molecules would get very far up, and by the time they got there they would have slowed down. Collisions tend to redistribute the velocities at each level, making an exact analysis somewhat more complicated, but it is clear that the constant and unidirectional pull of gravity tends to concentrate all the molecules near the bottom, whereas thermal agitation tends to redistribute them uniformly.   Consequently, some particles do reach any given high level, but their number decreases with the height of that level.   As the molecular weight increases, the effect of gravity increases and a smaller proportion of particles reach that level.   As the number of particles at any given level increases, so does the number that may reach any high level.   Finally, as the temperature is raised, the velocity of the molecules increases and so does their chance of reaching any higher level.

Thus, the kinetic theory leads readily, though qualitatively, to the same conclusions about the equilibrium distribution of a gas as does the barometric formula.   Let us, therefore, accept the correctness of the rigorously derived, quantitative result of the barometric formula and interpret it kinetically.

The barometric formula

$$\ln \mathfrak{C}/\mathfrak{C}_0 = -(M/\mathbf{R}T)(H - H_0)\mathbf{g} \qquad (7\text{-}1.12)$$

can be restated in terms of single molecules by introducing the weight of the individual molecule $m\ (= M/\mathbf{N})$ and the Boltzmann constant $\mathbf{k}\ (\ = \mathbf{R}/\mathbf{N})$ and expressing the concentration ratio in terms of the number $\mathfrak{n}$ of particles per unit volume as

$$\ln \mathfrak{n}/\mathfrak{n}_0 = -(m/\mathbf{k}T)(H - H_0)\mathbf{g} = -m\mathbf{g}(H - H_0)/\mathbf{k}T \quad (7\text{-}2.1)$$

The last rearranged expression shows two energy terms: one is $\mathbf{k}T$, the other is the work required to bring the molecule from height H_0 up to H, since $m\mathbf{g}$ is the weight of the particle and $H - H_0$ the distance traveled.

Thus, the natural logarithm of the ratio of concentrations established by thermal agitation at two levels is simply the ratio of the work involved in transporting one particle between these levels and of the kinetic energy term $\mathbf{k}T$.   If we call the work term w we can write the barometric formula simply as

$$\ln \mathfrak{n}/\mathfrak{n}_0 = -w/\mathbf{k}T \qquad (7\text{-}2.2)$$

or in an equivalent form

$$\mathfrak{n} = \mathfrak{n}_0 \mathbf{e}^{-w/\mathbf{k}T} \qquad (7\text{-}2.3)$$

This is the quantitative expression of the result of competition between thermal agitation and the force of gravity.

It will be apparent that w is also the potential energy difference of the particle between the two regions at which we measure the concentrations n and n_0.

In all this argument there was nothing particular about the force of gravity that would distinguish it from other forces independent of velocity such as centrifugal, electrical, or van der Waals forces.   Therefore it stands to reason that, if any other such force is in competition with thermal agitation, the resulting concentrations will be given by the same expression, with w being the work required to transport one particle against this force. With this generalization, Eq. 7-2.3 is called the Boltzmann distribution.

Instead of expressing the state of the column in terms of the collective behavior of molecules as measured by pressure or concentration, we can also look at it from the point of view of the individual molecule.   Each such molecule in the system is equivalent to any other and will, if given enough time, find itself at any given level.   However, the amount of time it will spend at this level will depend on its height, more time being spent on the average at the lower levels than at the higher ones.   In other words, the probability of finding a molecule in a certain volume depends on the level of this volume.   This probability can be readily estimated since the number of molecules in any volume, i.e., their concentration, is equal to the probability of finding there any given one, times the total number of all molecules. Hence in this case the probability is proportional to the concentration and must, like the latter, be given by the Boltzmann distribution.

If we denote the probability by $\mathcal{P}$ we have therefore

$$\mathcal{P} = \mathcal{P}_0 e^{-w/kT} \tag{7-2.4}$$

which means that the probability due to thermal agitation of finding a given molecule in a unit volume of a certain region, de-

pends on the work that would be required to bring it, deliberately, into that region.

Finally, we may note that the Boltzmann distribution gives us
an exact expression valid over all values of $w/\mathbf{k}T$.   Like all continuous functions, the Boltzmann distribution can be approxi-
mated by a power series which in this case is

$$\mathbf{e}^{-w/\mathbf{k}T} = 1 - w/\mathbf{k}T + (w/\mathbf{k}T)^2/2! - (w/\mathbf{k}T)^3/3! + \ldots \quad (7\text{-}2.5)$$

When $w/\mathbf{k}T$ is very small, the square and higher terms become
negligible so that a very simple yet useful approximation of Eq.
7-2.3 is

$$\mathfrak{n} = \mathfrak{n}_0(1 - w/\mathbf{k}T) \qquad (7\text{-}2.6)$$

7-3. Sedimentation Equilibrium in Solutions

We can now return to the problem of the distribution of particles in a liquid, under the combined effects of gravity and thermal
agitation.   This is a case where the Boltzmann distribution is
clearly applicable, and we need only to evaluate w, the work of
transporting a particle between heights H_0 and H.   As we have
seen in connection with sedimentation rate (Eq. 3-3.3), gravity
exerts upon the particle a force equal to

$$f_a = m(1 - \rho/\rho_2)\mathbf{g} \qquad (7\text{-}3.1)$$

where m is the unhydrated weight of the particle and ρ_2 its unhydrated density.   Since work equals force times distance, we
have

$$w = m(1 - \rho/\rho_2)\mathbf{g}(H - H_0) \qquad (7\text{-}3.2)$$

and introducing it into the Boltzmann distribution we obtain

$$\ln \mathfrak{n}/\mathfrak{n}_0 = -m(1 - \rho/\rho_2)\mathbf{g}(H - H_0)/\mathbf{k}T \qquad (7\text{-}3.3)$$

If we compare this result with the barometric formula, Eq. 7-2.1,
we see that the only difference is the term $(1 - \rho/\rho_2)$ which ac-
counts for the buoyant effect of the solvent on the particle, $m(1 - \rho/\rho_2)$ $\mathbf{g}$ being the effective weight of the particle in the solution.

Hence, here again the particles in solution behave much as molecules of a gas.

Since the ratio of the number of particles per unit volume is also the ratio of concentrations, $\mathfrak{C}$, expressed in any units per unit volume, we also have

$$\ln \mathfrak{C}/\mathfrak{C}_0 = -m(1 - \rho/\rho_2)\mathbf{g}(H - H_0)/\mathbf{k}T \qquad (7\text{-}3.4)$$

7-4. The Balance of Diffusion and Settling

Instead of drawing the analogy with a column of gas or applying the Boltzmann expression, we can consider our particles in solution as settling under the influence of gravity and diffusing upwards under the influence of the concentration gradient produced. This is reasonable since there is no reason why these two microscopic processes should stop at any time. However, when they exactly neutralize each other no macroscopic change will be perceptible, and a state of equilibrium will obtain. Hence, the equilibrium state must be such that the amount settling across any level equals exactly the amount diffusing upwards across this same level.

Quantitatively, the flux due to settling, j_s, is given according to Eq. 3-13.3 by

$$j_s = u\mathfrak{n} \qquad (7\text{-}4.1)$$

the settling velocity, u, is in turn given by $u\,\varphi = f_d$, where φ is the friction factor and f_d is given by Eq. 7-3.1. Combining these expressions, we get

$$j_s = m(1 - \rho/\rho_2)\mathbf{g}\mathfrak{n}/\varphi \qquad (7\text{-}4.2)$$

The upward flux, j_d, due to diffusion, is given by Fick's first law (Section 5-1)

$$j_d = -D(\partial\mathfrak{n}/\partial H) \qquad (7\text{-}4.3)$$

As we have said, at equilibrium these two fluxes must be equal and opposite, hence

$$-D(\partial\mathfrak{n}/\partial H) = m(1 - \rho/\rho_2)\mathbf{g}\mathfrak{n}/\varphi \qquad (7\text{-}4.4)$$

or

$$\partial \mathfrak{n}/\mathfrak{n} = -m(1 - \rho/\rho_2)\mathbf{g}\partial H/D\varphi \qquad (7\text{-}4.5)$$

Integrating this expression, in the same way as was done for Eq. 7-1.5, we obtain

$$\ln \mathfrak{n}/\mathfrak{n}_0 = -m(1 - \rho/\rho_2)\mathbf{g}(H - H_0)/D\varphi \qquad (7\text{-}4.6)$$

which gives us the equilibrium distribution of the particles. The difference between the present expression and Eq. 7-3.3 is that the latter involved $\mathbf{k}T$ whereas the former involves $D\varphi$. Yet both describe exactly the same state, and both have been derived rigorously for an ideal system. This means that both expressions must be equal and that there must be a relation between $\mathbf{k}T$ and $D\varphi$. Comparison of the two expressions shows that this relation is simply

$$D\varphi = \mathbf{k}T \qquad (7\text{-}4.7)$$

which proves Einstein's law of diffusion as we have stated it already in Section 5-12.

7-5. Sedimentation Equilibrium and the Stability of Colloids

After this interpretation of the barometric formula for solutions (Eq. 7-3.3) in terms of sedimentation and diffusion, let us translate it into macroscopic terms by introducing the general concentration $\mathfrak{C}$ and multiplying both m and $\mathbf{k}$ by $\mathbf{N}$ to get M and $\mathbf{R}$ respectively

$$\ln \mathfrak{C}/\mathfrak{C}_0 = -M(1 - \rho/\rho_2)\mathbf{g}(H - H_0)/\mathbf{R}T \qquad (7\text{-}5.1)$$

Evaluating the constants for 20 °C. and converting to common logarithms

$$\log \mathfrak{C}/\mathfrak{C}_0 = -1.75 \times 10^{-8}M(1 - \rho/\rho_2)(H - H_0) \qquad (7\text{-}5.2)$$

with H in centimeters.

Since a value of unity for $\log \mathfrak{C}/\mathfrak{C}_0$ means a ten-fold change in concentration, we see that for particles whose density differs markedly from water such a change in concentration per centi-

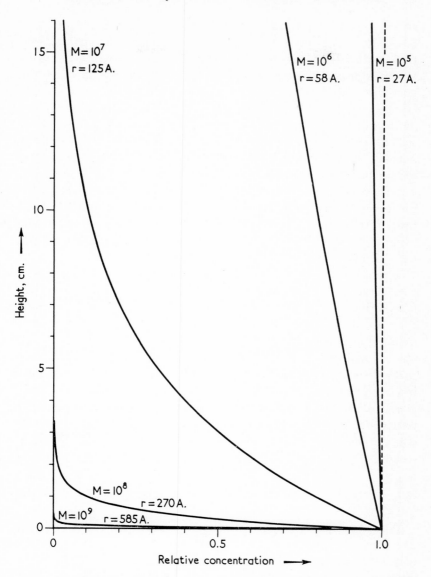

Figure 7-3. Gravitational equilibrium distribution in water of particles having a density of 2g/cm³. The radii are calculated assuming a spherical shape.

meter may be expected for particle weights of the order of 10^8. Much heavier particles will have even steeper concentration gradients and therefore will tend to gather very near the bottom, whereas much lighter particles will have lesser concentration gradients and will tend to be distributed almost uniformly. This is shown clearly in Fig. 7-3, in which the relative equilibrium concentrations in water are shown for particles having a density 2 and different particle weights. Since the height is given almost in actual size, the concentration changes are shown about as they would be directly observed.

Figure 7-3 shows clearly that, on the scale of a laboratory bottle, sedimentation equilibrium does not contribute toward a uniform distribution except for the lower extreme of the colloidal range. Hence, Brownian motion and diffusion alone are not capable of preventing the settling of most colloids on this scale. The reason for the apparent stability against settling of colloids is, therefore, as we have seen earlier (Section 3-22), the ubiquity of convection currents. The present considerations simply show that for the smallest particles there could be superimposed a factor due to thermal agitation. Since these are also the particles for which the rate of settling is particularly slow and convection currents particularly disturbing, this factor is of no practical importance.

Sedimentation equilibrium is, therefore, not even approached under ordinary laboratory conditions. Yet when realized it can be very valuable since it is directly related to the particle weight.

7-6. Experimental Methods

We have seen that sedimentation equilibrium is closely related to sedimentation rate since it is produced by a balance between this and diffusion. The rate of approach to this equilibrium must be of the same order as the rate of settling, which makes it very slow and extremely sensitive to convection currents.

Sedimentation equilibrium can be observed in vessels having

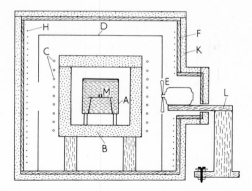

Figure 7-4. The experiment of McDowell and Usher. *M* indicates the two cells each 2 cm. high which are placed in a vessel filled with water and separated by an air-space and by insulation *B* from the outer circulating air-bath, whose temperature is maintained very constant by thermostat *C* and heater *H*. In order to reduce vibrations, the support of fan and motor *E* is not connected to the air-bath. (*From C. M. McDowell and F. L. Usher, Proc. Roy. Soc. (London)*, **A138,** *133 (1932)*.)

dimensions of the order of a centimeter only if the temperature control is excellent or if the settling rate is accelerated.

A very striking demonstration of the sedimentation equilibrium in a gold sol over appreciable distances and the production of a readily visible clear layer in the upper part of the liquid after a 3-week period has been given by McDowell and Usher[2] using the elaborate temperature control shown in Fig. 7-4.

The rate of settling can be accelerated by using an ultracentrifuge. This is of little value for larger particles whose equilibrium concentration gradient is already very steep (Fig. 7-3), but it can be very useful for small particles whose diffusion is rapid and tends to overcome completely the force of gravity. In contrast to sedimentation rate measurements where a sharp boundary undisturbed by diffusion is desirable, it is only a gradual change of concentration from top to bottom of the cell that is wanted in sedimentation equilibrium measurements. Hence, relatively weaker centrifugal fields are generally sufficient, and the method can be applied to very small particles. This procedure has been used

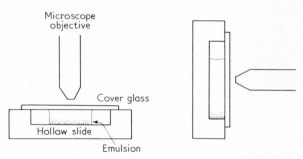

Figure 7-5. Perrin's illustration of his microscopic method of observing sedimentation equilibrium.   He mentions that the liquid layer is only about 0.1 mm. thick so that the proportions are completely distorted.   "Emulsion" refers to a suspension of spherical but solid particles of gamboge which is not the current meaning.   (*From J. Perrin, The Atoms, Constable and Co., London, 1923.*)

some in the past but is now being rapidly developed, and the difficulties connected with the length of the experiments[3] and with the accurate measurements of the concentration or the concentration gradient are being overcome.   (Probably the most up-to-date source of these procedures is in the manufacturer's manuals of the Spinco.)

It may be noted that the barometric formula has to be slightly modified when applied to a centrifuge.   The field $x\omega^2$ which replaces **g** changes with the distance, hence the work term w has to be estimated by integration of $dw = m(1 - \rho/\rho_2)x\omega^2 dx$.   Thus, $w = m(1 - \rho/\rho_2)\omega^2 (x^2 - x^2_0)/2$, and

$$\ln \mathfrak{C}/\mathfrak{C}_0 = -m(1 - \rho/\rho_2)\omega^2(x^2 - x_0^2)/2\mathbf{k}T \qquad (7\text{-}6.1)$$

In very small vessels, on the other hand, such as the space between the cover glass and a microscope slide separated by about 0.1 mm. (Fig. 7-5), sedimentation is readily established, and for larger particles can be observed microscopically.   It has been studied under these conditions for relatively large particles, such as those of the natural resin gamboge, by microscopic counting of the number of particles present at each level, and these measurements along with those of Brownian motion have played a role[4] in establishing the kinetic theory and determining Avo-

gadro's number.   When the observation is from above, as indicated in the left half of Fig. 7-5, advantage is taken of the very
small depth of focus of the microscope which makes visible only a
very thin layer of particles at one time.   By lowering the microscope, successive layers can be independently observed and their
concentration determined.

7-7. Meaning of Particle Weight

Since thermal agitation affects the particle as a kinetic unit and
does not change with its hydration or shape, and since the pull of
gravity is also unaffected by shape and hydration (Section 3-3),
the particle weight obtained from sedimentation equilibrium is
unaffected by these factors.   This resembles the result of colligative properties, but there is an important difference: there,
the actual concentration of the solution had to be known; here,
only the ratio at two levels is required.   A knowledge of the
pure material is required only in the determination of ρ_2.

Another way of looking at this problem is to note that both
the sedimentation rate and the diffusion rate are inversely proportional to the friction factor, φ, which depends on shape and
hydration.   Since sedimentation equilibrium depends on the op-
position of these two rates, the friction factor vanishes from the
result.

The particle weight thus obtained is, therefore, the same as
the one that is obtained if separate determinations of sedimentation velocity and diffusion constant are combined, as discussed in
Section 5-13.   Thus, a sedimentation equilibrium determination may be considered, in agreement with the kinetic picture, as
a single experiment balancing sedimentation rate against diffusion.

Although shape and hydration do not affect sedimentation
equilibrium, polydispersity does so markedly.   Each species
reaches a state of equilibrium given by Boltzmann's distribution,
but the total concentration no longer obeys this simple law.
This may be best seen from Fig. 7-6, which is a semilogarithmic
plot of concentration versus height.   For each species we have

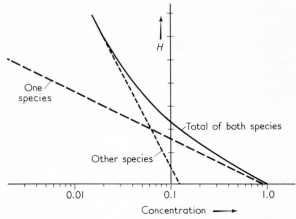

Figure 7-6. Sedimentation equilibrium of an ideal system of two species. While the concentration of each species corresponds to a straight line on a semilogarithmic plot, their sum necessarily gives a curved line.

a straight line according to Eq. 7-5.1. The sum of the two, however, is a curved line which cannot be represented by such an equation (because the logarithm of a sum is not the sum of the logarithms). In this simple case we can see that the two extremes of the curve approach the straight lines, and one could interpret the experimental result in terms of the two species. For polydispersed systems the situation is quite complicated and beyond the scope of this book. (A discussion of simple ideal systems may be found in reference 5.)

7-8. The Atmosphere

The gaseous atmosphere around the earth is a familiar though noncolloidal system under the influence of gravitational forces and of thermal agitation. One would therefore expect our considerations to apply directly. In fact, the barometric formula is well verified by air up to large heights. Its concentration and pressure decrease logarithmically according to its density. We know also that air is a solution of several gases and these differ markedly in molecular weight, N_2 being 28 and He

being 4.   According to the Boltzmann distribution, by the time
the concentration of nitrogen has decreased by a factor of 3 that
of helium should have decreased by only one-sixth, causing an
appreciable shift in composition.   In fact, however, the composition of the atmosphere is remarkably constant from the sea
level to the highest mountain tops.[6]

This apparent contradiction is due to the fact that the Boltzmann distribution deals with equilibrium systems, and equilibrium, as we have seen, has to be described with respect to specific processes.   Establishment of equilibrium with respect to air
as a whole requires only adjustment of pressure among the different levels with relatively minor bulk movements of large volumes of air.   This is a relatively rapid process, so that a state near
equilibrium prevails all the time from this point of view.   In
contrast, equilibration of the individual components requires
their relative transport by diffusion and sedimentation of individual molecules throughout the height of the atmosphere.   The
dimensions involved are so large that, despite the relatively high
diffusion coefficients of gases, the times involved are enormous.
The constant convection currents—winds and storms—are sufficient to completely obliterate any tendency toward this equilibrium and toward the applicability of the barometric formula to
individual gases within the atmosphere.

Thus the uniform composition of the atmosphere has basically
the same cause as the uniform concentration of colloidal solutions
under ordinary conditions.

Summary

When thermal agitation determines the relative equilibrium
concentrations and, therefore, the relative probabilities of finding a particle in two volumes, the Boltzmann distribution relates
these to the work required to transport a particle deliberately
from one volume into the other.   Sedimentation equilibrium is
an example of an equilibrium governed by this distribution.
Sedimentation equilibrium can also be considered as a balance
between the sedimentation and diffusion fluxes at all points.

Although generally slow to establish itself and easily disturbed by convection currents, sedimentation equilibrium can be used to determine particle weights.   Hydration and dissymmetry have no effect on sedimentation equilibrium, but polydispersity complicates it markedly.

References

1. M. Mason and W. Weaver, *Phys. Rev.*, **23**, 412 (1924); S. M. Klainer and G. Kegeles, *J. Phys. Chem.*, **59**, 952 (1955); also ref. 3.
2. C. M. McDowell and F. L. Usher, *Proc. Roy. Soc. (London)*, **A138**, 133 (1932); also N. Johnston and L. G. Howell, *Phys. Rev.*, **35**, 276 (1930).
3. R. A. Pasternak, G. M. Nazarian, and J. Vinograd, *Nature*, **179**, 92 (1957);   K. E. Van Holde and R. L. Baldwin, *J. Phys. Chem.*, **62**, 734 (1958).
4. J. Perrin, *The Atoms*, Constable and Co., London, 1923, Chap. 3.
5. W. D. Lansing and E. D. Kraemer, *J. Am. Chem. Soc.*, **57**, 1369 (1935).
6. R. M. Goody, *The Physics of the Stratosphere*, Cambridge University Press Cambridge, England, 1954, Sect. 3.4.

Problems

64. The friction factor φ enters the discussion of sedimentation equilibrium (*1*) in the evaluation of the work term in the Boltzmann distribution, (*2*) in the estimation of the driving force for sedimentation, (*3*) in the estimation of the rate of diffusion wihch maintains equilibrium (*4*) all of these, (*5*) none of these.

69. If a graph of log $\mathfrak{C}$ versus height in a sedimentation experiment is strictly linear, this does *not* indicate that (*1*) the particles are spherical, (*2*) the system is ideal over the range of concentrations involved, (*3*) the system is monodisperse, (*4*) the sedimentation was conducted in a gravitational field and not an ultracentrifuge, (*5*) all of these, (*6*) none of these.

47. The following graph represents the sedimentation equilibrium for two systems.   It could indicate that, all other things being equal, (*1*) the temperature is higher for *b*, (*2*) for the same particle

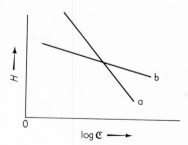

volume the density of the particles is greater in *a*, (*3*) for the same particle mass the density of the particles is greater in *b*, (*4*) all of these.

81. Vinograd and co-workers (ref. 9, chapter 3) observed a layer of colloidal particles at equilibrium in a density gradient. If the particles are strictly monodisperse (*1*) the height of the layer should be zero, (*2*) the concentration of the particles should be uniform throughout the height of this layer, (*3*) the spread of the layer should increase with the size of the particles, (*4*) the spread of the layer should depend on the particle weight but not on the friction factor.

CHAPTER VIII

Sorption

As we have already seen, thermal agitation tends to distribute all particles evenly through space, while forces acting upon the particles often oppose this tendency. We come now to the effect of attractive forces between particles, especially of van der Waals forces. When studying flocculation in Chapter 4, we examined some of the effects of these forces acting alone upon colloidal particles. In the present chapter we will be concerned mainly with the behavior of small particles as they are attracted to the surface of larger ones and even to macroscopic surfaces, i.e., adsorption. Thus we shall cover briefly some aspects of surface chemistry without attempting to survey this whole field. We shall restrict ourselves to what will be most needed for an understanding of the general behavior of colloidal systems; fuller treatments are given elsewhere.[1]

8-1. The Effect of Increasing Size

As mentioned above, we will be concerned mainly with the behavior of small particles under the combined influence of thermal agitation and of van der Waals forces. The reason is that for small particles an equilibrium distribution can be easily realized, whereas the particles become larger this becomes more and more difficult. This effect of size is shown, for example, in the quite important solubility behavior of long chain molecules.

Let us consider a saturated solution in equilibrium with the solid. As already stated in connection with Fig. 4-3, to dissolve a particle we must break some solute–solute and some solvent–solvent bonds and form some solute–solvent bonds. The first two require work, the last one can produce it. The resultant net work must be compared to $\mathbf{k}T$ in order to give us a measure of the probability of finding the particle in the liquid, i.e., its solubility.   The simple Boltzmann distribution cannot be applied to such a case because of the crowding of molecules in the solid, but we can still write

$$\mathfrak{C} = Ke^{-w/\mathbf{k}T} \tag{8-1.1}$$

where K is a constant.   Other things being equal, the solubility will vary with w.   If the work required to bring a particle into solution is large compared to $\mathbf{k}T$, the solubility will be low;   if it is small or negative, the solubility will be large.

The work term will always vary with the nature of the solvent. For a small particle the number of bonds involved is small, so that relatively great variations in the nature of the solvent are required to cause variations in w which are large compared to $\mathbf{k}T$ and correspond to very large changes in the solubility.   If we deal with a long chain molecule, the number of the bonds which have to be broken and formed is proportional to the number n_s of segments, and $w = n_s w_s$ where w_s is the net work per segment.   If n_s is very large, minute changes in w_s and, hence, in the nature of the solvent will cause great changes in solubility.

Thus, for example, if a long chain solute is dissolved in a good solvent and conditions are changed gradually, by lowering the temperature or adding a poor solvent, precipitation will gradually occur.   The longer chains, however, will be much more sensitive to changes in the solvent than the short ones.   They will precipitate earlier and over a narrower range of conditions than the shorter ones.   If particles of infinite chain length were present in such a system, they would, in principle, all precipitate at an infinitesimal change of conditions as soon as w_s became positive.   If the solute is polydispersed, fractionation will occur during precipitation, and the first fractions will be enriched in longer chains and the later ones in shorter chains.

If the transition from solution to two-phase system can be affected by changing the temperature, there will be a single temperature at which there will be a balance between the interactions determining w.   At this temperature the chain can behave as an ideal random coil since the segments neither attract nor repel each other.   Precipitation can begin when this temperature is crossed. It is generally called the Flory temperature, θ, of the system, after the contemporary physical chemist who brought out its importance.

8-2. Adsorption and Absorption

The term "sorption" is a very general description of the fact that a component has moved from one phase to another, particularly when this other phase is solid.   Thus, in the familiar titration of chloride with silver in the presence of dissolved dichlorofluorescein, the end point is indicated by a color change accompanying the attachment of the dye to the silver chloride.   We can say that the dye is sorbed by the precipitate;   it is the sorbate and the crystals are the sorbent.   In this case it is easy to establish that the dye is only on the surface of the small crystals, and we speak of *ad*sorption.   On the other hand, when a palladium cathode is used to electrolyze water, little or no hydrogen is evolved.   It is sorbed by the palladium.   In this case, the amount sorbed increases with the volume of the metal, and the gas is distributed throughout it, in part as a stoichiometric compound, in part as a solid solution.   Hence, the decision is again easy and we speak of *ab*sorption.

In other cases sorption may be easy to establish, but the question whether it is a surface or bulk phenomenon may not be readily settled.   An interesting phenomenon in which the distinction is not always clear at present is so-called "solubilization."

8-3. Solubilization

There are many substances, such as benzene, dibutyl phthalate, dodecyl alcohol, the dyes Orange OT or Pinacyanole* lauryl

---

* Pinacyanole is a cationic dye $[C_9N(C_2H_5)H_6]_2C_3H_3^+$ whose color changes markedly depending on environment.   Suspensions of its lauryl sulfate salt are red but the solubilized system is blue.   This color change can be used to determine the c.m.c., but the presence of solubilizable material has some effect on the equilibrium between monomers and micelles.[2]

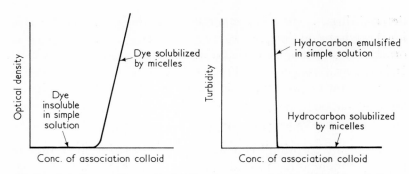

Figure 8-1. Some effects of solubilization by association colloids. *Left:* a water insoluble dye is unaffected at low concentrations but gives an intensely colored solution above the c.m.c. *Right:* if a small amount of a hydrocarbon is dissolved in a concentrated solution of an association colloid the solution stays clear upon dilution until precipitation and formation of an emulsion of high turbidity occurs near the c.m.c. (The turbidity due to micelles above the c.m.c. is negligible by comparison (see Chapter XX).)

sulfate, which are practically insoluble in water but dissolve markedly in solutions of association colloids, such as sodium lauryl sulfate (NaLS). The important fact is that as long as only simple ions of the association colloid are present, i.e., appreciably below the c.m.c., the solubility does not differ much from that in water. At higher concentrations it is almost directly proportional to the concentration of micelles (Fig. 8-1). Hence, the conclusion is readily drawn that the substance is attached to the micelle and, thus, held in solution or solubilized. We can safely say that the micelles have sorbed the substance. Whether it is adsorption or absorption, however, is a much more difficult question and the answer must be based mainly on a surmised structure of the micelles (Section 8-9).

8-4. Physical and Chemi-sorption

Any of the attractive forces exerted between particles may lead to adsorption. Their main classes are electric, van der Waals, and chemical. One sometimes distinguishes correspondingly between ion exchange, physical adsorption, and chemisorption.

We will consider the first one later (Chapter 17), and will be concerned here mainly with the second.   However, it should be remembered that different types of forces often combine to cause adsorption, and also that it is not always easy to distinguish between physical and chemisorption.   Essentially, the distinction involves the question of what kind of bond is formed rather than any simple experimental behavior.   It has been summarized by contrasting physical adsorption as surface condensation with chemisorption as surface reaction.

In some cases diagnosis of chemisorption is easy, as when upon adsorption of oxygen it is an oxide that is desorbed (e.g., from charcoal[3]), or when the energy of adsorption is more than could be reasonably due to van der Waals' forces.   Conversely, when an inert gas such as argon is adsorbed by inert surface, the adsorption can only be purely physical.   In other cases the distinction may be very uncertain.   Fortunately, it is also often unimportant.

8-5. Simple and Activated Adsorption

Whenever adsorption occurs, the adsorbate must reach the sorbent and must attach itself to it for at least a very short time. The rate at which the sorbent is reached depends on the concentration of the sorbate and on the rate of its Brownian motion. Using the same reasoning as in deriving Einstein's law of Brownian motion (Fig. 5-14), we can easily see that the number of particles having a diffusion coefficient D and concentration n which reaches a unit surface in time t is

$$q = (1/2)nl = n(Dt/2)^{1/2} \qquad (8\text{-}5.1)$$

where l is the average distance travelled by each particle in time t.   For gases, q is a large quantity except under high vacuum conditions, and even in aqueous solutions it is generally quite high.   Thus, in a 0.1% (by volume) aqueous solution of particles having a radius of 10 A., enough solute reaches the surface in 10 sec. to build up a layer 1000 A. thick, which means that each spot on the surface is reached by at least 100 particles in this time.   Thus, the rate of arrival is not, in general, the limiting factor in the rate of adsorption.   If the concentration is extremely low, however, or if the surface has deep cavities or thin capillaries, the rate of arrival may become significantly slow.

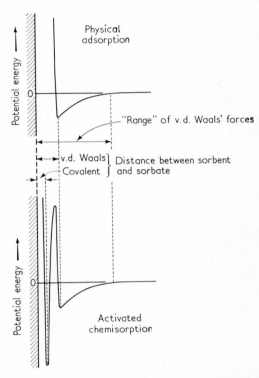

Figure 8-2. Potential energy diagram for physical adsorption (*top*) and activated chemisorption (*bottom*).

If there are no attractive forces between sorbate and sorbent, there will be no reason for attachment to the surface, and the state of equilibrium is readily reached.   Equilibrium is also reached rapidly if attractive forces can be exerted all along as the sorbate approaches the sorbent.   It does not matter whether the attractive forces are van der Waals, electrical, or chemical.

The energy distance diagram for this case has no hump but only a trough, as is schematically shown in the upper part of Fig. 8-2.

In the case of chemisorption, it sometimes happens that there is no interaction, or only a weak one, unless the sorbent and sorbate are brought together with great force and energy;   then a very strong bond is formed.   In ordinary terms: the reaction between sorbent and sorbate may be slow and require a large activation energy.   Of the many particles reaching the surface and attached to it by van der Waals' forces, only very few may acquire enough energy by random collisions to become chemisorbed. The bottom of Fig. 8-2 shows this situation.   The rate of reaching equilibrium with respect to chemisorption may be very slow or even negligible under such circumstances and will be greatly affected by temperature.   This is called activated adsorption.

Hence, activated adsorption on an accessible surface is always chemisorption, but chemisorption may be either simple or activated.   For example, the chemisorption of carbon monoxide on iron is instantaneous at liquid air temperatures.[4]   On the other hand, the chemisorption of nitrogen on iron (which seems to be a necessary step in the commerical synthesis of ammonia) does not occur appreciably until about 200 °C is reached.[5]

Another factor which may occasionally slow down adsorption is worth noting.   If large forces are involved in adsorption, considerable energy may be released as soon as adsorption occurs, which raises the temperature of the system, especially along the surface.   Hence, any equilibrium rapidly reached corresponds in this case to a higher temperature.   As heat is dissipated by radiation, conduction, and convection, the temperature of the surface will decrease and adsorption will approach a final equilibrium value which may be very different.   Thus, heat dissipation may be the rate determining factor.   This phenomenon is mainly important in gas adsorption at very low pressures where the heat capacity and conduction are both low.[6]

8-6. Coverage

The situation on a surface will depend greatly on the amount adsorbed, as indicated schematically in Fig. 8-3.   When the

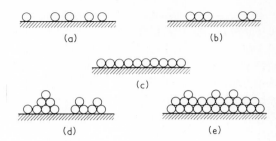

Figure 8-3. Coverage.   *Top:* low surface density; interparticle attraction (*a*) absent, (*b*) present.   *Middle:* a monolayer.   *Bottom:* multilayer adsorption; (*d*) preceding completion of monolayer, (*e*) following completion of monolayer.

amount adsorbed is very low, we deal essentially with a bare surface of adsorbent on which a few sorbate particles are present, far away from each other.   Hence, forces between sorbate particles are negligible whereas those between sorbent and sorbate are the only important ones.   This is low coverage of the surface.   As the amount adsorbed increases, the coverage becomes larger, the sorbate particles must be closer together, and their mutual interactions may, and generally do, become important.   Upon further increase in amount adsorbed, some sorbate particles no longer reach the sorbent but are separated from it by other sorbate particles.   Here forces between (adsorbed) sorbate and sorbate become very important.   This last situation is called multilayer adsorption and may or may not be readily reached, depending on the system.   If the surface is completely covered with a single layer of sorbate particles, we speak of the formation of a monolayer.   Again, depending on the system, multilayer adsorption may or may not precede the completion of the monolayer.

8-7. Competition

When dealing with a gas being adsorbed by a solid at low coverage, we are dealing only with forces between these two species, and whether these are chemical or physical they must always be attractive.   At higher coverages, sorbate–sorbate forces enter the picture, and these are also attractive.

When we deal with adsorption from solution, the situation is much more complicated.   The surface can no longer be bare; it must be covered by either the solvent or the solute.   Hence, adsorption of the solute involves (1) removing the solute from solution, (2) removing the solvent from the surface, and (3) attaching the solute to the surface (Fig. 8-4).   The last two steps will involve the breaking and making of bonds not only with the surface but also with adsorbed particles—of solvent at low coverages or of solute at high coverages.   The situation may be sim-

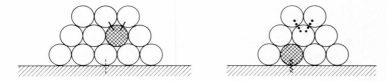

Figure 8-4. For adsorption from solution to occur, solvent-sorbent and solute-solvent bonds must be broken, while solvent-solvent and solute-sorbent bonds must be formed, as indicated schematically.

plified somewhat by looking at it as a competition between solvent and solute for the surface and considering the net work involved in adsorbing the solute at the expense of the solvent.   This may be negative or positive, and as a result adsorption itself may also be positive or negative.

Negative adsorption of a solute means that there is less solute near the surface than would correspond to a uniform distribution throughout all the solvent.   In other words, the number of solute particles per 100 solvent molecules is less at the surface than in the bulk of the solution.   This can only occur if the solvent is positively adsorbed.   In dilute solutions the amount of solute is very small even when it is uniformly distributed;   hence it is often difficult to determine precisely.   Negative adsorption is therefore hard to measure directly under these conditions and becomes more readily apparent in concentrated solutions.

As we have seen earlier, the forces between ions and the water of hydration are very large.   When single ions are brought out of the solution to the air–water interface, these bonds must be broken, and no significant forces are available to replace them. Hence, strong electrolytes formed by small ions are negatively adsorbed at the air–solution interface.

A similar situation prevails for the random coils formed by high polymers.   In the bulk of the solution the center of the coil can occupy any position without necessary deformation of its shape. If the center approaches a surface, the coil has to deform since segments cannot penetrate it and their thermal agitation forces the coil away from the surface.   Hence, in the absence of other forces, high polymers are negatively adsorbed.   This absence of other forces is rather unusual, but the existence of the negative adsorption could be verified experimentally.[7]

8-8. Orientation

If a particle is completely symmetrical, like an argon or tetra-methyl methane molecule, any position is equivalent to any other position and we need not concern ourselves with its orientation on the surface.   If it is unsymmetrical, like a nitrogen or benzene molecule, we may expect that thermal motion will tend to orient it randomly, whereas the forces responsible for adsorption as well as the effects of neighboring adsorbed molecules will tend to give it a preferred position.   Thus, there are indications that toluene and ethane molecules lie flat on the surface when only few of them are present and tend to stand up when crowded at higher coverages.[8]

In the case of polar particles having very different ends, the orientation may become very important.   The two ends, being part of the same particle, must stay close together, yet the force involved in breaking and forming bonds with them may differ widely.   When such a particle dissolves completely and individually within a phase, there is no choice as to the bonds to be broken and formed, and the total net work involved is determined.

However, at a surface, there is the possibility of the particle orienting itself so that this work is minimized.

Thus, we know that methyl alcohol is water soluble, which means that the work of breaking alcohol–alcohol and water–water bonds is less, or not much more, than that obtained from the formation of alcohol–water bonds; the alcohol group is hydrophilic.   On the other hand, hydrocarbons are insoluble in water because here the conditions are reversed, the water-hydrocarbon bonds are much weaker than the water–water ones, although they may be stronger than the hydrocarbon–hydrocarbon ones.   Hydrocarbons are hydrophobic.   If we consider a paraffinic solvent, on the other hand, the situation is reversed; the alcohol group is now lyophobic and the hydrocarbons are lyophilic.

A single molecule can often have both kinds of groups—one loving water, the other loving hydrocarbons.   Such a polar molecule may therefore be called amphipathic, having an affection for both.   An example of such amphipathic molecules are the higher aliphatic alcohols which combine a hydrophilic alcohol group with a hydrophobic paraffinic chain.   They become insoluble in water as this chain becomes longer.   Thermal motion is no longer able to break enough water–water bonds to bring the whole molecule into solution.   However, at a surface it is possible to bring the alcohol group into water without having to drag the hydrocarbon chain into it at the same time.   Hence higher alcohols, such as dodecyl alcohol, are strongly adsorbed at the surfaces of water, such as the air–water or benzene–water interface.

The orientation of the adsorbed alcohol will depend both on the nature of the other phase and on the degree of coverage, as indicated in Fig. 8-5.   The hydrophilic alcohol group will always tend to be in water.   At low coverage in the presence of air, the hydrocarbon chain will be weakly attracted by the water and lie more or less flat on it.   On the other hand, when the more polarizable benzene is present, it will be attracted more strongly by the water than the chain, so that the latter, being negatively adsorbed, will be directed more or less upward into the benzene. At somewhat higher coverages the forces between molecules will become important.   The hydrophilic heads in water and the hydrophobic tails in benzene will have little attraction for each other, but the tails resting on the water in the presence of air will tend to attract each other, and in this case the molecules will tend to congregate.   At still higher coverages, adsorption of additional polar

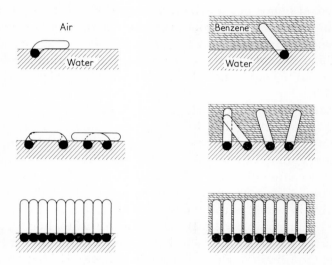

Figure 8-5. The orientation of amphipathic molecules at water-air and water-benzene interfaces depends on coverage.   Note that benzene competes successfully with the tails for the water surface and also for the other tails, whereas air does not.

heads to the air–water interface will have to displace some of the chains from the surface, but this will not involve much work. It will also permit the formation of additional hydrocarbon–hydrocarbon bonds as the alcohol molecules align themselves vertically on the surface.   Finally, in both systems the whole surface will be occupied by a tightly packed monolayer of aligned amphipathic molecules.

8-9. Association Colloids

Closely related to this surface orientation is the phenomenon of association which occurs in the bulk of the solution.   For very highly polar molecules, the work of bringing them into solution can be reduced, and solubility favored, if the molecules are not separated completely but only partially.   Thus, aliphatic acids dissolve in benzene as dimers, the strong hydrogen bond between the COOH groups still unbroken.   If they had to dissolve as monomers and this bond had to be also broken, the work of bringing them into solution would be much greater and the solubility much lower.

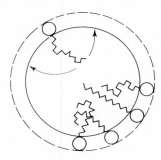

Figure 8-6. A possible spherical structure of micelles.   A few of the many amphipathic molecules are indicated to show that the outer part of the micelle contains the hydrophilic heads while the hydrophobic chains fill its interior in which they have much freedom of motion.   (*From G. S. Hartley in Progress in the Chemistry of Fats and Lipids, vol. 3, Pergamon Press, London, 1955.*)

In the case of aqueous solutions, a similar result is obtained if the hydrophilic parts of a highly amphipathic molecule are exposed to water while the hydrophobic ones remain in contact with each other.   This seems to be realized in the formation of micelles of association colloids, which are aggregates of such amphipathic particles with the polar heads exposed to water and enclosing, more or less, an interior formed by the hydrophobic tails.   The exact arrangement of the particles in such an aggregate and the reasons for its limited size are still not completely clear.   Figure 8-6 shows schematically a possible, spherical structure in whose interior the tails have much freedom of movement.   Such a micelle would be expected to solubilize hydrocarbons by incorporating them into its hydrocarbon interior. Solubilized amphipathic molecules, on the other hand, would be oriented in the surface of the micelle.

8-10. Traube's Rule

The properties of such amphipathic molecules having a hydrophilic head and a hydrophobic tail tend to change regularly with the length of the tail in a homologous series.   The bonds to be broken and reformed when the head is adsorbed are always the same, whereas expulsion of the tails from water permits an increasing number of water–water bonds to re-form as the tail becomes larger.   Hence, adsorption out of aqueous solutions, other things being equal, increases with the length of the hydrocarbon chain, so that the same amount of adsorption occurs at concentrations between about one-third and one-half as high for each added CH_2 group.   This generalization is often called Traube's rule.

8-11. Surface Tension and Adsorption

Surface tension (or surface free energy density) can be measured by the force needed per unit length to enlarge the surface. A very simple method of measuring it, the so-called Wilhelmy plate, is shown in Fig. 8-7.   A well-wetted plate, such as a microscope cover glass, dips into the solution while hanging from a balance.   Its vertical movement corresponds to a change in the surface of the liquid; hence, the balance measures this force per double widths of the plate.   If the plate is placed at the interface of two liquids, interfacial tension is measured.

From a molecular point of view, enlarging the surface means breaking bonds between molecules forming the phase, and, in the case of interfacial tension, also forming bonds between molecules belonging to different phases.   If a solute which is

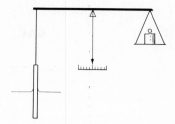

Figure 8-7. Principle of the Wilhelmy plate method of measuring surface tension.   The force acting upon a well wetted plate of known dimensions is determined.

adsorbed at the surface (surface active solute) is present, enlarging the surface must be easier, i.e., the surface tension must be lower.   The fact that the solute is adsorbed at the surface means that work can be obtained upon bringing it to the surface.   Thus, if we would first enlarge the surface of the solvent alone, not allowing any solute molecules to reach the surface, we would do work against the surface tension of the solvent.   If now we allow adsorption to take place, thus forming a surface of the solution, we get some of this work back.   The net (lower) work is the same as would be used to produce the fresh area against the surface tension of the solution.   The latter must, therefore, be lower.

Conversely, if the solute is negatively adsorbed in dilute solutions, the surface tension of the solution will be higher than that of the solvent.   However, the effect is slight, since negative adsorption itself is necessarily small.   The evidence for the negative adsorption of ions and of ideal random coils which we mentioned earlier (Section 8-7), comes mostly from surface tension measurements which show a slight rise with concentration.

8-12. The Surface Tension of Colloidal Solutions

Stable and diuturnal colloidal particles are generally quite inactive at the air–solution interface, and this is related to their size and stability.   If they were surface active, work could be readily obtained by bringing them to the surface, i.e., by remov-

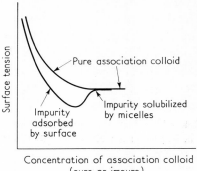

Figure 8-8. An association colloid containing a surface-active impurity may show a minimum near the c.m.c. as indicated by the lower curve. The minimum disappears when the impurity is removed. (*After G. D. Milles and L. Shedlovsky, J. Phys. Chem.*, **48**, *57 (1944)*.)

ing them from the water. Further work could then be obtained by bringing them together, because of attractive van der Waals forces freed of competition with the solvent. This would imply that they should also flocculate spontaneously and, hence, could not be stable or diuturnal.

This argument applies even to the behavior of solutions of association colloids which show a marked surface tension lowering. This is because the solution contains not only colloidal particles but also simple monomers. These highly polar monomers are very surface active, and despite their small size they do aggregate spontaneously, as shown by the formation of micelles. The micelles themselves with their hydrophilic exteriors are, however, surface inactive. They may be important, nevertheless, in surface phenomena as a reserve supply of monomers.

Apparently stable proteins, such as serum or egg albumin, also lower the surface tension of water and, thus, seem to be surface active. The surface tension lowering is, however, accompanied by denaturation, so that in the presence of surface these proteins are not truly stable. Egg whites, for example, show such surface activity and easy denaturation. It is this that permits their whipping and the making of meringues.

An interesting phenomenon, which puzzled chemists for years is a minimum which appears in the surface tension versus concentration curve of many association colloids, such as the one of NaLS shown in Figs. 8-8. This minimum has been traced to the presence of highly surface active and easily solubilized impurities, such as a trace of dodecyl alcohol in NaLS. Below the c.m.c., the impurity is strongly adsorbed at the surface and lowers the surface tension more than monomeric ions of NaLS would lower it by themselves. Above the c.m.c., however, it is strongly sorbed by the micelles, i.e., solubilized, and thus removed from the solution and even from the surface. Hence the surface tension increases to the value due to NaLS alone.

8-13. Polarization

As we have seen, a polar molecule adsorbed on a surface will be oriented so that it presents to other incoming molecules a very different picture from a randomly oriented one. Even a nonpolar and symmetrical molecule, once it is adsorbed, will lose this character because it is held by the van der Waals forces responsible for adsorption, and these forces are exerted along the perpendicular to the surface. As we have seen earlier, these forces are due in such a case to induced dipoles. Hence, the molecule ceases to be nonpolar once it is adsorbed and becomes polarized in the direction perpendicular to the surface.

Polarization by the surface will, of course, occur also with initially polar and unsymmetrical molecules, distorting them somewhat further.

8-14. Monolayers and Multilayers

Thus an adsorbed molecule differs appreciably from one that is free because it becomes oriented and polarized. This in turn must affect its interaction with other oncoming molecules and the formation of monolayers and multilayers. The number of approaching molecules is proportional to the pressure of the gas or vapor which is being adsorbed. At any fixed temperature the largest equilibrium pressure for a vapor is P_0, the vapor pressure of the pure liquid.   The number of molecules evaporating from the surface of the liquid is equal to that condensing on it when the pressure of the vapor is P_0.   This is merely the dynamic picture of the equilibrium between the two phases.

Now imagine a layer of these molecules unchanged in every respect except that they cannot leave this layer.   Since their attractive forces are the same as in the free liquid, molecules of vapor have the same chance of condensing here as on free surface and will tend to form a second layer; however, only molecules in the second layer can evaporate.   If the pressure of the vapor, P, equals P_0, the second layer will be complete, and successive layers may build up indefinitely in order to maintain the equilibrium conditions, since the surface of evaporating molecules must be equal to that of condensing ones.   If P is less than P_0, the second layer will be incomplete at equilibrium in order that the number of evaporating molecules be equal to the reduced number of condensing ones.   Portions of the second layer may, however, be covered by higher layers.

This imaginary situation is not to be expected in adsorption. An adsorbed layer of moleules is not likely to exert the same forces as the surface of a free liquid.   If formed by polarized nonpolar molecules, it would be expected to exert stronger forces upon other molecules.   If formed by polar molecules oriented by the surface so that the more weakly bonded tails are directed outward, it would be expected to exert weaker forces.   In the former case, formation of a second layer is favored, and it will be completed while P is still below P_0, and may be followed by other layers before P_0 is reached.   In the latter case, the second layer will not be completed even at P_0, and there may be little tendency even to begin its formation.   This last condition may prevail despite the fact that the first, highly oriented layer may be held firmly and formed readily.   An extreme case of this type is given by so called autophobic liquids, such as higher aliphatic alcohols, which do not spread on an adsorbed monolayer of their own molecules.[9]

Thus, depending on the particular system, multilayer adsorption may or may not occur, and when it does occur it may or may not tend to form complete layers (Fig. 8-3).

8-15. Capillary Condensation

It is a general phenomenon that a convex liquid surface, such as that of a small droplet, has a somewhat higher vapor pressure than a flat surface.   Conversely, a concave surface, for example in a well-wetted capillary, has a lower vapor pressure. From a molecular point of view this is readily seen as a consequence of the fact that a molecule is increasingly better surrounded by its neighbors as the surface changes from convex to concave (Fig. 8-9);   consequently, it is held more strongly by

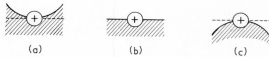

(a)   (b)   (c)

Figure 8-9. A molecule in the surface is more completely surrounded by its neighbors when the surface is concave (a), less completely when the surface is plane (b), and still less when it is convex (c).   The vapor pressure of a liquid increases accordingly in the same order.

them and has less tendency to evaporate, so that the vapor pressure is lowered progressively as the curvature changes in this direction.   This effect can also be regarded as a consequence of the fact that, on a droplet, surface tension exerts a positive pressure, whereas, on a concave meniscus it exerts a negative pressure.   As we have already seen (Section 6-2), these pressures raise and lower the vapor pressure respectively.*

---

* The quantitative expression—Kelvin's law:

$$\ln P/P_0 = 2M\gamma/\mathbf{R}T\rho R$$

where γ is the surface tension, ρ the density of liquid, R, the radius of the drop, and M the molecular weight of the vapor, is derived, for example, in reference 10. For water at 25° C., this gives $\log P/P_0 = 4.6 \times 10^{-8}/R$, which gives a 10% effect at $R = 100$ A. and a factor of 2 at $R = 15$ A.

Similarly, in adsorption, if the surface is not plane but forms crevices and capillaries, sorption is favored, because the surface tends to surround an adsorbed molecule and thus to hold it more strongly.   This effect continues as successive layers of molecules cover the surface, giving a concave meniscus so that filling of the capillary is favored below P_0.   This is the phenomenon of capillary condensation, which is often very important in the adsorption of vapors at higher partial pressures by porous materials. When capillary condensation is important, the maximum volume adsorbed is almost independent of the sorbate and is simply the total volume of the pores of the sorbent.

8-16. Dynamic Equilibrium and Mobility

There are some cases known in which it may be shown directly that adsorbed atoms are highly mobile, moving readily along the surface from one spot to another.   The most elegant experiment is probably the one described by Volmer and shown in Fig. 8-10,

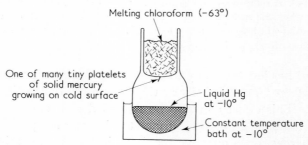

Figure 8-10. An experiment showing the surface mobility of molecules.   The rate of growth of the edges of the platelet corresponds to the rate of arrival of molecules upon its whole surface.   (*After M. Volmer and I. Estermann, Z. Physik, 7, 13 (1921).*)

in which a crystalline platelet of mercury was grown out of mercury vapor of known concentration.   The growth occurred only on the thin edges of the platelet, but it occurred at a rate corresponding to the accumulation of at least a thousand times more atoms than could reach this edge directly from the vapor phase.

The growth corresponded, however, quite well to the rate at which the atoms were reaching the faces of the platelet from the vapor phase. Hence, these atoms upon reaching the face must have become adsorbed on it and then moved, while adsorbed, to the edge where they finally came to rest.

There are many cases, however, where it is very difficult or impossible to demonstrate surface mobility directly, but it seems probable from general considerations that whenever a dynamic equilibrium is reached in adsorption, the main impediment to surface mobility will come not from the surface itself but from the other adsorbed molecules, and that it will come only at high coverages.

This argument runs about as follows: The existence of a dynamic equilibrium means that desorption occurs continuously, i.e., that thermal agitation is frequently able to overcome the forces causing adsorption. This is generally the case in physical adsorption but frequently is not the case for chemisorption, especially not at lower temperatures.

In order to move along the surface, the particle need not detach itself from the surface completely as in desorption. If the surface were microscopically homogeneous, there would be no resistance at all to the motion of the molecule in any direction along it. If the surface, because of its atomic structure, has spots to which the molecule is attracted more than to intermediate regions, only a partial detachment from one spot is needed to permit motion to the next spot. Hence, if dynamic equilibrium prevails, forces between surface and molecule are not sufficient to prevent it from moving occasionally away from the surface and therefore from moving along the surface much more often.

The reason why the molecule should tend to move along the surface is, of course, thermal agitation, which is exerted in all directions. Even when adsorption forces may prevent thermal agitation from removing the particle from the surface, the tendency to move it along the surface, as a result of all the collisions with atoms of the surface, incoming molecules, and other adsorbed molecules, will persist.

When the surface becomes crowded and adsorbed molecules cluster, then the restrictive influence of the neighbors may slow down any lateral motion, just as it is slowed down in a solid.

8-17. Heterogeneity of Surfaces

In speaking about adsorption, one generally speaks of *the* surface, i.e., of a homogeneous array of atoms or molecules, each offering the same opportunity for adsorption. This picture may correspond to reality in a few cases, such as the surface of a pure

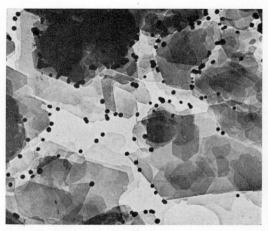

Figure 8-11. Electron micrograph of platelets of bentonite and specks of colloidal gold. Note that the gold particles are preferentially adsorbed by the edges, showing that the surface of the bentonite is not homogeneous. (Magnification 40,000 ×.) (*Courtesy P. A. Thiessen, Z. Electrochem.*, **48**, *675* (*1942*).)

liquid or a freshly cleaved mica sheet. Most surfaces, however, seem to depart markedly from this ideal state and are significantly heterogeneous. Extreme examples are known. Graphite powdered in high vacuum chemisorbs nitrogen rapidly and very strongly on the fresh edges where C—C bonds have been broken, but sorbs large additional amounts of nitrogen purely physically and much more weakly on the flat faces.[11] Platelets of the clay

Bentonite will bind negatively charged particles of colloidal gold along the edges only, as shown in Fig. 8-11, but also attach large amounts of various positive ions all along the flat faces.   There are some catalysts which, when their temperature is raised in the

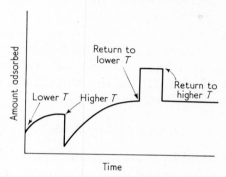

Figure 8-12. When the temperature of certain ZnO catalysts is raised in the presence of a constant pressure of hydrogen, both a rapid and reversible desorption and a slow and irreversible adsorption occur, indicating a heterogeneous surface.   (*After H. S. Taylor and S. C. Liang, J. Am. Chem. Soc.*, **69,** *1306* (*1947*).)

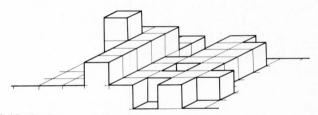

Figure 8-13. Surface irregularities of a crystal can provide a variety of faces, edges, and corners having different adsorptive power.

presence of a gas at constant pressure, first desorb rapidly a certain amount, then adsorb slowly a smaller or larger one (Fig. 8-12).   This shows that two opposite processes occur simultaneously, presumably on different parts of the surface.

In the case of crystalline solids, different forces must be exerted at the different plane surfaces and at the variety of corners, edges, troughs, and holes which can be formed by surface imperfections, as shown in Fig. 8-13.   Imperfections of the crystal lattice and impurities can produce additional heterogeneities.

As an extreme example of complications which can be caused by surface heterogeneity, we may consider a hypothetical surface whose one half adsorbs very strongly a monolayer of A, and the other half very strongly a monolayer of B, from a mixture of A and B.   This will lead to about equal amount of A and B adsorbed through most of the concentration range.   Hence, if the bulk mixture contains much more A than B, we have a strong negative adsorption of A, and vice versa if the concentrations are reversed.

8-18. The Amount Adsorbed

At constant conditions, the amount adsorbed is proportional to the available surface and therefore generally to the weight of sorbent.   Hence, the amount adsorbed is generally expressed per unit weight, e.g., as cubic centimeters of gas at **STP** or as grams or moles of sorbate, per gram of sorbent.   It may also be expressed in terms of monolayers or as per cent coverage when the adsorbing surface is known.   Under these latter conditions, particularly for a liquid surface, one often uses the inverse quantity, the surface available, in square Angstroms per molecule.   It may be noted that 166 A.^{2} per molecule is equivalent to 1 mole/km.^{2} or per 247 acres.

8-19. Adsorption Isobar

The amount adsorbed depends generally on the temperature, and decreases, at equilibrium, as the temperature rises.   This is due to the fact that the forces causing adsorption are essentially unaffected by temperature, whereas thermal agitation increases with $\mathbf{k}T$.   Alternatively, one can say that adsorption, being due to work done by forces causing it, is generally exothermic; hence, according to LeChatelier's principle it is favored by lower temperature.   The opposite type of behavior is encountered only when a competing adsorbate is present, so that the net work

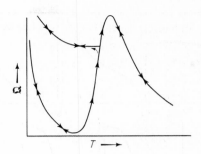

Figure 8-14. Schematic adsorption isobar for a system showing both simple and activated adsorption. The arrows indicate the reversibility or irreversibility of the adsorption along each branch of the isobar.

of absorption is negative. This is the case, for example, in the chemisorption of oxygen by platinum in the presence of carbon monoxide at 200–400 °C. As higher temperature reduces the adsorption of CO, more surface becomes available for O_2 and its adsorption increases.[12]

The above considerations apply only to the effect of temperature on equilibrium. If equilibrium is not reached, as often happens in activated adsorption, a rise in temperature may lead to an increase in adsorption simply because the rate now becomes noticeable, but this is not reversible upon lowering the temperature. When both simple and activated adsorption occur in the same system, one may encounter the behavior shown in Fig. 8-14. At low temperatures, a reversible decrease in physical adsorption occurs as the temperature is raised. At higher temperatures chemisorption occurs irreversibly and at still higher temperatures chemisorption, in turn, decreases reversibly. Upon cooling from a high temperature one may get additional reversible physical sorption superimposed upon an amount which is irreversibly chemisorbed.

8-20. The Adsorption Isotherm

Since temperature affects adsorption so markedly, the effects of changing bulk concentration are best observed at constant

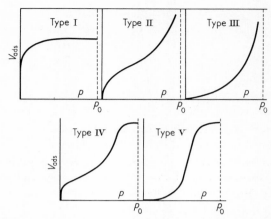

Figure 8-15. The five typical shapes of isotherms for physical adsorption. (*From S. Brunauer, L. S. Deming, W. E. Deming, and E. Teller, J. Am. Chem. Soc.*, **62**, *1723* (*1940*).)

temperature.   The curves summarizing them are called adsorption isotherms.   Since adsorption is a balance between forces which always tend to bring all the sorbate to the surface and thermal agitation which tends to distribute it uniformly, in two-component systems there can be no decrease in the amount adsorbed as bulk concentration increases.   In systems of more than two components other effects can occur, as we have seen in connection with the surface tension minima and with negative adsorption.

In most cases, the increase in amount adsorbed with concentration is gradual, and the isotherms tend to approach one of the five types shown in Fig. 8-15.   On very uniform surfaces, however, one has observed essentially vertical and horizontal portions.[13]

If conditions causing adsorption remain constant, one would expect that doubling the concentration of a dilute sorbate would also double the amount adsorbed, since twice as many molecules would now be reaching the surface.   As may be seen from Fig. 8-15, this condition seldom prevails.   Most of the time adsorption increases either faster or slower than concentration, and the isotherm is either convex or concave to the pressure axis. This means that conditions causing adsorption change, in one or the other direction, as adsorption proceeds. In general, if an adsorbed molecule renders the surface less attractive to the next one, the isotherm will be concave to the concentration axis. This is the case, for example, if a few most active spots of the surface are being occupied, or when the first layer is being filled by molecules having little attraction for each other. On the other hand, under reverse conditions when the surface becomes increasingly attractive with coverage, the isotherm becomes convex to the pressure axis. This is the case when a capillary is being filled or when molecules attract each other strongly so that they tend to bunch on the surface.

8-21. Isotherm Equations

There are three mathematical expressions which are most frequently used to express adsorption isotherms. These are due to Freundlich, to Langmuir, and to Brunauer, Emmett, and Teller (B.E.T.). The first one is empirical; the last two have been derived rigorously from simplified assumptions about the structure of the system and the mechanics of adsorption. But closer examination shows that these assumptions seldom apply to systems for which the expressions themselves are very useful. This is because the expressions contain constants which can be chosen to fit the data without regard to their original meaning in the premises of the theory. For this reason we shall simply present these expressions without derivation and with a minimum of interpretation.

We shall express them in terms of sorbate pressure, P, but this can be replaced directly by the concentration (or activity) of solute for adsorption from solutions.

The Freundlich Isotherm

The Freundlich isotherm gives the amount adsorbed per unit absorbent $\mathfrak{Q}$ as a function of the pressure, P, and two constants a and b

$$\mathfrak{Q} = aP^b \qquad \text{or} \qquad \log \mathfrak{Q} = \log a + b \log P \qquad (8\text{-}21.1)$$

The first form gives Ω explicitly, whereas the second is a linear relation between $log\ \Omega$ and $log\ P$.   Both Ω and log P are readily accessible from experimental data and if plotted against each other should define (if Freundlich's isotherm applies) a straight line of slope b and intercept log a.   This kind of plot makes it possible to ascertain readily whether the data conform to the equation, and if they do, to evaluate the constants.

The constant b varies between 1 and 0.1, so that the isotherm always increases but is concave to the pressure axis.   The smaller the b, the more rapid the curvature.   At constant b the amount adsorbed increases with a at any concentration.   It may be noted that the amount adsorbed, according to this isotherm, increases always until P cannot increase further at saturation.   At low concentration the slope of the isotherm tends to the vertical, indicating infinitely strong adsorption and great changes at the lowest coverages.

Thus the Freundlich isotherm tends to fit the isotherms of type I and the beginning of types II and IV of Fig. 8-15.

The Langmuir Isotherm

The Langmuir isotherm also introduces two constants, k and q, and is of the form

$$\Omega = qkP/(1 + kP) \qquad \text{or} \qquad P/\Omega = (1/kq) + (1/q)P \text{ (8-21.2)}$$

The second form, again, permits the evaluation of the constants from a plot of P/Ω versus P, which should be linear.

The Langmuir isotherm also increases with concentration at a decreasing rate, but it differs in two respects.   At high pressures, when 1 becomes negligible compared to kP, it gives $\Omega = q$, a limit to the amount adsorbed, which can be interpreted as a complete monolayer.   At low pressures, when kP is negligible in comparison with 1, it gives $\Omega = qkP$, so that the amount adsorbed is proportional to concentration, suggesting that at low coverages each particle is independently adsorbed in the same way.   The curvature of the isotherm depends on k, and, other things being equal, the amount adsorbed increases with q.

The Langmuir equation tends to fit the same types of isotherms as the Freundlich one and is particularly applicable to highly homogeneous surfaces.

The B.E.T. Equation

The B.E.T. equation in the commonly used, somewhat simplified form introduces explicitly the saturation value P_0 and two constants q and h to give

$$\mathfrak{Q} = qhP_0P/(P_0 - P)(P_0 + hP - P) \qquad \text{or} \qquad P/\mathfrak{Q}(P_0 - P)$$
$$= 1/qh + (h - 1)P/qhP_0 \quad (8\text{-}21.3)$$

where the second form again gives a linear plot of experimental quantities for the evaluation of constants.

When P approaches P_0, $\mathfrak{Q}$ goes to infinity, i.e., multilayer adsorption extends indefinitely.   If compared to P_0, hP is not negligible but P can be neglected, then one obtains the Langmuir isotherm in which $k = h/P_0$.   Again q is interpreted as a complete monolayer, but it corresponds to the amount adsorbed at an intermediate pressure.

The B.E.T. isotherm fits best the isotherms of type II and III of Fig. 8-15, but can be modified also to fit the other types.

8-22. Specific Surface

Both the Langmuir and the B.E.T. equations involve a constant q which is identified with the amount required to form a monolayer and which can be readily determined from the shape of the isotherm.   These values of q are very frequently determined for adsorbents from the B.E.T. equation, using nitrogen at its boiling point as the adsorbate.   From this, the area of the surface is calculated using a value such as 15.25 A². per molecule of nitrogen (i.e., 9.2×10^4 m²., or 23 acres, per mole).   The result is reported as the B.E.T. surface per gram (specific surface) of the adsorbent.   It is a very valuable single characteristic of adsorbents and frequently is quite close to the specific surface determined by other methods.

8-23. Particle Size

If the shape of particles forming an adsorbent is known or assumed, one can relate the specific surface to their size. For example, if we deal with monodisperse spheres having a smooth surface—so that the geometric surface corresponds to the one determined by adsorption—a radius r and a density ρ then the mass m of each is $4/3\pi r^3 \rho$ and its surface a is $4\pi r^2$. The number, n, of spheres per gram is $1/m$ and the specific area $A = na$. Hence

$$A = 4\pi r^2/(4/3)\pi r^3 \rho = 3/r\rho \qquad (8\text{-}23.1)$$

In general, for monodisperse systems the dimensions of the particles are inversely proportional to the specific surface, with the proportionality constant depending on their shape. Their mass is therefore inversely proportional to the cube of the specific surface. For polydisperse systems or for mixtures of shapes one obtains a so-called "surface-average" radius or mass.

Summary

Adsorption is the result of a balance between thermal agitation and attractive forces. The attractive forces include surface–particle as well as particle–particle effects. In solutions, competition between solvent and solute always plays a role and may lead to negative adsorption. Surfaces are frequently heterogeneous, and adsorbed particles are always polarized and often strongly oriented. If the amount forming a monolayer can be estimated, it provides a measure of the adsorbing surface, and can give an indication of the size of the particles which form this surface.

References

1. A. W. Adamson, *Physical Chemistry of Surfaces*, Interscience Publishers, Inc., New York, 1959; J. H. de Boer, *The Dynamical Character of Adsorption*, The Clarendon Press, Oxford, 1953; S. Brunauer *The Adsorption of Gases and Vapors*, Princeton University Press, Princeton, N. J., 1943.

2. P. Mukerjee and K. J. Mysels, *J. Am. Chem. Soc.*, **77,** 2937 (1955).

3. M. S. Shah, *J. Chem. Soc.*, **1929,** 2661.

4. P. H. Emmett and S. Brunauer, *J. Am. Chem. Soc.*, **59,** 310 (1937).

5. P. H. Emmett and S. Brunauer, *J. Am. Chem. Soc.*, **56,** 35 (1934).

6. S. W. Benson, D. A. Ellis, and R. W. Zwanzig, *J. Am. Chem. Soc.*, **72,** 2102 (1950).

7. H. L. Frisch and S. Al-Madfai, *J. Am. Chem. Soc.*, **80,** 3561 (1958).

8. C. Kemball and E. K. Rideal, *Proc. Roy. Soc. (London)*, **A187,** 53 (1946); S. Ross, *J. Am. Chem. Soc.*, **70,** 3830 (1948).

9. H. W. Fox, E. F. Hare, and W. A. Zisman, *J. Phys. Chem.*, **59,** 1097 (1955).

10. W. J. Moore, *Physical Chemistry*, Prentice Hall, Englewood Cliffs, N. J., 1955, p. 504.

11. R. H. Savage, *J. Am. Chem. Soc.*, **70,** 2362 (1948).

12. I. Langmuir, *Trans. Faraday Soc.*, **17,** 621 (1921).

13. J. H. Singleton and G. D. Halsey, Jr., *J. Phys. Chem.*, **58,** 1012 (1954); J. L. Shereshefsky and C. E. Weir, *J. Phys. Chem.*, **60,** 1162 (1956).

Problems

52. The adsorption of water vapor on a sorbent is rapid and liberates about 50,000 cal./mole. The water can be recovered unchanged by pumping at high temperature. This suggests that we are dealing with (*1*) chemisorption, (*2*) physical sorption, (*3*) ion exchange, (*4*) no way of telling.

66. The amount adsorbed increases as the temperature is raised at constant concentration. This suggests (*1*) a high activation energy, (*2*) chemisorption, (*3*) competition with another adsorbed species, (*4*) all of these, (*5*) none of these.

110. In general *a* will be more adsorbable than *b* if (*1*) molecular weight of *a* > molecular weight of *b*, (*2*) both are being adsorbed from solution and *a* is more soluble than *b*, (*3*) both are being adsorbed from solution and in the gas phase *a* is more adsorbable than *b*, (*4*) all of these, (*5*) none of these.

63. A toy boat can be propelled by a bit of camphor at its rear. This motion shows that the effect of camphor on the surface tension of water is to (*1*) raise it permanently, (*2*) lower it permanently, (*3*) raise it temporarily, (*4*) lower it temporarily.

CHAPTER IX

Some Applications of Sorption

In the previous chapter we have reviewed some principles of adsorption; in the present one we will touch upon some immediate applications: protective action and sensitization, which deal with the effect on colloidal solutions, and chromatography, which is of very general interest and often involves colloidal materials. In later chapters we will encounter other applications.

9-1. Transformation by Adsorption

The adsorption of a layer of sorbate may radically change the properties of a surface. We have seen that amphipathic long chain compounds tend to form compact monolayers on water (Section 8-8). This changes the outer aspect of the liquid from an aqueous layer to a hydrocarbon one. Similar changes can be wrought on other surfaces. An easily observed example is given by the behavior of glass in water and in solutions of long chain amines.[1] A clean glass microscope slide is hydrophilic; when dipped in water, it is readily wetted and a droplet of water spreads over its surface. If it is then dipped in a highly dilute solution of the amine, it becomes hydrophobic; droplets of water or of the solution do not spread over the surface. This is due to a tenaciously adsorbed monolayer of the amine which is oriented with the tails outward (as shown in Fig. 9-1a) so that a hydrocarbon surface is exposed to the liquid. Adsorption is favored here by the interaction of the negatively charged silicate groups of the glass with the cationic head of the amine. If the slide is now dipped in a relatively concentrated solution of the amine, it is readily wetted by it because a second layer of the amine which is oriented with the hydrophilic heads outwards (Fig. 9-1b) has become adsorbed. Finally, if the slide is now washed with

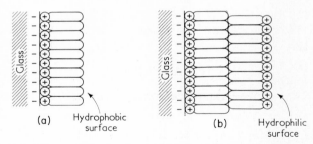

Figure 9-1. The negatively charged hydrophilic surface of glass can be changed to a neutral hydrophobic one by adsorption of an oriented monolayer of aliphatic amine molecules (*a*); and to a positively charged hydrophilic one by adsorption of a second layer (*b*).

water, this second layer is readily removed without affecting the first one, so that the surface again becomes hydrophobic.

Such a complete change of interaction with the surrounding liquid when it occurs at the surface of dispersed particles must of course cause corresponding changes in the flocculation-stability behavior and in the tendency of the particle to leave the bulk of the water and to stick to the air–water interface. This is frequently applied in the enrichment of ores by flotation. The finely ground ore composed of two types of particles is suspended in water. Air blown through the suspension collects one type and brings it to the surface, while the other remains in bulk. Either fraction may be recovered for further processing. A variety of surface-active agents is used to adjust the properties of the surfaces for most economical enrichment.

In later chapters we shall see how adsorption of charged particles can render a neutral particle charged and a charged one neutral, with corresponding radical changes in behavior. At present, we shall consider only some phenomena in which charge effects do not seem important.

9-2. Protective Action

As we mentioned often, if two colloidal particles tend to attract each other in preference to the solvent, they will tend to flocculate if they can come close together.   Adsorption of polar particles with their hydrophilic groups towards the solvent may reverse this tendency, since now the surfaces are effectively formed by hydrophilic groups and each prefers the solvent.   The colloid is thus protected against flocculation.   Gelatin is frequently used as a protective agent in this way.   Its long chains presumably have portions which are hydrophobic and become attached to a colloidal particle, such as gold, whereas the hydrophilic outer portions of the chain render the whole stable.   Another long chain molecule, carboxymethyl cellulose, is strongly adsorbed by cotton and protects it from many kinds of particles. It is, therefore, and important ingredient of commercial "detergents" containing no soap because it prevents the redeposition of soil and the "graying" of the wash.   Soap itself seems to have quite satisfactory protective action and does not require this additive.

9-3. Sensitization

Sensitization is the opposite of protection, it is the decrease of stability by small amounts of additives.   Sensitization is particularly interesting when caused by very small amounts of additives which act as protective agents if used in larger amounts. This behavior is encountered frequently and seems to be due to a variety of causes, some of them not well understood.   Sometimes it may be due to the type of behavior which we described above for long chain amines on glass.   Polar additives may form a first layer hydrophobic part outwards, thus sensitizing, and then a second layer oriented oppositely and giving protection. Another and interesting type of explanation seems to hold for some long chain additives, such as modified starches, which are very effective, within a narrow concentration range, in the flocculation of certain mine-tailing slimes.[2]   Flocculation will be favored if two particles become joined by a long chain adsorbed on both.   This will tend to keep the two particles close together and favor further links by other chains.   Why should this be more likely to occur when the concentration of the long chains is

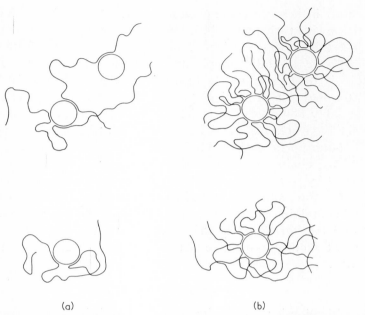

Figure 9-2. A possible mechanism of sensitization and protection by long chain molecules. Below: effect on a single particle; above: upon their interaction. (*a*) At low concentration coverage is low and bridging easy. (*b*) At high concentration bridging and close approach are both difficult.

low than when it is high?   In either case thermal agitation will permit only parts of a chain to be fixed to the surface, while many segments will be roaming the surrounding solution.   In dilute solution (Fig. 9-2*a*) the coverage of all particles will be low so that such a roaming segment can easily find a spot to which it can attach itself.   In a concentrated solution (Fig. 9-2*b*), on the other hand, the coverage will be high so that the chances for its attachment are low.   In this case the many roaming segments attached to each particle also exert a greater repelling force by their thermal agitation.

A similar flocculating mechanism is probably operating in the long chain compounds which are used in very small concentrations as soil "conditioners" (Section 4-1).

9-4. Chromatography

A very important application of sorption is chromatography.[3] This term covers the separation of materials during motion past a sorbing medium. The materials may be liquid or gaseous (vapor phase chromatography), but the sorbent is solid or, at least, supported by a solid. Sorption may be adsorption, or absorption, or a combination of the two. The principle of the process is, however, always the same. To illustrate it, let us consider the following system.

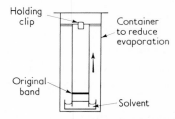

Figure 9-3. Ascending paper chromatography. The solvent ascends the filter paper strip by capillarity and elutes the original band.

Take a long strip of filter paper and paint across it a band with a dilute solution. After evaporation of the solvent, a definite band of solute is left. We will consider what happens to this band when a solvent is made to flow slowly along the strip. Such flow may be caused by dipping the lower end of the filter paper in the solvent which then rises by capillarity (ascending filter paper chromatography), as shown in Fig. 9-3. Alternatively, the strip may be hung over the edge of the vessel containing the solvent so that both capillarity and gravity cause its flow (descending filter paper chromatography Fig. 9-4). When the solvent reaches the band of solute one of several things may happen.

1. The solute is not affected by the solvent. Hence, the band remains as it was originally.

2. The solvent dissolves the solute completely so that none of it is sorbed by the paper. Hence, the solute is incorporated into

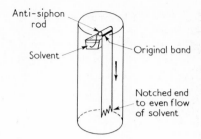

Figure 9-4. Descending paper chromatography. The solvent flows along the filter paper strip by capillarity and gravity eluting the original band. Compared to the ascending method, the rate of flow is faster and a larger volume of eluent can be used.

the moving front of the solvent and is carried with it as a narrow band, which may broaden with time because of diffusion and irregularities of flow. The band moves with the velocity of the solvent.

3. The solute dissolves in the solvent but is also significantly sorbed by the paper. Since this is clearly an intermediate case, the behavior of the solute will also be intermediate; it will not stay in the original position, nor will it advance with the front of the solvent. It will be transported along the paper but at a slower rate than the solvent.

This last situation is the one of interest in chromatography and must be considered more closely. It can be approached either from the macroscopic point of view as a solution–sorbent distribution, or from the microscopic one of the behavior of individual particles. In either case, one can begin by assuming local equilibrium to exist at each point, because the flow of solvent is slow compared to the rate of diffusion across the tiny channels between the paper fibrils.

9-5. Macroscopic View

The edge of the original band which is first exposed to solvent— the trailing edge—is also constantly exposed to fresh solvent, so that only solution and desorption can take place here. As a result, sooner or later all the solute will be removed from this line. The first portion of solvent passing over this trailing edge will come to equilibrium with the amount of solute which it will leave adsorbed here. Upon advancing to the next region, it will generally take up some more solute until it comes to equilibrium with the amount to be left there. This process will continue until the solvent reaches the other—advancing—edge of the band. It will now come in contact with fresh paper which will adsorb some of the solute until it reaches equilibrium with the concentration to be left in the solvent. This process of adsorption will continue until no solute is left in the solvent, and it will result in the transport of some solute along the paper.

The next portion of solvent coming in contact with the trailing edge will again reach equilibrium with the solute that it leaves adsorbed, and this must be less than the previous one. Again the process of dissolving continues as the solvent passes over paper rich in adsorbed material and is followed by gradual exhaustion as it passes beyond the original band.

In this way the trailing edge of the original band is gradually washed away, and the solute transported in the direction of flow forms a new, advancing, edge. Soon a steady-state is reached in which the adsorbed amount increases gradually from the trailing edge to the main body of the band and then decreases again to the front edge, and each portion of solvent removes solute from the trailing part and then redeposits it on the front part. In all cases, however, the solvent finally becomes completely freed of solute by the adsorbent paper so that the band advances more slowly than the solvent.

The edges of the band may be "sharp" or "diffuse" depending on how rapidly all the solute is removed from the paper at the trailing edge or from the solvent at the front edge. This in turn depends on the shape of the adsorption isotherm. In the usual case, when the isotherm is of the Freundlich or Langmuir type— concave to the concentration axis—the solute is most avidly adsorbed from dilute solutions and most strongly held by the sorbent when little is adsorbed. Hence, at the front edge the solvent will be cleaned out rapidly, and this edge will be sharp; while the paper will tenaciously retain small amounts of solute until many volumes of solvent have passed over it, and the trailing edge will be diffuse.

The rate at which the band advances depends on the sorptive power of the paper for the solute. The stronger the adsorption the less solute is in solution in the body of the band and the faster it is removed at the advancing front and, therefore, also the slower the rate of travel of the front of the band with respect to rate of flow of the solvent. This relative rate is generally designated as $\mathcal{R}_f$ and is characteristic of a given system and conditions.

9-6. Microscopic View

Another and very instructive way of looking at the same process is to consider that each solute molecule is constantly being adsorbed and desorbed so that on the average it spends a certain fraction of its time in the solvent and the rest on the paper. While in the solvent, it advances with it at the average velocity of flow of solvent, and while adsorbed, of course, it stays put. Its average velocity $\mathcal{R}_f$ is, therefore, this same fraction of the velocity of the liquid. The stronger the adsorption, the smaller the fraction of time spent in the liquid and the smaller the $\mathcal{R}_f$.

Let us now consider two bands, A and B, differing only in that the concentration of solute in the solvent is twice as large in A as in B. Let us neglect the edges and consider only the body of the bands where the concentration is uniform. If the adsorption isotherm is of the usual type, concave to the concentration axis, the amount adsorbed per unit surface will be *less* than twice as large in A as in B. Hence, the fraction of solute adsorbed on the paper will be less in A than in B. Conversely, the fraction in the solvent will be greater in A. The same will be true of the time spent by each particle in the flowing solvent. This means that the rate of movement of the solute will be faster in A than in B.

Instead of considering A and B as different bands, we can look at them as being part of the same band, A near the center, B near the edges. For this type of isotherm we see, therefore, that the center of the band (A) tends to move faster than the edges (B). As a result, the front edge will be constantly sharpened, and the tail edge will be becoming more and more diffuse, just as we indicated above.

The movement of the molecule along the paper may also be imagined as a kind of random walk, with a step being either taken in the liquid or omitted while the molecule rests adsorbed. As a result, the distance travelled by each molecule depends on the total number of steps which this molecule takes, and the band will acquire a certain width because of the random character of this walk. The assumption that adsorption equilibrium is always maintained locally during chromatography means that the number of steps is very large and the size of each is very small compared to the distance travelled. In the study of random walks (Section 5-6) we saw that under these conditions the relative deviation from the average is very small, and so is the resulting broadening of the band. It must be noted, moreover, that the probability of being adsorbed varies, as we have just seen, with the coverage of the surface so that this random walk is far from simple.

9-7. Chromatographic Separation

If more than one solute forms the original band, each will be carried by the solvent at a relative rate given by its own $\mathcal{R}_f$, which in turn is determined by its absorbability, as we have seen above. If these $\mathcal{R}_f$ values are different, the original band will soon be split into separate bands, each formed by one solute. The solutes thus become separated.

This chromatographic separation depends on the difference of adsorbability of the two components, and could, in principle, also be effected in a series of separate steps, as follows. If a solution of the two components is equilibrated with an adsorbent, one of them will be adsorbed more than the other so that some fractionation will occur. By treating the adsorbed portion with fresh solvent and the mother liquor with fresh sorbent further fractionations occur, and by repeating the process a large number of times and properly combining the fractions one could, in principle, also obtain a separation. The process is, however, completely impractical, unless the difference in adsorbability is so great that very few steps lead to the result.

Essentially, chromatography is a method of combining an incredibly large number of fractionating steps into a single and quite simple operation. It can therefore often produce complete separations on the basis of minute differences in adsorbability. It is, however, a batch process in that continuous supply of the mixture and withdrawal of the products is not generally possible.

9-8. Applications of Chromatography

Practical application of chromatography involves countless adaptations to specific problems. The most common application is the use of chromatography as a zone method of analysis or of preparation. As in the above example, one starts with a narrow zone containing a mixture. This may be a solid powder, a layer adsorbed from a poor solvent, or a layer of the adsorbent which has been exposed to a concentrated solution. Then the components of the mixture are separated by an appropriate solvent called the "eluent." This is the "development" of the chromatograph.

In order to obtain $\Re_f$ values which are sufficiently different to lead to a separation and yet large enough to give rapid results, the choice of eluent and sorbent is of great importance; this is still largely an empirical art with countless recipes being constantly published. Very frequently, powdered materials such as charcoal, silica, starch, and ion exchangers enclosed in glass tubes are used as sorbent columns.

In some cases of multicomponent mixtures, it is not possible to effect complete separation with only one eluent. An ingenious solution of this problem involves so called "two-dimensional paper chromatography" (Fig. 9-5). Here, the unknown is deposited as a spot near the corner of a sheet of paper, and elution proceeds in the direction of one of the edges of the sheet with a suitable solvent, forming a band along which the materials are

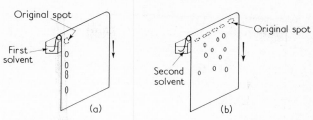

Figure 9-5. Two-dimensional descending paper chromatography. By eluting successively with two different solvents along perpendicular directions it is possible to separate components which move together in one of them.

more or less separated into groups. Then the paper is dried, and another solvent is used to elute at right angle to the first direction. Thus, each group in the original band is developed into a new band in which the individual components may be separated. The use of a different solvent in the two elutions permits the separation of materials which have identical $\mathcal{R}_f$ values in one of them.

After separation is obtained, there remains the problem of detection and identification. This is sometimes done *in situ*, for example, by spraying the paper with an appropriate reagent, giving color spots at the points where a material is located. In other cases the materials are eluted successively from the end of the paper or column and collected separately. Automatic fraction collectors permit the collection of hundreds of portions of eluent which may then be tested individually, or the efflux may be analyzed continuously. Any property which is strongly affected by the solutes may be used to identify the portions which contain individual materials. Color or ultraviolet light absorption, refractive index, conductivity, radioactivity, and in case of vapor, heat conductivity, are among those commonly used. In case of good separation, the first portions will contain pure solvent, the next ones a solute, then again only the solvent will be present, then another solute, etc. The identification may proceed along standard lines, but very often it is based simply on the $\mathcal{R}_f$ value, that is, on the position of the material in the chromatogram under standard conditions and comparison with a known. As

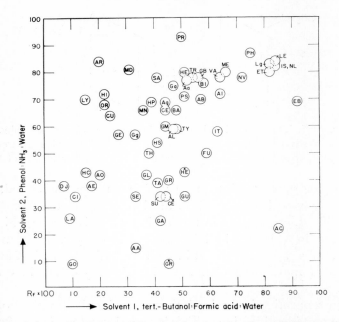

Figure 9-6. A chromatographic map showing the characteristic positions of 60 amino-acids, peptides, carbohydrates, and related products after two-dimensional chromatography under standardized conditions. (*From L. B. Rockland and J. C. Underwood, Anal. Chem.*, **26,** *1557 (1954).*)

shown in Fig. 9-6, two-dimensional chromatography can thus permit the identification of a very large number of components of a mixture by a single operation.

Chromatography is also sometimes used as a frontal method of analysis. In this case a solution flows continuously through a sorbent. Because of adsorption, the solutes move less rapidly through the column than does the solvent, so that the effluent is at first formed by the pure solvent. Then the least adsorbable solute makes its appearance and is later joined by the second least adsorbable, and so on, until after the most adsorbable solute emerges, the effluent has the same composition as the input. By observing changes in some property of the efflux, such as refractive index, conductivity, color, etc., one can determine the number of components and their rate of appearance. In this method, where solutes do not tend to become completely separated, competition between sorbates may become important in determining their rates of motion. A particularly simple form of frontal chromatographic analysis requires only a strip of filter paper dipped into a solution. Frequently, colored solutes may be distinguished visually, forming overlapping bands as the liquid ascends by capillarity.

Summary

The surface of a particle and therefore its properties can be radically affected by adsorption. Protective action and sensitization are among the effects produced by adsorption of small amounts of other materials by colloidal particles. Chromatography is a method of combining innumerable sorption–desorption steps into a simple operation and is extremely useful in the separation and characterization of compounds differing very little in their properties.

References

1. D. J. O'Connor and V. Sanders, *J. Colloid Sci.*, **11**, 158 (1956).
2. V. K. LaMer and R. H. Smelie, *J. Colloid Sci.*, **11**, 704 (1956).
3. A very clear introduction is given by H. H. Strain in *Frontiers in Colloid Chemistry*, R. E. Burk and O. Grummit, eds., *Frontiers in Chemistry*, Vol. VIII, Interscience Publishers, Inc., New York, 1950, and Dover, New York. More recent books include E. and M. Lederer, *Chromatography*, Elsevier, New York, 1957; H. G. Cassidy, *Fundamentals of Chromatography*, in A. Weissberger, ed., *Techniques of Organic Chemistry*, Vol. X, Interscience Publishers, Inc., New York, 1957.

Problems

45. In the case of the amine which can render glass both hydrophobic and hydrophilic, we deal with (*1*) only monolayer adsorption, (*2*) clear polarization, (*3*) marked orientation, (*4*) all of these, (*5*) none of these.

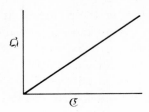

65. The adsorption isotherm shown above suggests that (*1*) if the system is used in zonal chromatography a sharp advancing edge will be obtained, (*2*) the surface has a few highly active spots, (*3*) there is little particle–particle interaction on the surface, (*4*) all of these, (*5*) none of these.

68. The graph below shows the state of a colloidal dispersion after the combined addition of varying amounts of an additive (abscissa) and then of varying amounts of a flocculating agent (ordinate). On the basis of this graph, one can conclude that the additive is (*1*) a good sensitizing agent and a good protective agent, (*2*) good sensitizing and poor protective, (*3*) poor sensitizing and good protective, (*4*) poor sensitizing and poor protective.

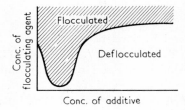

CHAPTER X

Fluctuations and Rubber Elasticity

After considering some interactions of thermal agitation with other forces, particularly gravitational ones, we can return to a simpler system in which only thermal agitation is important and consider fluctuations, i.e., spontaneously occurring deviations from average or equilibrium values. We can study them now because we have obtained the needed Boltzmann distribution from the interaction of thermal forces with gravitation. The study of fluctuations will lead us to that of rubber elasticity which, as we shall see, is a result of the interaction of thermal agitation with mechanically applied outside forces. Later in Chapters XII and XIII, we shall consider the effects of mechanical forces more generally, under the heading of rheology.

10-1. The Occurrence of Fluctuations

Thermal motion is intrinsically random. Each particle tends to move in a straight line and with uniform velocity, but collisions disrupt both the direction and the velocity after an extremely short time. Because we normally deal with innumerable particles, we measure the average results of their activities. Thus, we know that if we weigh the amount of oxygen in 22.4 liters at **STP** we will find 32.0 g., and the result will be as reproducible as our experimental technique of defining the volume, temperature, purity of gas, etc. This corresponds to 6×10^{23} molecules of oxygen. On the other hand, if we go to the best attainable vacuum of about 10^{-11} mm. Hg. and look at 1 mm.^{3}, we can readily calculate that we should find 267 molecules. If we had any good means of counting them under these conditions, it is obvious that 267 could only be an average of the variable number of particles darting through that volume. For $1\mu^3$ we can then calculate the presence of 2.67×10^{-7} molecules, which can have only the physical meaning that, on the average, a molecule will be found in such a volume less than three times in ten million observations. Thus, obviously, the concentration of particles animated with thermal agitation is never constant. It fluctuates randomly and spontaneously, just because of their thermal motion. Yet, when their number is large these fluctuations are imperceptible, again because of this motion. They become important only when the number of particles is small.

10-2. Observation of Fluctuation

The observation of the effect of small numbers of particles is not a frequent or easy accomplishment. It seems that under special conditions the human eye may be able to respond to just a few (4–8) quanta[1] of light, i.e., to energy changes of one electron in just a few atoms. And this response seems to be accordingly uncertain and fluctuating at these low levels.

The "counting" of radioactivity is the most common experiment in which the performance of the individual atom is individually recorded. The intrinsic fluctuation of this behavior gives the basic statistical counting error, and requires the counting of large numbers of disintegrations to give an accurate measure of the significant quantity, the average rate. Counting, however, deals with only a fleeting moment of an atom's existence, the instant of its disintegration.

In colloid chemistry, because of the increased size of particles, their effects sometimes become marked enough to permit individual observations. We have already mentioned the direct microscopic observability of Brownian motion and of sedimentation equilibrium. In the same systems fluctuations can also be directly observed. One uses a dilute enough suspension and a small enough field of view so that only a few particles occur in it at one time. Continuous observation then shows that some particles enter the field while others leave it, so that the number present varies irregularly. The average time that a particle remains in the field of view is related closely to $t = l^2/2D$, according to Einstein's law (where l is the radius of the field and D the diffusion coefficient of the particle). Hence, after an interval equal to a few times t, none of the particles originally present is likely to be left, and the number present is independent of the original number. Thus, by counting the number present at time intervals of this order, one can observe the occurrence of spontaneous fluctuations within the field of vision.

A further simplification of the counting procedure is obtained if the field of view is illuminated only by a flash of light at regular intervals.[2,3] This makes visible to the observer the instantaneous position and number of the particles present, without the confusing element of motion. Since the number of particles is small, it is readily counted mentally and recorded before the next fluctuation appears with the following flash. For example, 1557 observations[3] on a gold sol gave an average concentration of 2.168 particles in the field of view. The number of particles in this field fluctuated, however, from no particle present (in 12% of observations) to eight particles (in 2 cases, 0.013%), with two particles being the most frequent number but occurring in only 29% of observations.

By spacing the flashes closely it is also possible to measure the rate of fluctuation, which can be related to the diffusion coefficient of the particles.[4]

When we come later to optical phenomena, we will encounter the frequently used method of particle weight determination by light scattering (Chapter 20). We will see that the light is scattered because of fluctuations of concentration, and hence of refractive index, in minute volumes of the solution. It is therefore worthwhile to consider briefly the quantitative aspect of fluctuations.

10-3. Boltzmann Distribution of Fluctuations

If we consider a small volume v, in which the average concentration is $\mathfrak{C}_0$, it may occur that due to fluctuations the actual concentration is $\mathfrak{C}$.   We wish to estimate the probability $\mathcal{P}$ for the occurrence of such a fluctuation.   Although there are many ways of approaching this problem, the simplest one for us is to note that the probability of the occurrence of a fluctuation to a concentration $\mathfrak{C}$ is also the probability of finding a given particle within this volume while the concentration within is $\mathfrak{C}$.   We can now apply the Boltzmann distribution, which as we have seen (Section 7-2) gives the probability of finding a particle in a volume as a function of the work w required to place it deliberately into that region.   In the present case w is the work of changing the concentration from $\mathfrak{C}_0$ to $\mathfrak{C}$ within the volume v. In the next section we will evaluate this work, but for the time being we can write simply

$$\mathcal{P} \propto e^{-w/kT} \tag{10-3.1}$$

This means that the probability of a spontaneous fluctuation decreases exponentially with the work required to produce it deliberately.   Small fluctuations are, therefore, much more probable than large ones.   Furthermore, this work has to be compared to kT.   Thus, only those fluctuations which can be produced by work comparable to the kinetic energy of a single particle have any appreciable probability.   Such an amount of energy can produce substantial changes only in systems of very small numbers of particles.   Thus, we return to our original qualitative estimate.

Quantitative calculation of probability requires the knowledge of the proportionality constant in the above expression, or "normalization" of the probability function.   This is done by introducing the fact that the fluctuating system will always correspond to *some* value of w, which means that the sum of the probabilities for all the w's must be unity.   This sum is the integral of $\mathcal{P}$ over all values of w, from 0 to $+\infty$.

$$1 = \int_0^\infty \mathcal{P}(w)dw = \int_0^\infty Ae^{-w/kT}dw \tag{10-3.2}$$

where A is the sought proportionality constant. With the help of a table of definite integrals we obtain

$$\int_0^\infty A e^{-w/kT} dw = AkT \tag{10-3.3}$$

Hence,

$$A = 1/kT \tag{10-3.4}$$

and the probability of a fluctuation involving a work between w and $w + dw$ is

$$\mathcal{P} = (1/kT)e^{-w/kT} dw \tag{10-3.5}$$

We can now also calculate the average work involved in a fluctuation by summing over all the w's, each times its own probability, and then dividing by the sum of the probabilities. Since the latter is unity, because of the normalization, this last step can be omitted. We indicate this averaging by including w in angle brackets and obtain, again with the help of the table

$$<w> = \int_0^\infty w\mathcal{P}dw = \int_0^\infty (w/kT)e^{-w/kT} dw = kT \tag{10-3.6}$$

Hence, the average work involved in a fluctuation equals kT. It should not be forgotten, however, that the fluctuations occur spontaneously, and that what we are calculating is the work that would be required to produce the same effect deliberately.

Let us now evaluate the w term so as to obtain a measure of the extent of these fluctuations in terms of concentration and of the number of particles.

10-4. The Extent of Fluctuations

Let us imagine our small volume v to be enclosed in a cylinder and separated from the bulk of the solution by a semipermeable piston. At equilibrium, when the concentration is $\mathfrak{C}_0$ everywhere there is no pressure exerted on the piston. If the piston is moved, however, so as to increase the concentration to $\mathfrak{C}$, a pressure P, due to the corresponding difference in osmotic pressures, will be exerted on it. For small displacements, P will be proportional to the change in concentration produced, and the coefficient of proportionality will be the change of osmotic pressure with concentration, $\partial\pi/\partial\mathfrak{C}$.   This gives

$$P = (\partial\pi/\partial\mathfrak{C})(\mathfrak{C} - \mathfrak{C}_0) \tag{10-4.1}$$

Thus it is the change of osmotic pressure with concentration, $\partial\pi/\partial\mathfrak{C}$, which must be the determining factor in the work required to produce deliberately a fluctuation and which therefore also determines its spontaneous probability.

In order to change the concentration in the small volume v, the piston must cover the still smaller volume change Δ_v.   This is determined by the conservation of the amount of solute within the volume considered, i.e.

$$\mathfrak{C}_0 v = \mathfrak{C}(v - \Delta_v) \tag{10-4.2}$$

or

$$\Delta_v = v(\mathfrak{C} - \mathfrak{C}_0)/\mathfrak{C} \tag{10-4.3}$$

The work done by a piston is the product of the pressure it exerts times the volume it covers.   Since in our case the pressure increases linearly from zero to P, it is effectively half that value throughout the travel.   Hence, the work done is

$$w = [(\partial\pi/\partial\mathfrak{C})(\mathfrak{C} - \mathfrak{C}_0)/2] \times [v(\mathfrak{C} - \mathfrak{C}_0)/\mathfrak{C}]$$
$$= (\partial\pi/\partial\mathfrak{C}) (\mathfrak{C} - \mathfrak{C}_0)^2 v/2\mathfrak{C} \tag{10-4.4}$$

This is the term to be inserted into the Boltzmann expression when considering the probability of a fluctuation in concentration.

It may be noted that w is proportional to the square of the concentration change.   This means that equal increases and decreases in concentration are equally probable, but it holds only for small changes.

We can now estimate the average value of the fluctuation in concentration since we know already the average of w (Eq. 10-3.6)

$$<w> = (\partial\pi/\partial\mathfrak{C}) < (\mathfrak{C} - \mathfrak{C}_0)^2 > v/2\mathfrak{C} = \mathbf{k}T \tag{10-4.5}$$

or

$$<(\mathfrak{C} - \mathfrak{C}_0)^2> = 2\mathbf{k}T\mathfrak{C}/v(\partial\pi/\partial\mathfrak{C}) \qquad (10\text{-}4.6)$$

which shows that the average fluctuation increases with concentration, but only with its square root. The relative fluctuation, therefore, decreases with $\sqrt{\mathfrak{C}}$. It decreases also with the square root of the volume observed. The above expression is independent of units used to express the concentration, as these enter also the measure of the fluctuation and of the slope of osmotic pressure. In particular, if we use the weight per unit volume, $\mathfrak{W}$, the equation becomes

$$<(\mathfrak{W} - \mathfrak{W}_0)^2> = 2\mathbf{k}T\mathfrak{W}/v(\partial\pi/\partial\mathfrak{W}) \qquad (10\text{-}4.7)$$

The important factor $\partial\pi/\partial\mathfrak{C}$ which enters the above expressions will in general depend on the concentration. Since it refers to the average concentration, $\mathfrak{C}$ (and small variations around this value), it should be written $(\partial\pi/\partial\mathfrak{C})_{\mathfrak{C}=\mathfrak{C}_0}$ if one deals with nonideal solutions.

For ideal solutions, on the other hand, we have seen (Section 6-10) that $\pi = \mathfrak{W}\mathbf{R}T/M$, so that $\partial\pi/\partial\mathfrak{W}$ is constant in this case. A further simplification occurs if we use the molarity $\mathfrak{M}(= \mathfrak{W}/M)$ as a measure of concentration so that van't Hoff's law becomes (Eq. 6-5.6)

$$\pi = \mathfrak{M}\mathbf{R}T \qquad (10\text{-}4.8)$$

and

$$\partial\pi/\partial\mathfrak{M} = \mathbf{R}T \qquad (10\text{-}4.9)$$

Hence for ideal solution Eq. 10-4.6 becomes

$$< (\mathfrak{M} - \mathfrak{M}_0)^2> = 2\mathbf{k}T\mathfrak{M}/v\mathbf{R}T = 2\mathfrak{M}/\mathbf{N}v \qquad (10\text{-}4.10)$$

If both sides of this equation are multiplied by $\mathbf{N}^2$ we obtain the corresponding expression in terms of the number, $\mathfrak{n}$, of particles per unit volume since $\mathbf{N}\mathfrak{M} = \mathfrak{n}$

$$< (\mathfrak{n} - \mathfrak{n}_0)^2> = 2\mathfrak{n}/v \qquad (10\text{-}4.11)$$

Finally, if we consider n, the actual number of particles in the small volume v, we have $\mathfrak{n} = n/v$, and the above relation becomes

$$< (n - n_0)^2 > = 2n \qquad (10\text{-}4.12)$$

Thus if we observe a small volume containing on the average 10 particles, we can expect a root mean square deviation of about $\sqrt{20} = 4.4$ or 44% of the average, whereas, if it contains 100 particles, the value becomes about $\sqrt{200} = 14$, which is larger but represents only 14% of the average.

10-5. The Effect of Temperature

The last three equations do not include the temperature; the extent of fluctuation of ideal particles does not depend on temperature and therefore does not depend on the intensity of thermal agitation. This is because fluctuations are simply the result of the randomness of thermal motion which distributes the particles statistically independently of its intensity.

The role of temperature appears clearly if we note that the distribution of fluctuations is determined by the Boltzmann exponential $e^{-w/kT}$ (Eq. 10-3.1). Other things being equal, w is proportional to $\partial \pi / \partial \mathfrak{C}$ and, for ideal solutions, this is proportional to the absolute temperature (Eqs. 10-4.4 and 10-4.8). Hence the ratio w/kT is independent of temperature. Thus, increased thermal agitation increases the work required to produce deliberately a given fluctuation but does not affect its probability. The reason is that the probability depends on the comparison of this work with kT which increases in exactly the same ratio.

10-6. Fluctuations and Thermodynamics

If fluctuations would occur on a large scale as they are observed in Brownian motion, there would be no difficulty in constructing perpetual motions and motors. If the concentration of gas molecules would spontaneously tend to fluctuate by a large factor in a cylinder fitted with a piston, the latter could be directly coupled to any machine and would continue to drive it indefinitely, though erratically. While doing this work, the fluctuating gas would tend to cool itself below the surroundings, but spontaneous flow of heat would prevent an excessive drop in temperature. Thus the first law of thermodynamics would be obeyed, but the second would be violated.

As frequently enunciated, the second law is, indeed, violated by the fluctuations which are easily observable in Brownian motion, and the law should be properly restricted to large scale systems involving many particles and limited times. Under these conditions, the probability of a mechanically or thermally perceptible fluctuation is small enough to be negligible, and all consequences of the second law apply.

There still remains the problem whether work can be obtained from the fluctuations which occur frequently in the small systems to which the second law does not apply. The amounts of energy involved are small, and would require the coupling of an incredible number of elements to become useful, but this may not be an objection in principle. It seems, however, that the difficulty of devising a harnessing mechanism which would be sensitive to the amounts of energy involved without consuming them in the process cannot be surmounted.

10-7. Behavior of Long Chains

The Brownian motion of the n_s segments of a long chain produces constant fluctuations in its configuration. The distance between any two segments, particularly between the two ends is, therefore, not constant but fluctuates around an average value which, as we have seen, is proportional to $\sqrt{n_s}$ (Section 5-18). Positions differing greatly from this average value have a lower probability than those close to it. Since the probability of a fluctuation is related to the work required to produce it deliberately, this means that work is required to bring the ends of the wiggling chain either closer or further apart than the equilibrium distance. This in turn means that a restoring force is driving them to this average position and has to be overcome when they are removed from it.

The origin of this force may be visualized as follows.   Thermal motion of all the segments results in constant jerks and pulls transmitted to the ends.   In the equilibrium position, the chances of the jerk being in any direction are equal.   As the distance between the ends increases, the probability of jerks tending to shorten the distance increases, and vice versa.   One can perhaps imagine (and no lecture demonstration is contemplated) that one tries to hold a snake by its two ends in a stretched position. Any random wiggle of the beast will tend to bring the ends closer together.   Conversely, if one tries to hold the tail close to the head, any wiggle can only tend to separate them.

Thus, random thermal motion of segments of long chains results in a restoring force tending to bring them to an equilibrium position.   As we have seen, a rise in temperature does not affect the distribution of fluctuations but increases the work required to produce them deliberately (Section 10-5).   The restoring force must therefore increase with temperature, as would be expected from the greater thermal agitation.

10-8. Rubber Elasticity

An interesting application of these concepts is the explanation of rubber elasticity.   As is well known, rubber can be stretched several-fold in length yet returns rapidly to the original shape. There are several peculiarities of this behavior.   It is not accompanied by any appreciable change in the total volume of the rubber. At low temperatures rubber becomes hard and brittle and cannot be stretched, nor does it return spontaneously if cooled in the stretched condition.   Crude rubber tends to "creep" when stretched, and returns less and less completely to the original length if held long times in the stretched condition. The familiar complete return depends on the vulcanization of the rubber.   Synthetic rubbers and other similar materials— the "elastomers"—show this type of behavior over various ranges of temperature, although there are great variations in the rate of

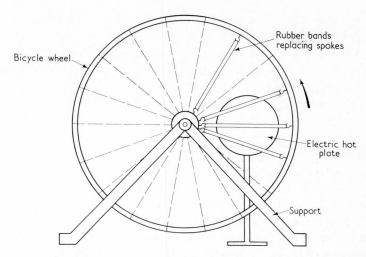

Figure 10-1. When the stretched-rubber spokes of a well-balanced wheel are heated on the right, they contract, shifting the center of gravity to the left of the axis, and causing the wheel to rotate as indicated.

return and in the amount of energy that can be recovered during contraction (the difference goes into heating which is generally undesirable).   All of these materials have in common a structure based on long and chemically rather inert chains, rubber itself being formed by repeating *cis* units of

$$\text{---CH}_2\text{---}\underset{\underset{\displaystyle \text{CH}_3}{|}}{\text{C}}\text{=CH---CH}_2\text{---}$$

There is a completely different type of structure which also has the ability to become greatly extended and then snap back. This is the ordinary coil spring, made of materials which, in bulk, show only small deformations but complete return under the influence of a force.   The coil spring structure is simply a device for greatly multiplying these small deformations.

The great difference between elastomers and springs lies in the effect of temperature.   When unextended, i.e., not subject to any force, both expand slightly with temperature.   When

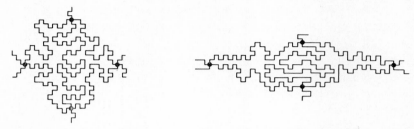

Figure 10-2. The stretching of rubber.   Great elongation can occur as the configuration of chains anchored at points of crosslinking changes from random to elongated or compressed.

extended, however, by a constant force, springs generally extend further as the temperature is raised, whereas elastomers contract markedly.   This unusual behavior of rubber is illustrated strikingly by a wheel with spokes made of stretched rubber bands as shown in Fig. 10-1.   If this vertical wheel is well balanced and a hotplate is placed near the spokes on one side of the wheel, these spokes contract and shift the center of gravity of the wheel so that it begins to rotate.   This permits these spokes to cool while others become heated, and the rotation continues as long as the heat is provided.

A less direct but simpler demonstration is to note the temperature change of a band during rapid (and therefore adiabatic) elongation and contraction.   Our lips being a very sensitive detector, it is enough to bring a band in contact with them to note that it is at room temperature, then stretch it rapidly and again bring it immediately to the lips.   A definite warmth is perceived.   After maintaining the elongation for a few moments to allow the temperature to return to ambient, the tension can be released and produces a definite cooling.   Thus contraction is an endothermic process, and according to LeChatelier's principle must be favored by higher temperature, and vice versa.

A consideration of the structural factors which are responsible for the elasticity of springs and of elastomers accounts for this effect of the temperature.

10-9. Kinetic Theory of Rubber Elasticity

Springs are formed by atoms lying close together in permanent relation and held together by short range forces.   An applied force tends to remove them from these equilibrium positions and is balanced by these short range forces.   Higher temperature and the resulting stronger thermal agitation of the atoms separate them from each other, the solid expands and weakens the short range forces.   Hence the same applied force can cause greater deformation at higher temperature.   Thermal agitation assists the expanding force.

In the case of rubber, on the other hand, the deformation is much too great to be accounted for by changes in interatomic distances.   As shown in Fig. 10-2 the chain structure permits elongation by rearrangement of the relative position of the segments, so that the random coils of unextended rubber become more or less deformed, stretched lengthwise and compressed crosswise.   This deformation of long chains generates, as we have seen, a restoring force which increases with elongation and also with temperature.   This is in agreement with observation. Thus, in contrast with what occurs in springs, thermal agitation counteracts the extending force—in fact it supplies the principal restoring one.   When the tension is released, thermal motion returns the chains spontaneously to their original random configuration.

This picture implies that the segments are quite free to move past each other under the influence of the outside force and of thermal agitation;   that is, they behave as if the rubber were liquid.   The reasonableness of this assumption is shown by a number of facts.   (1) The creeping of crude rubber is strictly analogous to the flow of a very viscous liquid.   In creeping, chains must move completely past each other and must overcome all the steric factors of entanglement, so that the phenomenon is much slower than the short range realignment involved in elasticity.   Vulcanization introduces crosslinks anchoring the chains to each other at relatively large intervals, which prevents any travel of chains with respect to each other but still permits the free motion of the many-segmented links between the anchors. If too many crosslinks are introduced, the elasticity is lost and the product is hard ebonite. (2) At low temperature, thermal agitation is reduced so that it no longer overcomes the attractive forces between the segments, the rubber becomes a solid, and rubber elasticity is lost. (3) Changes in structure which tend to hamper the free motion of the segments also tend to reduce the speed of the return and the extent of elongation.

Summary

The random character of thermal motion results in fluctuations which become increasingly significant as the number of particles involved becomes smaller. Hence colloidal systems are uniquely suited for their direct observation. The improbability of extensive spontaneous fluctuations is related to the work which would be required to produce them deliberately. Thermal agitation of long chains is equivalent to a restoring force tending to bring about the average dimensions of the random coil. Rubber elasticity is primarily due to this restoring force which increases with temperature.

References

1. S. Hecht, *Am. Scientist*, **32,** 159 (1944).
2. T. Svedberg and K. Inouye, *Z. physik. Chem.*, **77,** 145 (1911); for sources of error see ref. 3.
3. A. Westgren, *Arkiv. Mat.*, **11,** No. 8 (1916).
4. A. Westgren, *Arkiv. Mat.*, **13,** No. 14 (1918); S. Chandrasekhar, *Revs. Mod. Phys.*, **15,** 1 (1943), Chap. III; reprinted in N. Wax, ed., *Noise and Stochastic Processes*, Dover, N. Y., 1954.

Problems

67. The probability that the number of particles in a given volume deviates because of thermal agitation by 10 from the average increases if (*1*) the average number increases, (*2*) the volume increases for the same number of particles, (*3*) the concentration decreases for the same volume, (*4*) all of these, (*5*) none of these.

57. The force required to stretch a rubber band increases with temperature, yet the probability of any given configuration of an ideal random coil is independent of temperature. This is explained by the fact that (*1*) forces between the segments decrease with temperature, (*2*) thermal expansion affects the length of each segment, (*3*) the $\mathbf{k}T$ factor in the Boltzmann distribution also increases with temperature, (*4*) all of these, (*5*) none of these.

130. A semipermeable piston delimits a volume v in a cylinder. Originally this volume is v_0 and the number of particles in it is n_0. A travel of the piston over a small volume Δ_v changes the number of particles in v by Δ_n equal to (*1*) $n_0(v - \Delta_v)/v$; (*2*) $n_0\Delta_v/v$; (*3*) n_0v/Δ_v; (*4*) 0; (*5*) n_0/v_0.

87. If a wheel having spokes of stretched rubber is heated in the 9 o'clock position, it will rotate (*1*) clock-wise, (*2*) counter clockwise.

122. Relatively large local fluctuations in concentrations are observed in the immediate vicinity of the critical point of simple liquids and lead to so-called "critical opalescence." Their presence is due to (*1*) high pressure and temperature at this point, (*2*) the relatively small number of particles involved in critical phenomena, (*3*) the horizontal slope at that point of the isotherm on a pressure versus volume diagram, (*4*) the formation of a diuturnal colloidal dispersion of liquid in vapor at the critical point.

CHAPTER XI

The Preparation of Colloids

In the last chapter we examined fluctuations and some of their applications. We can now approach a field of quite general interest but of special importance for colloids, namely, nucleation—the beginning of the formation of a new phase. Closely connected with it is the subsequent growth of a phase. Both together are determinant in the preparation of many colloids, particularly the diuturnal ones, and when properly controlled can lead to the formation of monodisperse systems.

Before coming to this subject itself, we shall place it briefly within the broader field of the preparation of colloids in general. This will give us also occasion to survey the main methods used in the preparation of high polymers, whose industrial importance needs no emphasis.

11-1. Natural Colloids

Although the origin of all the materials of the chemist rests ultimately in nature, many of them are so highly refined and transformed that we consider them to be synthetic. Among colloids, there are quite a few which come rather directly from animals or plants and generally cannot, as yet, be otherwise duplicated. These include the proteins, highly organized polyaminoacids; starches and cellulose, which are branched and straight chain polysaccharides; agar-agar, pectin, and gum arabic, in which the polysaccharide chain carries acid or ester groups; natural rubber and gutta-percha, which are long chain hydrocarbons. Most of these natural products show, after some purification, a high degree of homogeneity as far as chemical structure is concerned but are very polydispersed. Thus, natural rubber is *cis*-polyisoprene, whereas gutta-percha is the *trans* isomer.   Occasionally an essentially monodisperse product is obtained, as in the case of serum albumin and a few other proteins, where only very sensitive measurements can reveal any inhomogeneity.[1]

An important industrial source of colloids lies in derivatives of natural colloids.   By far the largest group is formed by cellulose derivatives, such as cellophane, rayon, nitrocellulose, carboxymethyl cellulose (CMC), etc.   Others that should be mentioned are vulcanized rubber and leather.

The study of many of these materials has developed into semi-independent branches of knowledge, such as biochemistry and the various technologies.   The reader must be referred to more specialized textbooks for any details of their behavior and utilization.

11-2. Synthetic Colloids

From the point of view of their preparation, synthetic colloids fall naturally into three very different types.   One is illustrated by association colloids such as sodium dodecyl sulfate.   Here, one has to prepare a compound formed by small ions or molecules; when placed in a proper solvent under proper conditions this will dissolve and associate spontaneously into colloidal particles.   Another type is formed by high polymers such as polystyrene.   Here, one has to prepare covalently bound molecules of definite structure and of colloidal dimensions, and these, when placed in a proper solvent, will dissolve spontaneously.   The third type is represented by the diuturnal colloids, such as colloidal gold or sulfur, where the particles have to be prepared in the dispersed state.

The preparation of the first type, the association colloids, presents in principle no problems beyond classical organic or inorganic chemistry, and we shall not consider it further.   The synthesis of high polymers is a highly developed field of preparative chemistry with wide industrial applications.   We will touch on only some aspects of it.   The last type, the diuturnal colloids, involves specialized concepts which will be considered in somewhat greater detail.

11-3. Polymerization

Just as the term high polymer has been extended to any particle which can be considered as being formed from a large number of smaller units, so the term polymerization has been extended to any process of forming a polymer, whether this be polymerization strictly speaking (increase of molecular weight with conservation of total weight and composition) or condensation

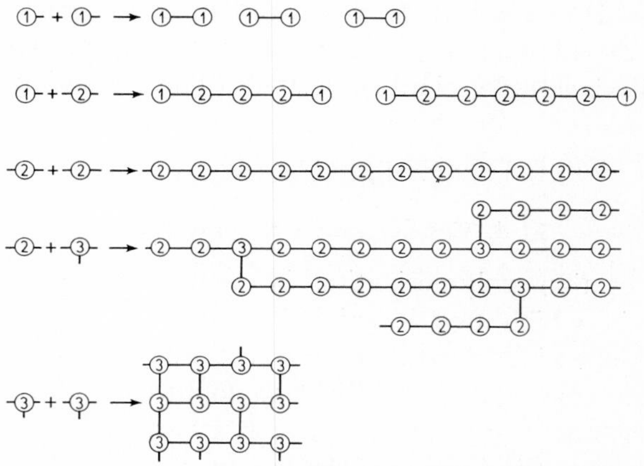

Figure 11-1. The role of functionality of monomers in the structure of polymers. Monofunctional groups can only terminate chains; difunctional ones can only give linear chains; trifunctional ones can give branching and networks.

(increase of molecular weight with elimination of some low molecular weight compound), and whether it involves only one monomeric species or whether it involves several. These different types are nevertheless distinguished as addition polymerization and condensation polymerization on one hand, and polymerization and copolymerization on the other.

The nature of polymerization and of the product depends, of course, on the chemical nature of the monomers involved, with an almost infinite possibility of variation. There are, however, also some general relations.

An important concept is the functionality of the monomer, that is, the number of groups capable of attachment to other monomers which it carries. As shown in Fig. 11-1, a unifunctional monomer can be attached to only one other of the same kind and therefore cannot become a link in any large structure. It can only terminate such a structure. A difunctional monomer can form a link of a chain but cannot be a branching point. A tri- or more functional (polyfunctional) monomer, on the other hand, can be a branching point and can serve as a basis for three-dimensional networks. If the branching becomes frequent enough, the network becomes practically infinite, leading to a necessarily insoluble, giant molecule. The formation of such a network corresponds also to a tremendous increase in viscosity and is commonly referred to as gelling.

11-4. Condensation Polymerization

Condensation polymerization is generally an equilibrium reaction in which two functional groups undergo one of the standard chemical reactions with the elimination of a small molecule. For example, in the manufacture of nylons an amide group is formed by reaction between a carboxyl and an amino group with the elimination of water

$$RCOOH + H_2NR' \longrightarrow R-\underset{\underset{O}{\|}}{C}-\underset{\underset{H}{|}}{N}-R' + H_2O$$

The R and R′ groups can be the original monomers or large molecules formed by condensation of many monomer units. The functional groups react essentially in the same way whatever length chain they are attached to. Each time a water molecule is eliminated, a polymerizing link is formed. Hence, by removing the water, polymerization can be favored and, in principle, could be pushed to the formation of a single giant molecule. Addition of terminating monofunctional groups, on the other hand, can reduce the average degree of polymerization. In practice, an average degree of polymerization of the order of a few thousands can be attained. However, because of the random distribution of links, there are always present both unreacted monomers and very high polymers, along with all the intermediates. In fact, on a number basis, it is the monomers

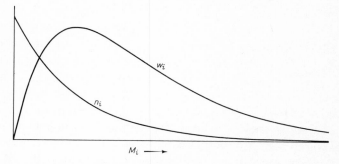

Figure 11-2. The "most probable" distribution of polymers produced by a condensation reaction. The number n_i of particles having the particle weight M_i decreases continuously while their total weight W_i passes through a maximum.

that remain the most numerous, but on a weight basis, there is a rather flat maximum in the distribution. This is the so-called "most probable" distribution and has the general shape shown in Fig. 11-2.

11-5. Addition Polymerization

Addition polymerization proceeds generally by a chain reaction mechanism in which a monomer becomes activated, reacts with another and activates it. The process continues until terminated by an impurity or an additive, or, very frequently, by the encounter of two growing chains. In the case of vinyl derivatives, the activated form is often a free radical, which can form spontaneously but is generally produced by an initiator such as a peroxide. The reaction may be represented as follows

$$CH\!=\!CH_2 + I\cdot \longrightarrow ICH\!-\!CH_2\cdot \qquad \text{(initiation)}$$
$$\overset{|}{X} \qquad\qquad\qquad \overset{|}{X}$$

$$ICH\!-\!CH_2\cdot + CH\!=\!CH_2 \longrightarrow ICH\!-\!CH_2\!-\!CH\!-\!CH_2\cdot$$
$$\overset{|}{X} \qquad\quad \overset{|}{X} \qquad\qquad\qquad \overset{|}{X} \qquad\quad \overset{|}{X} \quad \text{(propagation)}$$

$$R\!-\!CH\!-\!CH_2\cdot \quad \left\{ \begin{array}{l} R\!-\!CH\!-\!CH_2\!-\!CH_2\!-\!CH\!-\!R' \\ \quad\overset{|}{X} \qquad\qquad\qquad \overset{|}{X} \\ \\ \text{or } R\!-\!C\!=\!CH_2 + R'\!-\!CH\!-\!CH_3 \\ \qquad\overset{|}{X} \qquad\qquad\qquad \overset{|}{X} \end{array} \right. \quad \text{(termination)}$$
$$\overset{|}{X}$$
$$+ \longrightarrow$$
$$R'\!-\!CH\!-\!CH_2\cdot$$
$$\overset{|}{X}$$

Here X may be any of a large number of groups, such as C_6H_5 in polystyrene or Cl in polyvinyl chloride, and $I\cdot$ is the initiating radical. Polymerization can also be conducted with an ionic activated form.

For the simplest case of addition polymerization, a chain grows through the mass of monomers until it encounters the head of another chain. Other things being equal, the rate of polymerization is therefore proportional to the number of chains growing simultaneously at any one time. The length of a chain at termination depends on its life span and this, in turn, depends on its chances of meeting another. Thus, the degree of polymerization is inversely proportional to the number of growing chains existing simultaneously and therefore to the rate of polymerization. The largest molecule would be obtained if a single chain could be started and kept growing until it consumes all the monomer. But the rate of polymerization would then be extremely slow. In practice, average degrees of polymerization of the order of tens of thousands are obtained.

A high degree of polymerization and simultaneously a high rate of polymerization can be obtained by isolating the growing chains from each other in separate droplets. This is the basis of so-called emulsion polymerization and related techniques.

11-6. The Diuturnal Colloids

When a material in bulk form does not disperse spontaneously or easily, the problem of preparing a colloidal dispersion involves the production of small particles under such conditions that they remain separated in the solvent.   Thus, sulfur or gold do not dissolve spontaneously, yet by proper procedures it is possible to produce colloidal particles of these materials and keep them suspended indefinitely.   Their suspensions are basically formed by fragments of the bulk phase, tiny crystals or tiny droplets. These can be produced either by subdividing the bulk phase (dispersion methods) or by precipitating this phase in a finely divided form (condensation methods).

Dispersion by simple grinding or milling of the bulk phase generally does not lead to extensive subdivision, because the mechanical forces which cause the breakup of large particles also tend to cause the coalescence of smaller ones, so that a sort of equilibrium distribution of sizes is reached.   Hence special precautions have to be taken, such as the addition of an inert diluent which reduces the chances of the small particles meeting each other.   For example, the grinding of sulfur in the presence of sufficient urea or sugar gives a powder which, upon dissolving in water, yields colloidal suspensions of crystalline sulfur.[2] Continuous removal of the small particles by elutriation during grinding (Section 3-25) also permits complete comminution, but is practical only in the upper limits of the colloidal range and above.   Dispersion is also often facilitated by the addition of stabilizing agents which prevent or reduce coalescence of the small particles when they meet.   Many emulsions are thus made by more or less violent agitation of water with immiscible liquids in the presence of surface active agents.

Precipitation of the insoluble phase may be produced by any one of the multitude of methods available to the chemist.   Thus deposition from the vapor, substitution of a poor solvent for a good one, and innumerable chemical reactions are used.   The success of these condensation methods depends on the choice of conditions which lead to the formation of myriads of tiny discrete particles rather than of large chunks of the new phase.   Particularly critical is the choice which leads to the production of substantially monodisperse systems.   The key to the proper choice may generally be found in the details of the familiar process of precipitation.

11-7. Nucleation and Growth

It is frequently stated that water freezes when cooled to $0\,°C$. and that a salt precipitates when its solubility product is reached. In fact, however, the appearance of a new phase when equilibrium conditions for its existence are reached is the exception rather than the rule.   Water generally supercools by a few degrees and salts supersaturate readily.   We have already noted earlier superheating and negative pressures (Section 6-2).   It is only in the presence of seeds or nuclei that the growth of the new phase tends to occur until supercooling or supersaturation is relieved and equilibrium approached.   For water and many salts the rate of this growth is relatively rapid, though not instantaneous, but for some substances, such as sugar or magnesium oxalate, it may be quite slow.

Thus we have two fundamental processes, nucleation and growth, which are largely independent of each other and together determine the size and the shape in which a phase will precipitate.   The total amount of the new substance formed depends primarily on the chemical process involved.   Whether part or all of it will precipitate as a new phase depends on the supersaturation it reaches, on the presence or formation of nuclei, and on their rates of growth.   The state of subdivision of this total amount precipitated depends on the number of nuclei and hence of particles among which it is divided.   The uniformity of dispersion will depend on how simultaneous is the beginning and how equal the rate of growth of these nuclei.

11-8. Nucleation

For the sake of simplicity, let us first consider the formation of a liquid from a vapor phase.   Clearly, any large scale formation of the liquid phase must be preceded by the formation of very small amounts. If we neglect for the time being the effect of walls, these small amounts will be tiny droplets whose surface has a high curvature and therefore, as we have seen (Section 8-15), a higher vapor pressure than bulk liquid. Hence, if the vapor is saturated or even slightly supersaturated, a sufficiently small droplet will tend to evaporate rather than to grow, and any beginning of condensation will thus be inhibited. On the other hand, if supersaturation is adequate or if the droplet happens to be large enough, it will tend to grow and the formation of the bulk phase can begin; i.e., the droplet is an effective nucleus for the condensation. It is therefore interesting to examine more closely the factors which determine the occurrence of a nucleus.

A very important factor lies in foreign particles. These may adsorb the vapor and become covered with a monolayer or multilayer of liquid and thus become effectively a droplet. If hygroscopic, they may even dissolve in the adsorbed water. Single ions are very effective in promoting nucleation of water and act by attracting and orienting the dipolar water molecules around their charges. The term nuclei is generally extended to include such foreign or external agents.

Unless some care is exerted, foreign nuclei are likely to be present in most systems and initiate a phase change before high supersaturation is reached. Sometimes, as in the cloud chamber method of observing the path of radiation, the effectiveness of these foreign nuclei is put to very good use. On the other hand, by carefully excluding these foreign nuclei one finds that much higher degrees of supersaturation can be obtained. It is then that another limit to supersaturation is encountered due to the almost simultaneous appearance of very large numbers of nuclei in the bulk of the vapor. This is called spontaneous or homogeneous nucleation.

11-9. Homogeneous Nucleation

The origin of the nuclei effective in homogeneous nucleation seems to lie in the spontaneous fluctuations occurring in the vapor and leading to the accidental clustering of vapor molecules forming tiny droplets.   These clusters are somewhat stabilized by the same attractive forces which lead to liquefaction and are, of course, disrupted by thermal motion.   If below a certain critical size, they tend to evaporate spontaneously and are called embryos.   It is only when they reach the critical size that embryos become nuclei.   Because of spontaneous fluctuations in the arrangement of molecules of the supersaturated vapor, embryos form and disappear constantly.

The probability of a fluctuation producing a cluster depends, as we have seen (Section 10-3), on the work required to produce deliberately such a cluster.   This work will increase with the number of molecules in the cluster until the critical radius is reached, because, by definition, until that point molecules tend to evaporate rather than condense.   Therefore, the larger the embryo, the less probable its occurrence.   Since the energies involved are of the order of heats of evaporation, the work involved is large compared to kT, and the probability is very small and decreases very rapidly with the size of the cluster. Hence, when supersaturation is low and the critical radius correspondingly large, it is natural that the chances of spontaneous nucleation are utterly negligible.   As supersaturation increases, however, the critical size becomes smaller until it reaches a value for which spontaneous formation of clusters has a significant probability.   These clusters then become nuclei and spontaneous nucleation sets in.   Because of the large energies involved, the transition occurs over an extremely narrow range of conditions.

Essentially the same considerations, with minor changes, apply to freezing, boiling, or precipitation from solution.   The case of melting is somewhat different because this process almost always begins at the surface, and surface molecules are always intrinsically more loosely bound and form what is essentially an adsorbed liquid as the melting point is approached.   The surface thus acts as a built-in nucleus, and superheating is not normally observed in melting.   However, if a solid is heated only from the inside, as by concentrating sunlight with a lens in a piece of ice,[3] superheating can be readily observed.

The complete removal of external nuclei from bulk liquids and from solid walls is almost impossible. If liquids are subdivided into tiny droplets of fogs or emulsions, the influence of each external nucleus is confined to a single droplet, and the majority of these droplets can be kept free of external nuclei. It is thus possible to observe spontaneous nucleation, or its lack, in most of the liquid. For example, a fog or emulsion of water droplets can be supercooled to about $-39\,°C.$, and it is only then that spontaneous nucleation occurs.[4]

It is known that certain materials can interfere with the nucleation of solid phases. This is probably due to their being incorporated into the clusters, which prevents the formation of the crystal structure required of an effective nucleus. We will encounter an example of this shortly in connection with gold sols.

11-10. Growth

The rate of growth of a new phase involves a number of processes, each of which may limit its speed. Thus, molecules must reach the surface, must be incorporated into it, and the heat of formation must be dissipated. The last factor is important in the condensation of vapors on the walls of a vessel, and sometimes in the rapid crystallization of melts. It is of little concern in the growth of colloidal particles with their enormous specific surfaces.

The difficulty of incorporation into a surface is particularly striking in the slow rate of crystallization of certain liquids, such as glycerin whose maximum rate of crystal growth is about 0.002 cm./sec.[5] (Phosphorus has a corresponding rate of over 100 cm./sec).[6] There can be no question here that molecules are in the immediate vicinity of the surface and that temperature equilibrium prevails. The difficulty is more likely to lie in the need for the proper orientation of the molecules.

In general, the rate of growth tends to increase with increasing

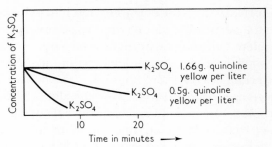

Figure 11-3. The effect of an adsorbable impurity on the rate of crystallization. (*From T. Svedberg, Colloid Chemistry, Chemical Catalog Co., Reinhold,
N. Y.*, 1928.)

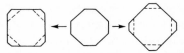

Figure 11-4. It is the slowest growing faces of a crystal which develop most
fully whereas the fastest growing ones disappear.

supersaturation and to decrease with increasing viscosity and the
corresponding loss of mobility of the molecule in the liquid.
Lowering the temperature not only increases supersaturation
but also the viscosity of the liquid.   This generally leads to a
maximum rate of growth at an intermediate temperature.

Another and very important obstacle to growth may be the
presence of impurities which are adsorbed on the surface and
prevent the incorporation of additional molecules.   Thus the
dye quinoline yellow is adsorbed by potassium sulfate, and in
concentrations as low as 0.16% virtually prevents the growth of
its crystals (Fig. 11-3).   Unequal adsorption on different faces
of a crystal may lead to unequal reduction of their rates of growth
and subsequent development of unusual crystal faces and habits
(Fig. 11-4).   Thus ordinary salt in the presence of urea forms
octahedral crystals instead of the usual cubic ones.

The rate of approach becomes an important factor in the
condensation of vapors and in precipitation from solutions.
Here, it is often the rate of diffusion to the growing surface that

determines its rate of growth.   The growing nucleus acts as a "sink" for the molecules in its immediate vicinity, and these must be replaced by diffusion from further away.   As a corollary, each nucleus reduces supersaturation in its neighborhood, but the effect decreases with distance.

Let us now illustrate these general concepts by the preparation of gold sol, one of the earliest and perhaps most studied examples of a diuturnal colloid, and then turn to the preparation of monodisperse systems and of sulfur sols.

11-11. Gold Sols

It is possible to produce gold vapor and make it condense to colloidal particles by striking an electric arc between gold electrodes under water or in a stream of nitrogen leading directly into water.   This method is applicable to many metals and is often called the Bredig method.   Although seldom used, it permits the preparation of systems in which components other than gold and water, and their ions, are virtually absent.   Under these conditions the sols have only a fleeting existence and flocculate rapidly.   In the presence of small amounts of Cl^- ions, however, stable sols may be obtained.   We will return in Chapter 15 to the stabilizing effect of the charge on the particle and to its origin in the adsorption of this anion.

Gold sols are prepared most frequently be reduction of the common trivalent compound, chloroauric acid, $H(AuCl_4)$. Almost any reducing agent can be used[7] to precipitate gold from its solutions, but the size and stability of the resulting particles depend markedly on the specific conditions.   Thus phosphorus, added as a small volume of an ethereal solution, gives particularly fine particles indicating that nuclei form readily.   Formaldehyde behaves similarly.   On the other hand, when hydroxylamine is the reducing agent, the formation of nuclei is greatly inhibited and coarse particles are obtained, sometimes so coarse that they settle out readily.   The addition of ammonium or ferricyanide ions can similarly interfere with nucleation and leads to fewer and larger particles during reduction, for example, with formaldehyde.

Growth, separated from nucleation, may be observed when a finely dispersed sol (formed with phosphorus or formaldehyde) is added to a reduction mixture in which nucleation is very slow. A particularly striking effect can be observed during the reduction with hydrogen peroxide according to the net reaction

$$2 \text{ AuCl}_4^- + 3 \text{ H}_2\text{O}_2 \longrightarrow 2 \text{ Au} + 8 \text{ Cl}^- + 6 \text{ H}^+ + 3 \text{ O}_2$$

The progress of the reduction in this system can be measured by the increase of electric conductivity, while the disappearance

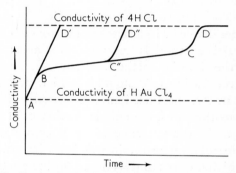

Figure 11-5. Nucleation in the formation of a gold sol. Conductivity measures the formation of elemental gold. Curve *ABCD* in the absence of external nuclei; *ABD'*, with nuclei present from the beginning; *ABC"D"* with nuclei added at *C"*. (*From T. Svedberg, Colloid Chemistry, Chemical Catalog Co., Reinhold, N. Y., 1928.*)

of the faintly yellow gold complex and the appearance of the intensely red colloidal gold can be observed visually. If no nuclei are added, the conductivity of the system changes as shown by the solid line in Fig. 11-5. There is a rapid initial increase in conductivity (*A–B*) and a decrease in the yellow color, showing that part of the gold is rapidly reduced. Then both processes slow down and the system changes, but slowly, until point *C*. Presumably a high degree of supersaturation has been rapidly reached and the reaction correspondingly slowed down.   Then, rather suddenly, the red color of colloidal particles appears and darkens rapidly, while the reaction proceeds to completion $(C-D)$.   This corresponds to homogeneous nucleation and rapid growth of nuclei.   By adding external nuclei at any point, the supersaturation can be immediately relieved, as shown in the figure for nuclei added before the beginning of reduction $(B-D')$ or in the middle of the slow state $(C''-D'')$.

Hydrazine, which interferes with nucleation, has no effect on growth, whereas other additives, such as H_2S, KI, or gelatin, can slow down the rate of growth considerably.

11-12. Monodisperse Gold Sols

Sols produced by the growth of external nuclei have particles whose final size is determined by the initial size of each nucleus and by its rate of growth.   If a fine gold sol is used as a source of external nuclei, the initial size is generally polydisperse, but since the particles are all small their absolute range is also small and can often be neglected in comparison with the final size.   The rate of growth depends primarily on the rate at which the gold reaches the surface of the particle by diffusion. If the external conditions are uniform, i.e., the solution is well mixed, this is a random process.   The deviation from the average can therefore be expected to vary with the square root of the number of elementary events (steps in a random walk), and each event corresponds to the accretion of one gold atom. Hence the growth of a sizable particle involves a tremendous number of random events, so that the deviation becomes very small compared to the total size.   Thus the particle size distribution of sols produced in this way can be very narrow, and for many purposes these sols can be treated as monodisperse.   This is the basis of the so called Zsigmondy nuclear method of preparing monodisperse gold sols.[8]

The same principle of providing uniform external growth centers and uniform growth conditions can be used to prepare many other monodisperse systems, such as aerosols[9] or high polymers.[10]

11-13. Sulfur Sols

A rather coarse and unstable sulfur suspension can be produced by adding some alcohol, which has been boiled with sulfur, to a large volume of water. The small amount of sulfur which originally dissolved in the hot alcohol precipitates upon dilution. In this suspension, as in all finer ones, the sulfur is in the form of droplets of supercooled sulfur, showing no anisotropy of shape and properties. This is in contrast to the suspensions obtained by grinding, as described above, where the crushed crystals tend, for example, to align in magnetic fields.[11]

A more common method of preparing sulfur sols is, again, by chemical reaction such as that of H_2S with oxygen (which can be so troublesome in qualitative analysis), or, better, by the decomposition of thiosulfate in acid solution

$$3 \ HS_2O_3^- \longrightarrow 4 \ S + 2 \ SO_4^{2-} + H^+ + H_2O$$

The mechanism of this reaction is quite complicated. Polythionic ions are formed at the same time and probably serve to stabilize the sol. When performed with concentrated solutions, the reaction is relatively rapid and gives quite polydisperse particles because of continuous growth and nucleation in a very highly supersaturated solution. The gradual increase in size of the particles can give rise to a gradual change of colors of transmitted light, the so-called "chemical sunset." The resulting particles have little tendency to coalesce and may be repeatedly flocculated by the addition of salts and then redispersed in pure water. Since ease of flocculation increases with larger particle size and lower temperature, it is possible to fractionate such polydisperse sols to produce more monodisperse ones.[12]

If the reaction is conducted at very low concentrations,[13] of the order of 0.003 M in thiosulfate and in acid, it becomes

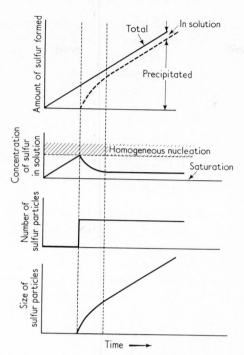

Figure 11-6. The processes occurring during the formation of a monodisperse sulfur sol.   While elemental sulfur is continuously formed, nucleation is delayed until the concentration of homogeneous nucleation is reached.   This reduces supersaturation and prevents further nucleation, while all the particles grow at the same rate.

very slow and leads to the processes shown schematically in Fig. 11-6. The reaction generates sulfur continuously over many hours, as can be ascertained by ultraviolet absorption. During the first hour or so, this sulfur remains in solution causing a tremendous and gradually increasing supersaturation.   Then, when supersaturation reaches the point of homogeneous nucleation, a large number of nuclei appear spontaneously within a very short time.   These grow rapidly and thus relieve the supersaturation sufficiently throughout the solution to prevent further nucleation.   Hence these nuclei, all formed at the same time, grow all at the same rate from then on as sulfur continues to be generated in the system.   This leads, for the same reasons as discussed in connection with seeded gold sols, to an essentially monodisperse system of growing particles.   Addition of KI, which reacts rapidly with the remaining thiosulfate, can stop the growth at any desired point.   These sols, which can show beautiful colors, the so-called higher order Tyndall spectra (see Section 20-15), are often called LaMer sols, after the contemporary American chemist who has studied them extensively.

Summary

The preparation of colloids involves much of the normal preparative skill of the chemist, with additional emphasis on factors controlling the size of the particles produced.   Specifically, in condensation methods it is the presence of nuclei, either external or spontaneously generated, which determines the number of particles.   The growth of these nuclei determines the rate at which supersaturation is relieved and in turn affects the formation of the nuclei.   The conditions for monodispersity are obtained when all the nuclei grow at the same time and under the same conditions.

References

1. A. Alberty, E. A. Anderson, and J. W. Williams, *J. Phys. & Colloid Chem.*, **52,** 217 (1948).
2. S. Utzino, in J. Alexander, *Colloid Chemistry*, Vol. I, The Chemical Catalog Co. (Reinhold), New York, 1926, p. 659.
3. J. Tyndall, *Phil. Trans. Roy. Soc. (London)*, **148,** 211 (1858); *Heat as a Mode of Motion*, Appleton and Company, New York, 1873, p. 129.
4. V. J. Schaefer, *Ind. Eng. Chem.*, **44,** 1300 (1952); G. M. Pound, L. A. Madonna, and S. L. Peake, *J. Colloid Sci.*, **8,** 187 (1953).
5. M. I. Volmer and M. Marder, *Z. physik. Chem.*, **A154,** 97 (1931).
6. R. E. Powell, T. S. Gilman, and J. H. Hildebrand, *J. Am. Chem. Soc.*, **73,** 2525 (1951).
7. R. Zsigmondy and P. A. Thiessen, *Das Kolloide Gold*, Akademische

Verlagg., Leipzig, 1925; H. B. Weiser, *Inorganic Colloid Chemistry*, Vol. I, John Wiley & Sons, Inc., New York, 1933, Chap. II.

8. A. Westgren, *Z. anorg. Chem.*, **93**, 151 (1915); **94**, 193 (1916).

9. D. Sinclair and V. K. LaMer, *Chem. Revs.*, **44**, 245 (1949).

10. R. Waack, A. Rembaum, J. D. Coombes, and M. Szwarc, *J. Am. Chem. Soc.*, **79**, 2026 (1957).

11. T. Svedberg, *Colloid Chemistry*, 2nd ed., The Chemical Catalog Co. (Reinhold), New York, 1928, p. 199.

12. S. Oden, *Acta Nuova (Upsala)*, (4), **3**, No. 4 (1913); through T. Svedberg, ref. 11, p. 265; or *Der Kolloide Schwefel;* through Weiser, ref. 8, Chap. 12.

13. E. M. Zaiser and V. K. LaMer, *J. Colloid Sci.*, **3**, 571 (1948).

Problems

112. Equal large portions of a mixture of gold chloride and hydrogen peroxide are seeded with small volumes of a "phosphorus" gold sol. These small volumes are in the ratio of 1:4:16. Hence the radii of the final particles should be approximately in the ratio of (*1*) 1:4:16, (*2*) 16:4:1, (*3*) 1:2:4, (*4*) 4:2:1, (*5*) 1:1.6:2.5, (*6*) 2.5:1.6:1, (*7*) none of these.

118. In the preparation of monodisperse sulfur by LaMer's method, if an additive would reduce the probability of a surface molecule's becoming attached to a nucleus upon reaching it, this would probably require (for the maintenance of monodispersity) (*1*) no change in procedure, (*2*) lower concentrations of reagents, (*3*) higher concentrations of reagents.

104. Colloidal particles may be expected to be particularly small if formed under conditions causing (*1*) rapid nucleation and rapid growth, (*2*) slow nucleation and rapid growth, (*3*) rapid nucleation and slow growth, (*4*) slow nucleation and slow growth.

100. In producing a monodispersed gold sol you would try to use (*1*) large colloidal gold particles for seeding, (*2*) a reducing agent which produces elemental gold very rapidly, (*3*) additives which slow down the growth of nuclei, (*4*) all of these, (*5*) none of these.

CHAPTER XII

Descriptive Rheology

We are now reaching the last of the chapters dealing with the behavior of colloidal systems in the absence of electrical charges. These chapters will consider those aspects which become perceptible when the systems flow. We shall first give a brief summary of the phenomenological description of these systems— what kind of behavior is observed and how it is measured and classified. In the next chapter we shall proceed to the interpretation of this behavior in terms of structure. Throughout, we shall be interested particularly in measurements which can give us an estimate of the shape, and hence in some cases of the size, of the particles or which can shed light on their interactions.

The ability to flow is, by definition, the most general property of liquid and semisolid materials, and comes into play continuously whenever we deal with these. Rheology, the science of the flow of matter, is therefore of tremendous practical importance. It includes hydrodynamics, which is often treated as a separate subject. Whereas hydrodynamics deals only with simple liquids, rheology is particularly interested in the more complicated behavior of solutions, suspensions, gels, pastes, doughs, etc. In dealing with colloidal systems, therefore, a knowledge of rheology is most useful. Unfortunately, precise treatment of these phenomena runs into great mathematical difficulties and complications, and we will have to skip it almost completely. We can only introduce some of the basic concepts and interpretations.

12-1. Viscosity

Let us begin by considering again the laminar flow of a simple liquid, such as water or the much more viscous glycerin. We

253

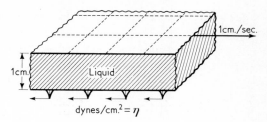

Figure 12-1. Viscosity is the force required per cm.² to maintain a relative velocity of 1 cm./sec. between two parallel planes separated by 1 cm. of fluid.

have defined (Section 3-1) their viscosity in poises as the force in dynes required per square centimeter to pull two large planes, 1 cm. apart, with a relative velocity of 1 cm/sec. In this definition the force is computed per unit surface and may be properly called the shearing stress or, briefly, stress (Fig. 12-1). If the velocity or the spacing change, the stress will change also, unless it is computed per unit of velocity-per-unit-spacing, $\Delta u/\Delta x$. This quantity is called the rate of shear strain or, briefly, the rate of shear. We can thus restate the definition of viscosity as

$$\eta = \text{Stress/Rate of shear} = (F/A)/(\Delta u/\Delta x) \qquad (12\text{-}1.1)$$

where F is the total force acting over the area A. In the c.g.s. system, the dimensions of viscosity are dynes-sec/cm.² or g/sec.-cm. As we have already seen, the c.g.s. unit of viscosity is the poise although the centipoise is most frequently used.

It may be noted that this definition considers the force on the plane and not on the liquid, and that this force is independent of the separation as long as the rate of shear is constant. Yet the force clearly is required by the friction within the liquid. This implies that there is no slip between the plane and the immediately adjoining liquid, for if there were such a slip its effect would vary with the separation. In fact, slip seems never to have been observed with liquids,[1] and for gases becomes significant only when the mean free path of the molecules is comparable to the dimensions of the apparatus. The reason for this lack of slip lies in the smallness of the forces involved in viscous flow when compared to the intermolecular forces between the liquid and the wall.

For water, glycerin, and many other liquids, the viscosity is a well defined constant for a given temperature and pressure and is independent of the stress or rate of shear (Table 3-1 in Chapter 3). We shall now see how viscosity is measured and later see how such measurements fail to yield a constant for many other fluids.

12-2. The Couette Viscometer

It is rather difficult, experimentally, to provide the infinite planes moving with respect to each other at a constant velocity that are required by the above definition of viscosity. The result can be approached, however, by curving both planes so as to form concentric cylinders and limiting their height. This is the

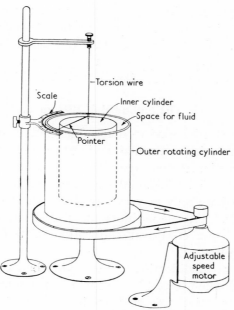

Figure 12-2. The principle of a Couette viscometer. (*From R. B. Dean, Modern Colloids, D. van Nostrand Co., New York*, 1948.)

principle of viscometers of the Couette type. Generally the outer cylinder or "cup" is rotated at a known speed by a motor (Fig. 12-2) while the inner one or "bob" is suspended from an elastic torsion wire whose twist measures the force, so that one has the basis for computing the viscosity of the liquid. If the spacing, Δ_R, of the two cylinders is small compared to their radius, R, the rate of shear is $2\pi R\alpha/\Delta_R$, where α is the rate of rotation in revolutions per second. The area over which the viscous force F is exerted is $2\pi RH$, where H is the height of the cylinders. Thus

$$\eta = F/(2\pi RH)(2\pi R\alpha/\Delta_R) = F\Delta_R/4\pi^2 R^2 H\alpha \qquad (12\text{-}2.1)$$

In practice, disturbing factors, such as the "end effects" of forces acting upon the upper and lower end of the bob and the finite width of the gap between the cylinders, have to be taken into account.

Under proper conditions, an accuracy of the order of a per cent and a precision of the order of a tenth of a per cent seem to be attainable. The main advantage of Couette viscometers is that the rate of shear is quite uniform and can readily be varied by changing the rate of rotation or the width of the gap.

12-3. The Falling Ball Viscometer

Stokes' law can be used to determine viscosity by measuring the terminal velocity of a sphere falling through a column of the liquid. In practice, the passage of the ball between two reference marks is timed (Fig. 12-3). As we have seen, however, Stokes' law applies strictly only at very low Reynolds numbers and for infinite liquids. These conditions are seldom approached sufficiently, and some empirical calibration of the apparatus is generally required.

A convenient modification of the falling ball principle is the Höppler viscometer (Fig. 12-4), in which a sphere is allowed to descend in a relatively narrow, inclined tube. The motion of the sphere is a complicated combination of sliding and rolling, so that the apparatus requires empirical calibration. This in-

Figure 12-3. Principle of the falling-ball viscometer. The time of travel of the sphere between the two fixed marks is measured. Note the breather hole and the narrow tube for gently introducing the sphere.

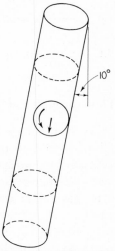

Figure 12-4. The principle of the Höppler viscometer. The time of travel of the sphere along the inclined tube between the two fixed marks is determined. (*Adapted from materials courtesy Fish-Schurman Corp., New Rochelle, N. Y.*)

strument has the great advantage that, by simply changing balls, one can cover the whole range of viscosities from gases to very

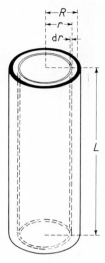

Figure 12-5. The total flow in a capillary is the sum of the motions of concentric lamellae of uniform velocity, each satisfying the basic viscosity equation.

viscous liquids, and that the measurement can be made very precise.

12-4. Flow through Capillaries

The most precise and convenient method of measuring the viscosity of ordinary liquids is based on their flow through capillaries. We shall therefore consider now the laws governing this flow and then describe the viscometer used.

The liquid, in order to pass from one reservoir to another through a capillary, has to (*1*) overcome the viscous forces which it encounters while flowing in this capillary, (*2*) be accelerated from rest and then brought to rest again, and (*3*) be squeezed into the capillary and emerge from it. The first effect is the main one and is the one that can serve to measure the viscosity. The other two can be made negligible or require small corrections and are generally referred to respectively as the kinetic energy correction and the end effects. We will neglect these corrections

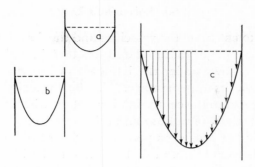

Figure 12-6. Laminar flow through capillaries. (*a*) Liquid which originally occupies a diameter of the tube becomes a symmetrical parabola during flow. (*b*) If the pressure is doubled, flow velocity is also doubled. (*c*) If the radius is doubled, corresponding velocities are quadrupled. Note that the velocity is greatest at the center and vanishes at the wall (*left side of c*) but the velocity gradient is greatest at the wall and vanishes in the center (*right side of c*).

and consider only the steady flow of a liquid through the body of a capillary.

The volume of liquid which flows through a capillary is, of course, proportional to the time during which the flow occurs. It also increases directly with the pressure difference which causes the flow. The longer the capillary, the greater the resistance and the less the flow. A most important factor, however, is the radius of the capillary.

For reasons of symmetry, the lamellae of the flowing liquid must be concentric cylinders, one of which is shown in Fig. 12-5. The total volume flowing through the tube is the sum of the volumes carried by all such lamellae, each having its own velocity. The lamella immediately adjacent to the wall must have a negligible velocity, since one of its surfaces is formed by the wall. The velocity increases towards the center, and at each point there is a radial velocity gradient such that the viscous forces just balance the force exerted by the driving pressure. These simple premises are sufficient to derive the exact distribution of the velocity given by Eq. 12-5.5 and illustrated in Fig. 12-6, as well as the total flow given by Poiseuille's law, Eq. 12-5.8.

12-5. Poiseuille's Law

In order to calculate the velocities and the flow, let us consider (Fig. 12-5) a tube of radius R and length L in which the liquid of viscosity η flows under the influence of a pressure P exerted uniformly over its upper surface. The flow velocity u varies with the distance r from the center but is constant with height. A thin cylindrical lamella of radius r and thickness dr encloses a cylinder having an upper area πr^2 upon which pressure P exerts a force $\pi r^2 P$. In the steady-state this force has to be balanced by the viscous forces over the lateral surface $2\pi rL$ of this cylinder. These viscous forces are due to the velocity gradient $-du/dr$ within the lamella (the sign is negative since u increases with decreasing r). From the definition of viscosity we have therefore

$$\eta = -(\pi r^2 P/2\pi rL)/(du/dr) \qquad (12\text{-}5.1)$$

or

$$du = -(P/2\eta L)r\, dr \qquad (12\text{-}5.2)$$

which is the differential expression for the velocity as a function of the distance from the center. It shows that the rate of shear, du/dr, changes from zero at the center when $r = 0$ to a maximum equal to $PR/2\eta L$ at the wall. To obtain the velocity itself we integrate, which gives

$$u = \int du = -(P/4\eta L)r^2 + C \qquad (12\text{-}5.3)$$

where C is an integration constant. The fact that the velocity is zero at the wall of the tube gives

$$0 = -(P/4\eta L)R^2 + C \qquad (12\text{-}5.4)$$

which defines C. Hence the velocity at any point is given by

$$u = (P/4\eta L)(R^2 - r^2) \qquad (12\text{-}5.5)$$

which shows that the maximum velocity is at the center of the tube and is equal to $(P/4\eta L)R^2$. The velocity decreases parabolically to the walls, as shown in Figure 12-6.

The volume of liquid per unit length of a lamella is $2\pi r \, dr$. The volume flow dV it delivers in time t is therefore

$$dV = 2\pi r u t \, dr = 2\pi r (P/4\eta L)(R^2 - r^2)t \, dr$$

$$= (2\pi P t/4\eta L)(R^2 r - r^3)dr \quad (12\text{-}5.6)$$

which is the differential equation for the volume of flow. The total flow V through the tube is the sum of volumes delivered by all the lamellae or

$$V = \int dV = (2\pi P t/4\eta L)\int_0^R (R^2 r - r^3)dr$$

$$= (2\pi P t/4\eta L)[(R^2 r^2/2) - r^4/4]_0^R \quad (12\text{-}5.7)$$

which gives

$$V = (\pi/8)PR^4 t/\eta L \quad (12\text{-}5.8)$$

This is Poiseuille's law and shows that the flow increases with the fourth power of the radius. It is named after the French physician who discovered it while investigating the flow of blood in small blood vessels.

12-6. The Ostwald Viscometer

When the pressure difference, P, causing flow through a capillary is produced by the level difference, H, of the liquid, we have $P = \rho H g$, where ρ is the density of the liquid. Hence, Poiseuille's law (Eq. 12-5.8) becomes

$$V = \pi \rho H g R^4 t/8\eta L \quad (12\text{-}6.1)$$

or

$$\eta/\rho = (\pi H g R^4/8 V L)t \quad (12\text{-}6.2)$$

The Ostwald viscometer (Fig. 12-7) is based on this relation. It is essentially a convenient instrument for making the whole expression within the bracket a constant, so that the measurement of only t gives η/ρ. This last value is called the kinematic viscosity* and, with a knowledge of density, is directly converted

* or viscosity/density ratio (see footnote on p. 276).

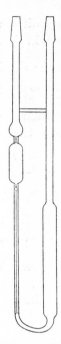

Figure 12-7. A precision viscometer of the Ostwald type. The time of emptying the oblong reservoir on the left is determined. To reduce the effect of surface tension the diameter of this reservoir is the same as that of the receiver on the right. *(From G. Jones and H. J. Fornwalt, J. Am. Chem. Soc.,* **60,** 1683 (1938).)

to the viscosity. As shown in Fig. 12-7, the instrument is a rigid assembly of a capillary and two reservoirs. The radius R is therefore constant, and when a known volume of liquid is introduced H and L are fixed. The upper reservoir serves also as a pipet for measuring the volume V. Hence, a measurement of the time of emptying this reservoir determines the kinematic viscosity once the constant is known. This, in turn, is determined by measuring the flow time of water or of another liquid of known viscosity and density.

The Ostwald viscometer permits ready measurements with an accuracy of the order of 0.1%, and with special refinements can give a precision of some 0.002%. The time of flow of an Ostwald viscometer should be at least of the order of 200 sec. to permit ready measurement of time and volume and also to reduce kinetic energy effects. As the viscosity of the liquid increases, the time increases proportionately and soon becomes impracticably long. Hence, each viscometer is useful over only a limited range of viscosities. In addition, the rate of shear in the capillary varies (Eq. 12-5.2), from zero in the center to a maximum at the wall, so that it is neither uniform nor easily changed. As we shall see, this can be a definite handicap under some circumstances.

12-7. Viscoelasticity

A solid (in contrast to a liquid) when subject to a small stress becomes deformed, but this deformation is limited and does not increase with time. To maintain a constant deformation, a constant stress must be maintained. Furthermore, when the stress is removed, the original shape is spontaneously restored. These are the characteristics of perfectly elastic behavior and are shown, for example, by good steel or by silica. A viscous liquid, on the other hand, also deforms under these conditions, but the deformation is proportional to time and shows no reversal when the force is removed. This is the behavior of water, oil, glycerin, etc.

There are many materials which show neither of these ideal behaviors. For example, when subjected to a force they deform continuously, but when the force is removed they return spontaneously, though not completely, towards the original shape. When the elastic part of this behavior predominates, we speak of the creep of a solid; when the viscous prevails, we speak of viscoelastic behavior of a fluid. We have already encountered the former in unvulcanized rubber, and it is shown by many metals, especially at higher temperature. Viscoelasticity on the other hand, is shown by concentrated systems of long chain molecules and is exemplified by the familiar raw egg white.

An important characteristic of this viscoelastic behavior is

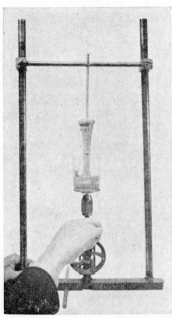

Figure 12-8. One of the remarkable phenomena shown by a viscoelastic material.   It leaves the rotating cup and climbs up the stationary rod.   (*From J. J. Hermans, ed., Flow Properties of Disperse Systems, Interscience, N. Y.,* 1953.)

that the elasticity is more marked in rapid deformation.   Thus, if a deformation is produced and then only enough force is applied to maintain it, this force decreases gradually until almost none is needed, and there is no return after the force is removed. The fluid has "relaxed," and the time in which the force decreases to a specified fraction (generally to $1/e = 0.368$) of the original value is called the relaxation time.   If the relaxation time is sufficiently short, it becomes, of course, unobservable, and the behavior is viscous.   Conversely, if it is sufficiently long, the observed behavior tends to the purely elastic.   Silicone putty, "Silly Putty," has a quite short relaxation time, so that it bounces but shows little elasticity when slowly stretched.

Another characteristic of viscoelastic behavior is that it tends to cause flow at right angles to the applied forces.   For example, in a Couette viscometer the fluid may climb up the supporting wire.   An extreme type of this behavior is shown in Fig. 12-8. This is readily understood if one visualizes a strand of the fluid attached at one end to the cup and at the other end to the rod. Rotation of the cup stretches this elastic strand so that it tends to wrap itself tightly around the rod.   In so doing, it tends to squeeze out any interfering portions of the fluid, and the only place where these can go is upward.   As other strands become attached higher up to the rod, the same effect continues to push the fluid up this only avenue of escape.

12-8. Viscoelastic Models

One way of considering the behavior of viscoelastic materials is to consider them as a mechanical combination of ideally elastic and ideally viscous elements.   As shown in Fig. 12-9, the viscous element can be symbolized by a dashpot (filled with oil) and the elastic element by a spring.   These basic elements can then be combined in various ways in an attempt to reproduce the behavior of real systems.   Combined in series, they form the model of the so-called Maxwell fluid which shows the relaxation behavior discussed above.   Combined in parallel, they illustrate the Voigt solid which deforms to a limit under constant stress and then returns completely after its removal just like an ideal solid, but does this slowly and dissipates energy in the process. This corresponds to the behavior of some rubbery plastics which show little bounce.

These models are very useful in illustrating the types of behavior to be expected and in developing their mathematical description under ideal conditions.   Most real viscoelastic systems, however, show much more complicated behavior whose representation requires the combination of many such elements. The simplicity of treatment is thus rapidly lost.   In addition, there seems to be no direct correlation between the real, molecular structure of the material and the elements used to symbolize its behavior.

Viscoelasticity, as may be readily seen from the above survey, is a highly complicated type of behavior.   It is also still very incompletely understood.   Having pointed out its existence and

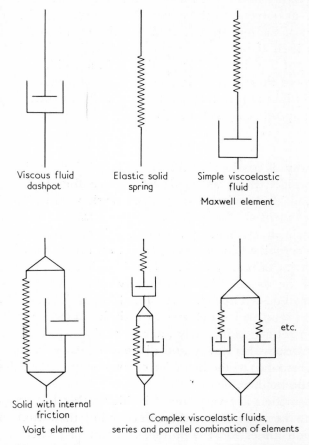

Viscous fluid
dashpot

Elastic solid
spring

Simple viscoelastic
fluid

Maxwell element

Solid with internal
friction

Voigt element

Complex viscoelastic fluids,
series and parallel combination of elements

Figure 12-9. Schematic models of viscous liquids, elastic solids, and viscoelastic fluids.

importance, we shall therefore neglect it through most of the following.   (A number of articles on various aspects of this subject can be found in reference 2.)

12-9. Newtonian and Non-Newtonian Behavior

As already stated, simple liquids, such as water, have a constant viscosity at a given temperature and pressure. In particular, the viscosity is independent of the rate of shear and of the previous history of the sample. Concretely, this means that when the liquid is placed in a Couette viscometer and subjected to a given rate of shear, the observed stress becomes constant as soon as inertial effects are overcome, and it is directly proportional to the rate of shear (Fig. 12-10). Such a fluid is called Newtonian. All liquids formed by small particles seem to show this Newtonian behavior, whether pure or a solution.

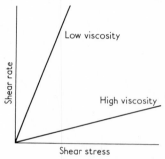

Figure 12-10. Newtonian liquid: the shear rate increases in direct proportion to the shear stress.

There are, however, many systems which show deviations from Newtonian behavior. Neglecting the elastic effects discussed above, these deviations may be of two principal types, or a combination of these. When subject to constant shear in a Couette viscometer, the system may show either a force which varies with time and the previous history of the sample (time or hysteretic effects), or one which is constant but is not proportional to the rate of shear (steady state phenomena). Time effects, in turn, may be reversible or not.

Since it is, as we shall soon discuss, the structure of these systems that is responsible for their non-Newtonian behavior, the term "structural viscosity" is sometimes used as a catchall.

The nomenclature involved in the more detailed consideration of the non-Newtonian behavior is still far from established. We shall use one which is common among chemists, but the reader should always remember that it is the concepts and their relations which are of primary importance in understanding nature, whereas the names are only a tool for the communication of this understanding.

12-10. Steady-State Phenomena

Pseudoplasticity is characterized by a stress which increases more rapidly at low rates of shear than at high rates of shear, so that the graph of stress versus rate is concave to the rate axis (Fig. 12-11).

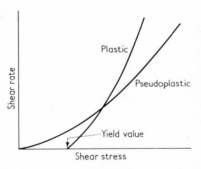

Figure 12-11. Plastic and pseudoplastic fluid: the shear rate increases faster than proportionally to the shear stress. A yield value characterizes plastic behavior.

Plasticity resembles pseudoplasticity, but the rate of shear does not acquire a finite value until the stress exceeds a "yield value" (Fig. 12-11). If, beyond the yield value, the relation is linear or rapidly becomes linear, we speak often of a Bingham solid. The distinction between plasticity and pseudoplasticity is not always easy. When the curvature is strong, the rate of shear for small forces may be so low that it is difficult to detect experimentally. A useful criterion is then the appearance of the surface of the fluid. If it is smooth, the extremely small surface-tension forces are capable of making it flow; hence, it has no true yield value and is pseudoplastic. On the other hand, one can also speak of a practical yield value at which the rate of shear simply becomes negligible for the purpose at hand.

Modeling clay is a typical product in which plasticity is desirable, since the clay should hold its final shape indefinitely yet should yield readily when molded. Pseudoplasticity is shown frequently by concentrated dispersions of small particles and by solutions of long chain molecules.

Figure 12-12. Dilatant fluid: the shear rate increases slower than proportionally to the shear stress.

Dilatancy is the opposite of pseudoplasticity. The force increases faster than the rate of shear (Fig. 12-12). This is a seldom encountered type of behavior, shown by deflocculated pastes of uniform particles with barely enough liquid to wet the mass.[3] When undisturbed, the particles arrange themselves regularly and occupy a small volume so that there is enough liquid to spare. As movement disturbs this order, the particles tend to occupy a larger volume, but the surface tension of the liquid prevents them from doing this. Hence, they are pressed against each other and offer increasing resistance to flow. Starch in a water-glycerin mixture shows this characteristic behavior over a relatively narrow concentration range.

12-11. Apparent Viscosity and Fluidity

When a system shows any non-Newtonian behavior we can no longer speak of its viscosity.   Yet, knowing the dimensions of the viscometer, we can relate any simultaneous stress and rate of shear to an apparent viscosity equal to that of a Newtonian liquid

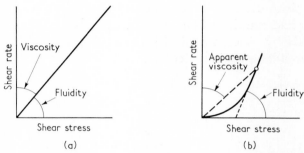

Figure 12-13. Geometric representation of viscosity, apparent viscosity, and fluidity.   The tangent of the angle shown gives the indicated quantity.

giving the same results.   Graphically, the viscosity of a Newtonian liquid (Fig. 12-13a) is measured by the tangent of the angle of the line representing its behavior with the rate of shear axis. By analogy, in a non-Newtonian system (Fig. 12-13b) apparent viscosity is measured by the same angle formed by a line joining the origin with the point corresponding to a given measurement. This angle and, therefore, the apparent viscosity vary with the conditions of this measurement.

Fluidity of a Newtonian liquid is the inverse of its viscosity. It is therefore measured by the complementary angle, as shown in Figure 12-13a.   In non-Newtonian liquids, however, particularly in the Bingham solids, fluidity is generally measured by the angle of the stress axis with the straight portion of the diagram or with a tangent to the curve (Fig. 12-13b).

12-12. Time Effects

Thixotropy is a reversible and noninstantaneous decrease of apparent viscosity upon shear, the effect increasing with the rate

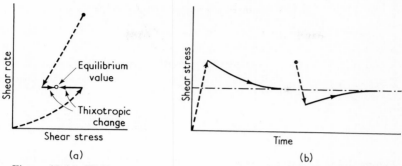

Figure 12-14. Thixotropy. The shear stress at constant shear rate depends on the previous history (indicated by the dashed lines) but gradually reaches an equilibrium value. (*a*) and (*b*) are two different representations of the same experiment.

of shear. Thus, if a thixotropic system is allowed to rest and then a certain rate of shear is applied, the stress will gradually decrease until it reaches a steady value (Fig. 12-14). This steady value is an equilibrium value, because if the system is now sheared at a much higher rate and then immediately returned to the initial rate, the stress will be smaller than the steady value but will return to it gradually.

The term, thixotropy, means "touch changing" and was originally applied only to the reversible liquefaction of some gels upon shaking, but now it is used in the broader sense. Thixotropy is always accompanied by instantaneous and equilibrium plasticity or pseudoplasticity, and it is sometimes confused with these. The latter, however, need not be accompanied by any observable thixotropy.

If a thixotropic system is studied in a Couette viscometer under gradually increasing and then decreasing rates of shear without waiting for equilibrium to be reached, one obtains a so-called thixotropic loop, as shown in Fig. 12-15. This loop is reproducible under standardized conditions and gives a measure of the thixotropy and plasticity of the system.

Rheopexy is the increase of viscosity with time upon shearing. It is less frequently observed and then mostly for small rates of

Figure 12-15. Thixotropic loop obtained by continuous variation of shear rate from zero to a maximum and back to zero.

shear.   It seems to be often an acceleration of thixotropic recovery during slow stirring as opposed to rest.   Thus certain bentonite suspensions which show marked thixotropy set only slowly on standing but quite rapidly when gently tapped.

The irreversible phenomena of increasing apparent viscosity under the influence of shear, or *work hardening*, and its opposite, *rheodestruction*, are of less general interest.

Summary

For Newtonian liquids, viscosity is a constant which is readily measured by a variety of instruments.   Deviations from this simple behavior are frequently encountered in colloidal systems and require special care in measuring and in expressing the results of a measurement.   The deviations may involve elastic effects, equilibrium effects (such as plasticity, pseudoplasticity, or dilatancy), and time effects which may be reversible, as in thixotropy, or may be irreversible.

References

1. E. C. Bingham, *Fluidity and Plasticity*, McGraw-Hill Book Co., Inc., New York, 1922, pp. 29 ff.; E. C. Bingham and T. R. Thompson, *J. Am. Chem. Soc.*, **50**, 2878 (1928).
2. F. R. Eirich, ed., *Rheology*, Academic Press, Inc., New York, 3 vols., 1956–, especially Vol. II.

3. E. K. Fischer, *Colloidal Dispersions*, John Wiley & Sons, New York, 1950, pp. 194 ff.

Problems

48. The ratio of rate of rotation to torque required to produce it is plotted versus rate of rotation in the graph. This shows that the system is (*1*) non-Newtonian, (*2*) without yield value. (*3*) pseudoplastic, (*4*) all of these, (*5*) none of these.

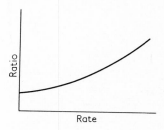

56. A system is known to be thixotropic. After a long time of shearing at rate α, its "rheological state" is represented by point *A*. The rate of shearing is then increased to β and then again reduced to α. Of the indicated points the only ones through which the "rheological state" may pass in this process are _____

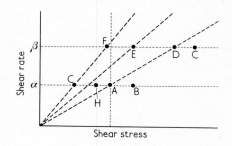

49. A material in a Couette viscometer gives the following values of rate of rotation and torque respectively: 1, 5; 2, 6.5; 4, 9.5. This suggests that the system is (*1*) non-Newtonian, (*2*) plastic, (*3*) a Bingham solid, (*4*) of constant fluidity, (*5*) all of these.

121. In the c.g.s. system, the rate of shear is best expressed in (*1*) radi-

ans per second, (2) per second, (3) square centimeters per second, (4) seconds per square centimeter.

70. If a dashpot is placed parallel with a Maxwell element and the system subjected to a constant force, it will extend at a rate which will (1) gradually decrease to a constant value, (2) gradually increase to a constant value, (3) gradually decrease to zero, (4) remain constant.

CHAPTER XIII
Structural Rheology

Having described briefly in the last chapter how flow properties are observed, measured, and classified, we can now consider
their relation to the structure, i.e., to the nature of the particles
present and their interaction.

The simplest problem may seem to be the behavior of a liquid
formed by small molecules. In principle, its viscosity may be
attributed to the difficulty which a molecule has in changing
neighbors. The details of this picture are still largely incomplete
however, and need not concern us in the study of colloids. The
next simplest problem is the one we will consider first: the effect
of a single particle of solute upon the behavior of a solvent. Here
only solute–solvent interactions are important. Much is known
about this subject so that structural interpretation can be quite
fruitful, but the behavior is of importance only in the laboratory.
Still more complicated is the effect of many solute particles on
the behavior of the system. Here, not only solute–solvent but
also solute–solute interactions become important, and the latter
often predominate. Despite their great practical importance,
much less is known about these systems, and we will return to
them later.

13-1. Intrinsic Viscosity

A discussion of the interaction of an isolated particle with the
solvent acquires real usefulness only if it can also be measured.
The increase in viscosity due to the introduction of enough solute
to make an infinitely dilute solution, is, of course, an infinitely
small quantity and cannot be measured directly. On the other
hand, such increase per molecule or per gram of solute is a ratio

of two small quantities and is likely, therefore, to have a finite value even at infinite dilution.   This is therefore the quantity to be measured.   It can be arrived at by extrapolation from measurements on dilute (but not infinitely dilute) solutions whose increase in viscosity is measurably large.

Let η_0 be the viscosity of the solvent.   A dilute solution of concentration $\mathfrak{C}$ will generally have a slightly higher viscosity, η. The quotient η/η_0, called* the relative viscosity of the solution, η_{rel}, is slightly larger than unity and includes the effect of the solvent (unity) and of the solute (the "slightly").   To isolate the effect of the solute, we compute $\eta_{rel} - 1 = (\eta - \eta_0)/\eta_0$, which is called the specific viscosity, η_{spec}, and is a small number measuring the increase of viscosity due to the solute. This becomes larger with concentration but not necessarily in direct proportion.   To take the concentration into account, we compute $\eta_{spec}/\mathfrak{C} = (\eta_{rel} - 1)/\mathfrak{C}$, which is called the reduced viscosity, η_{red}, and is a relatively large quantity, which does not change much with concentration in dilute solutions.   It would not change at all if η_{spec} were proportional to the concentration. It measures the increase of viscosity per unit concentration in solution of concentration $\mathfrak{C}$.   If this value is determined at several low concentrations, it can generally be extrapolated to zero concentration and give the contribution of the solute at infinite dilution per unit concentration.   This extrapolated value is called intrinsic viscosity, $[\eta]$, and is precisely the desired quantity measuring the solute–solvent interaction.

Table 13-1 summarizes these relations, which are also illustrated in Fig. 13-1.

The values of η_{red} and of $[\eta]$ depend, of course, on the units of concentration used, and these are a matter of convenience.

---

* The Council of the International Union of Pure and Applied Chemistry has recommended in 1951[1] the more rational nomenclature: η/ρ, viscosity/density ratio; η/η_0, viscosity ratio; $\eta_{sp}/\mathfrak{C}$ viscosity number; and lim viscosity number ($\mathfrak{C} \to 0$), $[\eta]$, limiting viscosity number.   The concentration $\mathfrak{C}$ to be expressed in g./ml.   Thus the new $[\eta]$ is 100 times larger than the customary one.   Its unit is to be called a Staudinger (18th Conference, Zurich, 1955).

TABLE 13-1

η	$= \eta_0\eta_{rel}$	$= \eta_0(1 + \eta_{spec})$	$= \eta_0(1 + \eta_{red}\mathfrak{C})$	$=$	in the limit $\eta_0(1 + [\eta]\mathfrak{C})$
η_{rel}	$= \eta/\eta_0$	$= 1 + \eta_{spec}$	$= 1 + \eta_{red}\mathfrak{C}$	$=$	in the limit $1 + [\eta]\mathfrak{C}$
η_{spec}	$= (\eta/\eta_0) - 1$	$= \eta_{rel} - 1$	$= \eta_{red}\mathfrak{C}$	$=$	in the limit $[\eta]\mathfrak{C}$
η_{red}	$= [(\eta/\eta_0) - 1]/\mathfrak{C}$	$= (\eta_{rel} - 1)/\mathfrak{C}$	$= \eta_{spec}/\mathfrak{C}$	$=$	in the limit $[\eta]$

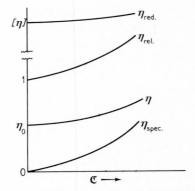

Figure 13-1. The quantities involved in defining intrinsic viscosity and their relative variation with concentration.

There is a considerable measure of unanimity in the customary choice, which depends on whether the viscosity is to be used in the study of the molecular weight of high polymers or of shape and hydration.

In most work with high polymers concentration is expressed in weight-volume per cent, i.e., the number of grams per 100 ml. of solution.[1] The reason for using this unit is the ease of preparation of such solutions from a dry solute using only a balance and a volumetric flask. When the symbol $[\eta]$ is used without any remark it generally[1] refers to these units. In considerations of shape and hydration, on the other hand, the volume fraction $\mathfrak{V}$ i.e., the volume of solute per unit volume of solution, is generally

used, for reasons which we shall consider very soon.   This is
frequently indicated by the subscript $_\phi$, but we shall use $[\eta]_v$.

13-2. Theories of Solute-Solvent Interaction

Let us return to the infinite planes moving with respect to
each other on both sides of a liquid subject to a constant rate of
shear, but let us make them move in opposite directions with
equal velocity.   Then, as shown in Fig. 13-2a, the middle lamella of the liquid will not move.   If we now place a particle across
this lamella, it will not tend to move to the right or left but will
tend to rotate, since its top is pushed in one direction and the
bottom in the opposite one, as shown in Fig. 13-2b.   In this
process, the particle disturbs the streamlines of flow and thus

Figure 13-2. Solute-solvent interaction.   The force required to move two
planes with respect to each other, i.e., the viscosity of the liquid is increased
as the straight streamlines (a) are distorted by the presence of a particle (b).
Note that the particle is made to rotate by the flow of the liquid.

increases the viscous forces acting on the planes.   Hence the
presence of the particle increases the viscosity of the system.
The problem is to calculate this increase quantitatively for different shapes of the particles.   These calculations involve the
same kind of difficulties as calculations of terminal velocities of
fall (Section 3-7) plus additional ones due to the effect of the ro-
tational forces, which in this case are never negligible, and of the
counteracting thermal agitation.   We can therefore, again, only
indicate some simple results.

If our particle is a sphere, its rate of rotation under the action
of the streamlines will be uniform, since each position is equivalent to any other.   If the particle were an infinitely thin rod, its
rate of rotation would depend greatly on orientation.   When perpendicular to the stream lines it would rotate rapidly (Fig. 13-

Figure 13-3. The torque exerted by the flowing liquid upon a rod-shaped particle varies greatly with orientation and tends to align it with the streamlines.

3a), whereas, when oriented along the resting streamline, it would have little or no tendency to rotate (Fig. 13-3b).   Hence, a system composed of such rods would tend to have them all aligned with the streamlines and offer little resistance to flow. If the particle is not an ideal rod, the orientation is not as complete, but unless the particle is spherical there is always some orientation.   Such orientation can be made readily apparent by stirring a turbid suspension of tiny unsymmetrical crystals, such as those of bismuthyl nitrate or of calcium stearate.   The observed silkiness of the streaming suspension is due to the reflection of light from crystals in parallel orientation.

Thermal motion counteracts this uniform orientation in two ways.   First, by disturbing the perfect orientation it brings the rods back into rotation.   In addition, and this is more important, thermal motion tends to produce a uniform orientation of the rods and, hence, causes them to redistribute themselves against the pressure of the streamlines.[2]   This redistribution is possible because the interaction of rod and streamline is a viscous one and permits a relative motion but requires an additional force.   The interaction is analogous to the compressing of a gas with a porous piston which permits diffusion across it, with corresponding transformation of mechanical energy into heat.   Thus, the existence of thermal motion increases the viscosity.

The final orientation of the particles in the flowing liquid must therefore depend on a compromise between thermal motion and the orienting effect of the streamlines.   The latter in turn depends on the size and shape of the particles.   A measure of this orientation is possible by an optical method (determining the streaming birefringence of the system), and it provides some information about the nature of the particles.[3]   The theory of this effect is, however, somewhat too complicated for this book.   It is mentioned mainly to point out that there is independent evidence for the interacting effect upon orientation of both streamlines and thermal motion.

13-3. The Effect of Spheres

The simplest case, that of spheres, has been treated by Einstein under assumptions similar to those of Stokes (Section 3-7). His final conclusion[4] is that the intrinsic viscosity, $[\eta]_v$, of a suspension of spheres is 2.5.   We may all find some comfort in the fact that his original calculations contained a numerical mistake and that the first published result[5] gave 1 instead of 2.5.

If $[\eta]_v = 2.5$, then the reduced viscosity will not differ greatly from 2.5 at high dilutions.   Hence, η_{spec} will be equal to $2.5 \, \mathfrak{B}$; $\eta_{rel} = 1 + 2.5 \, \mathfrak{B}$ and

$$\eta = \eta_0(1 + 2.5\mathfrak{B}) \qquad (13\text{-}3.1)$$

for sufficiently dilute suspensions of spheres.

Einstein's law does not specify anything about the size of the spheres.   The assumptions of the derivation require that the spheres be large compared to the discontinuities of the solvent, but small compared to the dimensions of the apparatus and to the distance from one sphere to the next one.   Within these limits it does not matter how large they are; the effect upon viscosity depends only on the total volume they occupy in the solution. Thus, Einstein's law shows that for spherical particles measurements of viscosity are useless in the determination of particle weights or of polydispersity.

13-4. Hydration

We shall now consider the effect of hydration on the intrinsic viscosity of spheres.   It will be convenient to introduce for this purpose a "hydration factor," $\mathfrak{K}_v$, which measures hydration as the ratio of the hydrated volume to the anhydrous volume. Thus, if the volume fraction of the solute calculated from its anhydrous volume is $\mathfrak{V}$ and its real, hydrated volume fraction is $\mathfrak{V}_h$, the hydration factor is

$$\mathfrak{IC}_v = \mathfrak{V}_h / \mathfrak{V} \qquad (13\text{-}4.1)$$

The hydration factor is, of course, directly related through the density to the customary measure of hydration in grams of water per gram of solute.

Einstein's formula is based on a consideration of hard spheres suspended in a homogeneous liquid. Hence, the volume fraction used by him and appearing in Eq. 13-3.1 is based on the hydrodynamic volume actually existing in solution; i.e., it is $\mathfrak{V}_h = \mathfrak{IC}_v \mathfrak{V}$.   In order to obtain the true viscosity of a solution we have therefore to introduce the hydrated volume fraction, $\mathfrak{IC}_v \mathfrak{V}$, into Eq. 13-3.1

$$\eta = \eta_0 (1 + 2.5 \mathfrak{IC}_v \mathfrak{V}) \qquad (13\text{-}4.2)$$

When the spheres are unhydrated $\mathfrak{IC}_v = 1$, and this equation reduces to Einstein's.   This equation shows also that the intrinsic viscosity of hydrated spheres becomes

$$[\eta]_v = 2.5 \mathfrak{IC}_v \qquad (13\text{-}4.3)$$

Hence intrinsic viscosity is directly proportional to the hydration factor and can be used to measure hydration if the shape is known to be spherical.

13-5. Nonspherical Particles

The calculations for nonspherical particles, even the simple ellipsoids, are much more complicated than for spheres,[6] and where final results can be obtained they are far from the simplicity of Einstein's formula.   There is no doubt, however, that for any given shape the intrinsic viscosity is a constant, and that this constant increases rapidly with the dissymmetry of the shape. For elongated ellipsoids, intrinsic viscosity is approximately proportional to the square of the axial ratio.   In other words, the relatively small constant of 2.5 in Einstein's formula is replaced

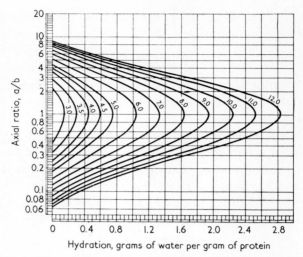

Figure 13-4. The relation between hydration, dissymmetry, and intrinsic viscosity for ellipsoidal proteins. The contours correspond to indicated intrinsic viscosities and delineate the combinations of hydration and axial ratio which can account for it. (*From J. L. Oncley in E. J. Cohn and J. T. Edsall, Proteins, Amino Acids and Peptides, Reinhold Publishing Co., New York, 1943.*)

by a larger constant when the shape of the particles departs from the spherical.

Thus, just as for spheres, viscosity measurements cannot give any indication of size for particles of similar shape. The reader can readily show that consequently, just as for spheres, $[\eta]$, is directly proportional to the hydration factor for particles of the same shape. Thus, measurements of intrinsic viscosity are sensitive to both hydration and to dissymmetry. Unfortunately, both increase the experimentally measured $[\eta]$, so that a whole range of axial ratios and corresponding hydrations can account for a given experimental result, as shown in Fig. 13-4.

This situation is similar to the one we encountered in sedimentation rate and diffusion, where the frictional ratio, φ/φ_0, could be interpreted in terms of a similar graph (Fig. 3-3) giving a range of hydrations and dissymmetries. More careful examination of the two graphs shows that they are slightly different, so that the two ranges, each corresponding to a line on a different graph, have generally only two points in common, as shown in Fig. 13-5.   One intersection corresponds to an oblate, the other to a prolate, ellipsoid.   This suggests that by determining both $[\eta]_v$ and φ/φ_0 for a system, one could be able to reduce the uncertainty about hydration and dissymmetry to a choice between

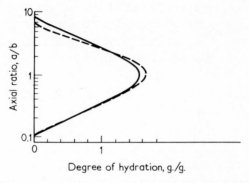

Figure 13–5. The range of hydrations and axial ratios corresponding to a given fractional ratio (1.45, solid line) and a given intrinsic viscosity (8.0, dashed line), based on Figs. 3-3 and 13-4.   In principle, the lines for a given particle intersect at only two points.

oblate and prolate shapes.   Unfortunately, the two lines intersect at such an acute angle that small experimental variations can restore much of the original uncertainty.   In some cases, nevertheless, this approach has been useful.

13-6. The Determination of Particle Weights

As just pointed out, viscosity measurements cannot distinguish between particles of different size but same shape, yet they are very sensitive to the shape and hydration.   Hence, it is only if shape or hydration varies with size that viscosity measurements become a method of determining particle weights.   Thus, if some systems consist of particles that are rigid rods of constant cross section (Fig. 13-6a), their intrinsic viscosity will vary, in analogy with elongated ellipsoids, with the square of the length, and hence with the square of the particle weight.

$$[\eta] = KM^2 \tag{13-6.1}$$

where K is a proportionality constant depending, among other things, on the cross section of the rod.

Similarly, if some systems consisted of spheres having a hydration shell of constant thickness (Fig. 13-6b), their intrinsic viscosity would tend to be 2.5 for very large particles and increase markedly as the particles became small.

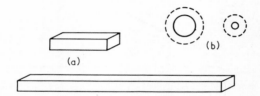

(a)

(b)

Figure 13-6. Particles of same shape and hydration and different size give the same intrinsic viscosity, but certain *similar* shapes and hydrations can give values differing with size: (a) rods of same cross section; (b) spheres with same hydration-layer thickness.

13-7. Staudinger's Equation

The most important application of this idea is to long chain molecules. As we have seen, these form more or less random coils, whose over-all outer shape though indefinite should not depend on length. On the other hand, the size of the coil does not increase proportionately to the length of the chain, but faster.

The distance of the two ends of the chain increases with the square root of the number of segments, hence, with $M^{0.5}$ (Section 5-18). Other dimensions keep proportion to this distance, so that the over-all volume of a random coil increases with $(M^{0.5})^3 = M^{1.5}$, i.e., faster than the molecular weight.

The anhydrous volume is proportional to M for particles of a given material, and the hydrated volume is, as we have just seen, proportional to $M^{1.5}$. Hence the hydration factor is proportional to their ratio

$$\mathcal{H}_v \propto M^{1.5}/M = M^{0.5} \tag{13-7.1}$$

Thus random coils of different molecular weights have different hydration factors, and this will permit us to measure their size.

Since intrinsic viscosity is proportional to the hydration factor for particles of same shape, we have, for ideal random coils

$$[\eta] = KM^{0.5} \tag{13-7.2}$$

where K is a proportionality constant whose value depends on the nature of the segments forming the coil.

When it comes to real linear high polymers instead of ideal random coils, the situation is somewhat more complicated and the result is slightly different. As we have seen in Section 5-18, real long chains tend to form coils which are more extended than the random ones, because of both the excluded volume effect and the usual interaction with the solvent. This tends to increase the apparent hydration and to increase the exponent in Eq. 13-7.2. On the other hand, as the coil expands it also tends to become more free-draining, so that the effective shape changes. This has the opposite effect on the exponent. The exact calculation of these and related effects is a very difficult and still uncompleted task, but even our approximate discussion shows why, empirically, one finds relations of the form

$$[\eta] = KM^a \tag{13-7.3}$$

where a is generally between 0.5 and about 1.1, and for any given solvent increases slightly with molecular weight. For the same particles, a always decreases as the solvent becomes poorer, showing that the coils tend to become more compact.

Equation 13-7.3 is often called Staudinger's law, in honor of the Swiss organic chemist who pioneered the concept of high polymers and the use of viscosity to determine their molecular weights. Strictly speaking, however, Staudinger believed that a is always unity.

Thus, the measurement of the viscosity of a few solutions readily gives an estimate of relative molecular weights for high polymers of the same structure.   If, in addition, the molecular weight of a few fractions is measured independently, so that the values of K and a can be determined, the absolute values of M are obtained from such viscosity experiments.   Because it is so easy, as we have seen, to obtain precise values of viscosity with an Ostwald viscometer, this is by far the most convenient and the most frequently used method of molecular weight determination.

13-8. Higher Concentrations

The relative viscosity always increases with concentration more than proportionately, except in the case of some charged particles to which we will return later (Section 17-10).   A proportionate increase would mean that each added particle contributes as much to the viscosity as if it were alone.   In fact, however, each particle interferes with the other particles, so that the increase is larger.   The interference may be purely hydrodynamic if there are no forces exerted between the particles,[6] or it may be complicated by attractive or repulsive forces between them. The most striking effects are observed when the attractive forces are large enough so that particle–particle bonds are formed and yet are not large enough for these bonds to withstand the shearing stresses applied.   We will consider this situation with the assumption that the system remains grossly homogeneous and does not separate into two visible phases.   This will generally be the case if it is not too dilute.

13-9. Pseudoplasticity and Thixotropy

If the particles form aggregates and the aggregates can be broken up by shear, their size will depend on the rate of shear. At any constant rate of shear, an equilibrium distribution of sizes will be established as the rate of breaking up balances the rate of aggregating.   At higher shear rates the average size may be expected to be smaller, since the breaking-up forces increase with the rate of shear while the aggregating forces remain constant. At sufficiently high and generally unattainable rates of shear, all aggregates should be broken up and only simple particles persist. Higher rates of shear should also change the nature of the aggregates, rendering them more compact, since the looser aggregates should break up more readily than the dense ones in which there are more particle–particle bonds for the same volume and shearing force. Thus, the apparent degree of solvation, due to entrapment of solvent between the particles, decreases with rate of shear, and as a result the apparent viscosity decreases. This gives one of the frequent reasons for pseudoplasticity.

Another and overlapping reason for pseudoplasticity is that the breaking of bonds during flow requires work and, thus, contributes to the viscosity of the system. The rate of formation of bonds will generally not increase as fast as the rate of shear, since some bonds are generally being formed at rest. Hence the work of breaking them, and the shearing stress required, will not increase so rapidly as the rate of shear, and again we have pseudoplasticity.

Under either picture, the rate at which the state of equilibrium is established between breaking and forming of bonds at any given rate of shear may be observable and lead to thixotropy. It will take time for a system which was sheared at a lower rate and has a higher apparent viscosity to reach a steady value, and the same is true for a system which was sheared at a higher rate and, hence, has a lower apparent viscosity.

13-10. Yield Value

When the system is at rest, the formation of bonds may proceed to the point of formation of continuous bridges of particles between the solid parts of the viscometer. To break these bridges a definite stress will be necessary, and smaller stresses will cause no flow. This produces a yield value and plasticity. When the yield value is exceeded, the bridges are at least partially broken and flow proceeds.

The interpretation of yield value in terms of interparticle forces and of bridging can be demonstrated readily in some systems by independent measurements. For example, certain types of magnetic clutches are based on the free flowing behavior of iron suspensions in the absence of a magnetic field and on the immediate rigidity (i.e., high yield value) of the system upon application of such a field.[7]   That iron particles attract each other and form strong aggregates in a magnetic field is a well known macroscopic phenomenon.   Another example is given by suspensions of carbon blacks in oil which often tend to acquire yield values on standing.   At the same time they become electrically conducting.[8]   Since the oil does not conduct and the carbon (graphite) does, this means that continuous carbon-to-carbon contact is established from electrode to electrode.   Upon stirring, the conductivity is reduced or disappears.   In the presence of deflocculating agents, both yield value and conductivity disappear.

There is an important difference in behavior depending on whether the bonds of the bridging network are weak enough for thermal agitation to break them occasionally or so strong that thermal agitation does not affect them appreciably during the period of observation.   Sufficiently small stresses will always deform the bridging network elastically.   If the network remains unaffected, there will be no further movement and no relaxation of the stress.   If, on the other hand, thermal agitation does, from time to time, break a link of the network and re-forms one at another point, the new link will be formed in an unstressed state, whereas the removal of the first one will permit some flow or relaxation.   Thus, if the energy of the bonds is of the order of a few kT we can expect no true yield value and only pseudoplastic behavior, despite the formation of a bridging network.

In the above discussion we have not specified the nature of the bonds.   They may be caused by any of the forces tending to flocculate dispersions.   But they can also be due to a simple mechanical interference of particles, especially the highly unsymmetrical ones.   Even spheres may have difficulty squeezing past each other in concentrated systems, whereas long chain molecules may be intertangled even at very high dilutions.   In general, the more unsymmetrical the particle, the greater the possibility of formation of bridging networks in dilute systems. But even spherical particles may show similar effects, if they tend to form thread-like aggregates.

13-11. Gels, Jellies, and Pastes

Semisolid systems having either yield values or very high viscosities are often called gels, jellies, or pastes. The meaning of these terms is far from standardized, and the types of systems involved vary greatly. Here are a few typical examples with some characteristic properties, but the list is far from exhaustive and the structural interpretation often uncertain.

Pastes

Suspensions of relatively large and very unsymmetrical crystals may form a network of needles or plates having little elasticity but a high apparent viscosity with a definite yield value. This high viscosity and yield value may disappear abruptly at the melting point of the crystals.[9] This type, especially if coarse, is generally called a paste and is represented by certain shoe polishes and some grease-like dispersions of calcium oleate in mineral oil. Dispersions of platelets of the clay bentonite in aqueous and non-aqueous media probably belong in this category. Because of the large size of the clay particles which reduces the importance of thermal motion and because of their thermal stability, the rheological properties of these systems are relatively unaffected by temperature. On the other hand, they are very sensitive to the addition of flocculating and deflocculating agents. The bonds between the platelets seem to re-form upon contact, which occurs slowly by Brownian motion or more rapidly during flow. Hence, thixotropy is marked and readily observed, but there is little irreversibility—the system "heals" well.

Silica

Sodium silicate sets to a gel upon acidification. This is presumably due to the formation of three-dimensional —Si—O—Si

—O— network.   This network can be obtained anhydrous by
simple evaporation of the water, but the structure suffers considerable and irreversible collapse by the surface forces of the re-
treating water menisci during evaporation.   A much better
preserved structure can be obtained if water is replaced with a
miscible liquid of lower surface tension, and a still better one if
this liquid is removed above its critical temperature so that no
menisci form at any time.[10]   Such dehydrated skeletons or
aerogels are widely used under the name of silica gels as dehy-
drating and adsorbing agents and as catalysts or catalyst supports.
Once the network is formed, it has little ability to mend any
breaks.   Hence it shows elasticity and yield values, but any flow
tends to lead to irreversible rheodestruction.

Linear Polymers

Long chain molecules in good solvents at high concentrations
form highly viscous systems in which the intertanglement of the
long chains causes their strong interaction.   Brownian motion of
the segments constantly mixes and unmixes them, whereas shear
stress deforms the structure, causing first an elastic movement
which then relaxes to become flow.   Since entanglement is due
mainly to thermal motion and occurs at an approximately constant rate, pseudoplasticity is present, and, since there are no
permanent strong links, there is no true yield value.   In the
presence of additional solvent, the particles tend to dissolve
and the gel swells without limit, becoming weaker and weaker
until it gradually changes to a simple solution of normal viscosity.   The term "jelly" is sometimes restricted to this type of
system.

If the solvent is poorer, in addition to intertanglement there
will be attractive forces between segments of different molecules,
so that the particle–particle interaction is stronger and the apparent viscosity higher.   This is in contrast to the intrinsic viscosity, which, as we have seen (Section 13-7) is lower in the poorer
solvent because at infinite dilution the segment–segment interactions must be satisfied within the particle.   In the presence of

excess solvent, complete solution may not be possible, and the swelling is then limited. This may be considered as a result of a balance between thermal agitation, which tends to disperse the segments and molecules as uniformly as possible, and the inter-segment attraction, which tends to bring them closely together.

In both this and the previous type of linear polymer systems, equilibrium conditions are reached under any set of conditions, since Brownian motion can restore all intertanglements and links destroyed by shear (unless the stresses are large enough to break the chains), but this restoration takes time. The systems, there-fore, heal well and show thixotropy.

Crosslinking

If the long chains are all crosslinked by covalent bonds, as in vulcanized rubber, the situation is different. Thermal motion cannot break the crosslinks, and once broken they cannot re-form. Hence, there is a true yield value and considerable ir-reversibility in flow phenomena. In the presence of excess sol-vent, no matter how good it is, swelling is only limited and de-termined by the balance between thermal agitation and inter-action with the solvent, on one hand, and the rubber-like elas-ticity of the stretched network of crosslinked chains on the other.

Thermal Revertibility

Gelatin solutions are well known to set upon cooling in a rever-sible way. This is probably the case of long chain molecules slowly forming crosslinks which are readily broken at higher tem-perature. The transition from a liquid of relatively low viscos-ity to an elastic gel occurs revertibly over a narrow temperature range, and the more concentrated the solution the higher the temperature at which this happens. The transition is also slow, so that equilibrium conditions are hard to reach at any one temperature and hysteretic effects are marked. The rate is very temperature-dependent, so that a system which sets upon slow cooling may remain liquid if rapidly chilled to the same tempera-ture.[11] Upon drying, the gelatin network collapses completely to form a nonporous transparent mass, the gelatin of commerce. The collapse is, however, largely revertible and gelatin swells to many times its dry volume when exposed to water. The gel is elastic and can heal to some extent, especially at higher temperatures. Large aggregates persist above the transition range, especially in dilute solutions, and give typical thixotropic behavior.

13-12. Syneresis

The opposite of swelling is the spontaneous exudation of liquid and shrinking of the gel. This is called syneresis, and is frequently observed in dilute gels formed by cooling (gelatin) or precipitation (silica). It means, of course, that the network as originally formed is unstable and slowly changes to a more stable state of smaller volume. The reduction may be due occasionally to gravitational forces, but more often it is caused by attraction between the particles and formation of additional bonds which bring the particles closer together. Other things being equal, syneresis is slowed down by viscous solvents, which are more difficult to squeeze out and impede the approach of the particles. It may be prevented by the adhesion of the network to the walls of the containing vessel. This may produce large internal tensions and lead to "ringing gels."[12] On the other hand, vibration and other mechanical treatment which tends to bring the particles together may speed up syneresis markedly.

Summary

Intrinsic viscosity measures the solute–solvent interaction and eliminates the complications of solute–solute effects. It is independent of the size of the particles but is sensitive to their shape and hydration. In special cases, in particular for linear high polymers, it can therefore serve as a very sensitive measure of the molecular weight. In systems of finite concentration, and especially in relatively concentrated ones, the variety of shapes of colloidal particles and the many ways in which they can interact produce the observed richness of rheological behavior.

References

1. *J. Polymer Sci.*, **8**, 257 (1952).
2. W. Kuhn and H. Kuhn, *Helv. Chim. Acta*, **28**, 97 (1945) (in German); *Proc. Intern. Congr. on Rheology, Holland, 1948*, North-Holland Publishing Co., Amsterdam, 1949, II-77, III-30 (in English).
3. E. J. Cohn and J. T. Edsall, *Proteins, Amino Acids, and Peptides*, Reinhold Publishing Corp., New York, 1943, pp. 527 ff.
4. A. Einstein, *Ann. Physik*, (4) **34**, 591 (1911); *Investigations on the Theory of Brownian Movement*, Methuen & Co., Ltd., London, 1926; Dover, New York, 1956, Chap. III.
5. A. Einstein, *Ann. Physik*, (4) **19**, 289 (1906).
6. H. L. Frisch and R. Simha, in F. R. Eirich, *Rheology*, Academic Press, Inc., New York, 1956, Vol. I, p. 525.
7. *Rev. Sci. Instr.*, **19**, 375 (1948); also J. Rabinow, U. S. Pat. 2,622,-713 (1952).
8. C. M. McDowell and F. L. Usher, *Proc. Roy. Soc. (London)*, **131A,** 564 (1931); A. Voet, *J. Phys. Chem.*, **61**, 301 (1957).
9. F. Höppler, *Fette u. Seifen*, **49**, 700 (1942).
10. S. S. Kistler, *J. Phys. Chem.*, **36**, 52 (1932).
11. L. Arisz, *Kolloid Beih.*, **7,** 1 (1915); also K. J. Mysels, *J. Colloid Sci.*, **2**, 375 (1947).
12. H. N. Holmes, W. E. Kaufmann, and H. O. Nicholas, *J. Am. Chem. Soc.*, **41,** 1329 (1919).

Problems

44. The properties of four systems of compact particles of same density are as follows:

	A	B	C	D
Particle weight	10^4	10^5	3×10^4	5×10^3
Axial ratio	1	3	3	2
Hydration, g./g.	2	0	2	1

The intrinsic viscosity will be the highest for _____.

46. If a in the viscosity equation is unity, then the average molecular weight obtained from viscosity measurements is (*1*) the weight-average, (*2*) the number-average, (*3*) none of these.

53. The degree of hydration of particles has a marked effect on their (*1*) intrinsic viscosity, (*2*) diffusion coefficient, (*3*) sedimentation rate, (*4*) all of these, (*5*) none of these.

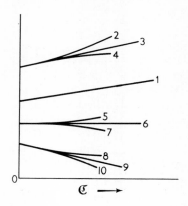

42. If 1 represents the reduced viscosity of a system, then its viscosity can be represented schematically only by line number _____.

89. Appreciable electric conductivity of a carbon-in-oil dispersion suggests that (*1*) thermal agitation is unable to overcome particle—particle attractions, (*2*) the system shows a yield value, (*3*) mixing will tend to reduce this conductivity (at least temporarily), (*4*) all of these, (*5*) none of these.

83. In interpreting viscosity determinations on dilute polymer solutions, one often uses the so-called inherent viscosity (or logarithmic viscosity number[1]), defined as $(\ln \eta_{rel})/\mathfrak{C}$. This is plotted against $\mathfrak{C}$ and extrapolated to zero concentration. This extrapolation gives (*1*) $\ln [\eta]$, (*2*) $[\eta]$, (*3*) $[\eta]/\mathfrak{C}$, (*4*) nothing that is simply related to $[\eta]$.

90. Two experimenters work with the same material. *A* using it as is, *B* using it after drying carefully which removes 20% of moisture. Other things being equal, one may expect *B* to report a higher (*1*) sedimentation rate, (*2*) molecular weight by osmotic pressure, (*3*) intrinsic viscosity, (*4*) all of these, (*5*) none of these.

85. The viscosity of a solvent is 0.3000; for a solution of 1 ml./liter, it is 0.3010, and for one twice as concentrated, 0.3020. Hence $[\eta]_v$ is _____.

CHAPTER XIV

Electroneutrality

Until now we have avoided the complicating factors introduced by electrical effects, despite their importance. Uncharged colloids exist and are important, both in aqueous solutions and in nonaqueous ones. In addition, as we shall see, charge effects can be neglected in the presence of sufficient simple salt, the so-called "swamping electrolyte" condition. Thus the results obtained so far have quite a broad field of applicability. There are, however, many phenomena involving charged colloids which can be understood only by taking into account their electrical properties. We shall begin with macroscopic behavior, in which it will be shown the electric forces are always overwhelming. In the following chapters we shall consider the balance between electrical and other forces on a microscopic scale, the measurement of this balance by electrokinetic methods and, finally, its effect upon the behavior of the system.

14-1. The Electric Forces

Much of our consideration of electrical effects will be based on simple electrostatics, which are presumed to be known but may be worth restating and illustrating to bring out their meaning in molecular terms.

As chemists, we shall measure charges mainly in electronic units, ϵ, and Faradays, $\mathbf{F}$. For computations these will have to be given a numerical value, and here the different systems of electrical units introduce a complication which has to be kept in mind. For current flow calculations ϵ is $= \mathbf{F}/\mathbf{N} = 96,500/6 \times 10^{23} = 1.60 \times 10^{-19}$ coulombs and 1.60×10^{-20} electromagnetic c.g.s. units (emu) or abcoulombs. (The abcoulomb and related

units must not be confused with the *absolute* coulomb, etc.   The
absolute units differ from the usual or "International" units by a
very small fraction, but differ by powers of ten from the ab- or
emu units.)   The number of these electronic charges per particle
is generally symbolized by z when referring to the electrovalence
of a small ion and by p when referring to a colloidal particle.

From the point of view of current flow, the electronic charge
appears very small.   To maintain for 1 sec. a current of 1 micro-
ampere, which is quite small but measurable, requires 10^{-3} coulombs or 6.25×10^{12} electronic charges.   This is also $1.03 \times
10^{-11}$ moles of electrons or of monovalent ions.   Thus very large
numbers, but still unweighably small amounts, of ions correspond
to small flows of current.

The force between two charges is given by Coulomb's law

$$F = q_1 q_2 / \vartheta L^2 \tag{14-1.1}$$

where ϑ, the dielectric constant, depends on the medium separating them and L is their distance.   In vacuum ϑ is unity, whereas
in water it is about 80.   In order to obtain the force in dynes, the
charges q must be expressed in electrostatic c.g.s. units (esu).
In these units $\epsilon = 4.80 \times 10^{-10}$ esu, and $\mathbf{F} = 2.89 \times 10^{14}$ esu.

From this point of view of force, the electronic charge becomes
quite respectable.   Thus one mole of positive monovalent ions
and one of negative ions ($6 \times 10^{23} \times 4.8 \times 10^{-10} \approx 2.9 \times 10^{14}$
esu each) if separated by the distance equal to that from New
York to Los Angeles or about 4×10^8 cm. would exert upon each
other a force of about $8 \times 10^{28}/16 \times 10^{16} = 5 \times 10^{11}$ dynes or
half a million kilograms or 500 tons.   This is about the weight of
a 18-ft. cube of solid concrete.   To put this in a more familiar
scale: a force of about 10 kg. (10^7 dynes) would be required to
keep 1 cm. apart two small balls made each of 6.6×10^{12} monovalent ions of opposite sign, or each containing about 10^{-11}
moles.   Thus, large numbers but immeasurably small weights of
ions correspond to very large mechanical forces.

The force exerted on a unit charge at a point in space is the
electric field intensity, and the work required to bring a unit

charge from infinity to this point is the electric potential at this point. For a single point charge, the intensity at a distance L must be, according to Coulomb's law, $-q/\vartheta L^2$. The potential, V, is the integral of this force from infinity to L

$$V = \int_{\infty}^{L} (-q/\vartheta L^2)dL = -q/\vartheta \int_{\infty}^{L} dL/L^2 = (q/\vartheta)1/L = q/\vartheta L \quad (14\text{-}1.2)$$

The units to be used are, again, the esu–c.g.s. units, and the esu potential unit is equal to 300 v. Thus a mole of univalent positive ions in New York would produce in Los Angeles a potential of $3 \times 10^2 \times 2.9 \times 10^{14}/4 \times 10^8 = 2.2 \times 10^8$ v.

Sparks begin to fly through air when the potential gradient is of the order of 30,000 v./cm. Hence only 2×10^{11} monovalent ions would be enough to draw a 1 cm. spark through air to the ground. This is about 3×10^{-13} moles.

If we consider a single monovalent ion in air or vacuum, its potential at 1 cm. distance is $3 \times 10^2 \times 4.8 \times 10^{-10}$ v. or about $0.15 \mu v$. As we approach this ion, the potential increases rapidly, and at 10 A. it becomes 1.5 v. If the ion can be approached to within 1 A. of its center, the potential becomes 15 v. In these and similar calculations, it is the distance from the center which is important, because it can be shown that charges distributed uniformly over a sphere act as if they were concentrated at its center.

The potential gives us directly the energy required to bring together or to separate two charges. Thus one electron, moving between two points whose potential differs by 1 v., will produce or consume $(1/300) \times 4.8 \times 10^{-10} = 1.6 \times 10^{-12}$ ergs, which is about 40 $\mathbf{k}T$ at room temperature. Alternatively, 1 $\mathbf{k}T$ is the equivalent of an electronic charge traveling through 0.025 v., or of bringing two such charges to within 600 A. of each other in vacuum. A mole of ions traveling through 1 v. gives $1.6 \times 10^{-12} \mathbf{N} = 9.65 \times 10^{11}$ ergs $= 9.65 \times 10^4$ joules or w.-sec. or 1 v.-$\mathbf{F}$, just as calculated from direct current considerations.

Thus the electric effects when considered in terms of forces, potentials, or work, become very substantial on a macroscopic scale when large numbers but unweighable amounts of ions are concerned, and when compared with thermal agitation on a molecular scale they become important even for single charges.

In the presence of water, these effects of charges are reduced by a factor of 80 from the values considered above through the dielectric constant of this solvent.   This is, of course, what makes possible the ionization of salts.   Nevertheless, the magnitude of these electric effects remains quite large, especially in the case of colloids which along with their large size can also have large charges.

14-2. Electroneutrality

We can now obtain an answer to a question of basic importance to chemists: To what extent can ions of opposite charge separate from each other?   The answer depends on the scale in which we are interested.   No macroscopically significant separation can occur because of the tremendous potentials and energies involved.

On the other hand, separations which are insignificant from this point of view can produce major, macroscopically significant, electric and mechanical effects.   Hence in any experiment involving ions, we may attempt to measure potentials, currents, pressures, and forces, but there is no point in trying to measure separated amounts of ions of one kind.   In other words, the system must remain electrically neutral as a whole, except for infinitesimal variations which can give rise to potentials within a few powers of ten of a volt.   In aqueous systems, the decomposition potential of water puts a limit of the order of 2 v. on the potentials that can occur.

We may therefore say that on a macroscopic scale ions are tied together so that wherever there are positive ions there must be also an equivalent number of negative ions.   This is the principle of electroneutrality.

On a microscopic scale, however, the individual ions can, and do, separate over distances which do not involve large electrical energies.   In particular they can, and do, keep their individual thermal motion, since this represents an energy of the order of

$k T$. We will discuss the effects of this motion further in the next chapter.

14-3. Counterions and Similiions

An obvious consequence of the requirement of electroneutrality is that, if charged colloidal particles are present in a system, oppositely charged ions must also be present in an equivalent amount. These are often called counterions, or by the German word gegenions.

A colloidal electrolyte is formed, like any electrolyte, by equivalent amounts of oppositely charged ions. It is colloidal if it has at least one kind of ion of colloidal dimensions. (We shall see later that it is very unlikely to have both kinds in this class.) Occasionally, the term colloidal electrolyte is restricted to association colloids, but this leaves all other ionized colloids without a descriptive name, and since many association colloids are uncharged, this term cannot cover them all. We shall therefore use colloidal electrolyte as a broad term and refer to association colloidal electrolytes when designating this subclass.

Thus a solution of a pure colloidal electrolyte, for example a protein chloride, contains, in the simplest case, colloidal ions (the protein cations) and their counterions (Cl^-). The addition of a simple electrolyte such as salt complicates the situation. The total charge of oppositely charged ions is now greater than that of the colloidal ones. The term counterions is nevertheless generally used to denote all of them. The similarly charged small ions (Na^+) seem not to have an accepted name. We shall use "similiions" for short.

14-4. Lack of Discrimination

Electroneutrality thus requires that in the immediate vicinity of charged colloidal particles there be a neutralizing excess of counterions over similiions. This requirement is, however, completely unspecific as to which ions satisfy it, or whence they came. This is because of the intrinsic lack of discrimination by electrostatic forces. They are only concerned with the charge.

A result of this lack of discrimination is that the situation differs greatly when dealing with a pure colloidal electrolyte and when dealing with one in which there are many small similiions. In the former case, the only ions available to satisfy electroneutrality are the original gegenions.   Hence, any shift of the colloidal ions must be accompanied by a corresponding shift of these gegenions, and vice versa.   In the latter case, the movement of any ions may satisfy electroneutrality.   In particular, a small shift of all the gegenions in the same direction, or of all similiions in the opposite direction, or a still smaller shift of both can suffice. It is generally the last one which occurs, being the path of least resistance.

14-5. Potentials in Dynamic Phenomena

The lack of discrimination of the electric forces caused by the requirement of electroneutrality can be expressed in a way better adapted to exact calculations if we note that any net motion of the charged colloidal ions corresponds to an electric current. In order to maintain electroneutrality, an equal and opposite current must flow in the system because of the motion of all the other ions.   The origin of this current can be visualized as follows: The motion of the colloidal ions leads to an accumulation of charge in the region to which they are moving, and therefore to a potential difference which tends to repel these ions and the similiions and to attract the counterions.   The flow of the latter two produces the neutralizing current.

According to the requirement of electroneutrality the intensity, I_n, of the neutralizing current is determined solely by the motion of the colloid.   The potential difference, E, required to produce I_n depends, according to Ohm's law, on the resistance R of the solution

$$E = RI_n \qquad (14\text{-}5.1)$$

If only colloidal ions and their counterions are present, the resistance is relatively high and the potential difference must be large.   If similiions and additional counterions are present, the resistance is reduced and the potential gradient is smaller. Finally, when "swamping" amounts of these ions are present, the resistance and the potential become negligible.

The potential, E, affects not only the gegenions and similiions but also the colloidal ions—that is part of the lack of discrimination. Hence, when the potential is high in the absence of other electrolytes, the motion of the colloidal ions will be affected and in fact may be affected quite radically as we shall see. When swamping electrolytes are present, on the other hand, the potential and its effects are negligible; hence the colloidal ion can move freely, just as if it were an uncharged particle.

If, instead of moving the colloidal ion in the first place, we move the gegenions, the same situation prevails in reverse, the neutralizing current stemming from the motion of the colloidal ions and the similiions.

Because it affects all the ions present, the potential E can be measured directly by any of the conventional electrodes introduced into the system.

Let us now apply these ideas to some dynamic phenomena already familiar in the case of uncharged particles, namely, sedimentation rate and diffusion. For simplicity we will consider quantitatively only the two extremes, the pure colloidal electrolyte without any similiions, and the colloid in presence of swamping electrolytes.

14-6. Sedimentation Rate

Gravity and buoyancy are of course unaffected by charge. The friction factors include any electrical effects but, as a first approximation, we may neglect the effect of charge on Stokes' law.

If only colloidal ions and their gegenions are present, the sedimentation of the former must be accompanied by an equal movement of the latter. All the ions must move with the same velocity. The driving force for sedimentation will be the difference of the gravitational and buoyant effect on all the ions. In practice, this force on the small counterions may be neglected.

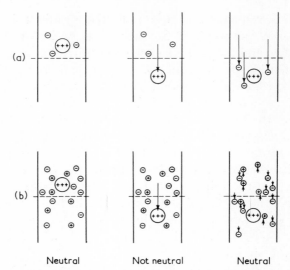

Neutral   Not neutral   Neutral

Figure 14-1. The maintenance of electroneutrality in a transport process. The motion of a colloidal ion (*middle*) must be accompanied by a neutralizing motion of other ions (*right*).   In a pure colloidal electrolyte (a) the counterions travel the same distance in the same direction.   In the presence of swamping electrolytes (b) the distance is small and the direction corresponds to the sign.

Sedimentation occurs, therefore, because of the tendency of the colloidal ions to sediment, but these ions must drag along all the small ions and are thus slowed down.   Hence, all the ions will sediment at a rate which is slower than would be expected for the colloidal particles in the absence of charge, but faster than expected for the small ions if they were uncharged.

In other words, any sedimentation of the colloidal ions sets up a potential which retards their sedimentation and forces the gegenions to move downwards (Fig. 14-1a).

The sedimentation velocity u is easily calculated for the case in which similiions are absent.   If the charge of the colloidal ions is p and the system is monodisperse, we have for the driving force, f_d, on the colloidal ion and its p counterions in analogy with Eq. 3-3.1

$$f_d = v_2(\rho_2 - \rho)\mathbf{g} + pv_3(\rho_3 - \rho)\mathbf{g} \qquad (14\text{-}6.1)$$

where the subscript $_2$ refers to the colloidal ions and $_3$ to the gegenions. The densities are again denoted by ρ and the volume of a particle by v. For the resistant force, f_r, we can similarly write, in analogy with Eq. 3-6.2

$$-f_r = u(\varphi_2 + p\varphi_3) \tag{14-6.2}$$

where φ denotes the friction factors. The terminal velocity is, again, given by the equality of these two opposite forces in analogy with Eq. 3-11.1

$$u = \mathbf{g}\,[v_2(\rho_2 - \rho) + pv_3(\rho_3 - \rho)]/(\varphi_2 + p\varphi_3) \tag{14-6.3}$$

In practice, as already mentioned, the contribution of the gegenions to the driving force is negligible, but that to the resistance may be of the order of half of the total. This is because the former increases with the cube of the anhydrous radius and the latter linearly with the hydrated radius. The equation can therefore be simplified only to

$$u = \mathbf{g}v_2(\rho_2 - \rho)/(\varphi_2 + p\varphi_3) \tag{14-6.4}$$

and can be rewritten in analogy with eq. 3–11.2 as

$$u = m_2(1 - \rho/\rho_2)\mathbf{g}/(\varphi_2 + p\varphi_3) \tag{14-6.5}$$

where m_2 is the particle weight of the colloidal ion. As the weight of the p counterions is generally negligible in comparison, this is also the particle weight of the colloidal electrolyte as a whole. It is given explicitly by

$$m = u(\varphi_2 + p\varphi_3)/\mathbf{g}(1 - \rho/\rho_2) \tag{14-6.6}$$

Comparison with Eq. 3-11.2 shows that if m were to be estimated from the observed sedimentation velocity u, neglecting the presence of charges, the result would be in error by a factor of $\varphi_2/(\varphi_2 + p\,\varphi_3)$.

In the other extreme case of swamping electrolyte conditions, the situation is very different. The conducting solution prevents the appearance of significant potentials, and the motion of the colloid is unimpeded. To express it otherwise, electroneutrality is maintained by a motion of all small ions through a very small distance (Fig. 14-1b). This motion is therefore very slow and requires a negligible amount of energy; consequently, it has no retarding effect on the sedimentation velocity of the colloidal ions, and the treatment of Chapter 3 applies despite the charge. (For the intermediate case, see reference 1.)

14-7. Diffusion

Diffusion, as we have seen (Chapter 5), is due to thermal agitation and is slowed down by viscous forces. Again, charge effects have no influence on the basic forces involved but, in the absence of similiions, electroneutrality requires that the net movement of colloidal and gegenions proceed at the same rate. The small ions tend to diffuse faster than the colloidal ones because of their smaller friction factor. Because of electroneutrality they must, however, drag the latter along and are thus slowed down. Hence, all the ions will diffuse at the same rate which (in contrast to what happened in sedimentation) is faster than expected for the colloidal particle in the absence of charge but slower than would be expected for the small ions if they were uncharged.

In other words, the tendency of the smaller gegenions to diffuse more rapidly will produce a potential difference which will slow them down and accelerate the motion of the colloidal ion. This potential is the same as the junction potential encountered in the study of concentration cells.

The driving force will now be the thermal energy of all the particles, that is, $(1 + p)\mathbf{k}T$, and the resistance will be due, again, to the friction factors of all the particles, i.e. $(\varphi_2 + p\varphi_3)$, giving, in analogy with Einstein's law (Eq. 51-2.2),

$$D = \mathbf{k}T(1 + p)/(\varphi_2 + p\varphi_3) \qquad (14\text{-}7.1)$$

Compared to the diffusion of an uncharged particle, where $D = \mathbf{k}T/\varphi_2$, we see that the resistance is increased by a factor of the order of 2, whereas the driving force is multipled by $p + 1$, which is generally many times more. Hence charge effects can greatly accelerate the rate of diffusion in the absence of added electrolytes.

If the simple electrolyte is present in swamping amounts, any potentials generated by differences in the rates of diffusion are readily dissipated by small motions of all the ions, and the colloidal particle can again diffuse just as if it were uncharged.   (For the intermediate case, see reference 2.)

14-8. Potentials in Equilibrium Phenomena

Let us now consider the closely related problems of sedimentation equilibrium and colligative properties.   These equilibrium phenomena were treated in the absence of charge effects in Chapters 6 and 7.   The basic pattern is the same here as for rate phenomena; charge effects are marked in the absence of added electrolyte but disappear in swamping electrolytes.   There is, however, a somewhat subtle difference in the meaning and effect of the potentials involved.

We are dealing here with equilibrium systems in which the concentrations are not uniform.   The nonuniformity is due to a constraint (gravity or membrane) which affects the distribution of the colloidal ion.   Because of electroneutrality, this in turn affects the distribution of the small ions.   Because the constrained system is in equilibrium, there can be no current flowing in it or drawn from it, and there is therefore no potential present between electrodes reversible with respect to the small unconstrained ions (Fig. 14-2).   However, if the constraint is removed, or bypassed, the system is no longer at equilibrium and it can produce electric currents and generate potentials by the movement of the small ions.   In principle, the actual constraint could be replaced by electrical potentials capable of maintaining the same concentration differences of the small ions.   Either of these potentials measures the tendency of the small ions to return to unconstrained equilibrium with uniform concentration throughout.   These are the potentials about which we may speak in these equilibrium systems.

Experimentally, these potentials may be approximately measured by by-passing the constraint, especially the membrane, by means of an electrolyte and measuring the potential developed

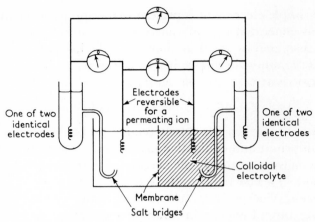

Figure 14-2. The potentials in a membrane equilibrium. A potential can develop in a constrained equilibrium system only when the electric circuit bypasses the constraint. The relative directions and magnitudes of the galvanometer deflections are significant.

within this electrolyte. In practice, salt bridges are immersed in the solutions on both sides of a membrane (Fig. 14-2). They provide the by-pass and permit the system to approach equilibrium by diffusing into the salt solution at both ends. The other ends of the salt bridges are connected to identical electrodes, e.g., Ag/AgCl ones, and the potential between these is measured. It gives the tendency of the small ions to equalize their concentration, just as in an ordinary concentration cell.

Electroneutrality determines only the absolute differences between the concentrations of small ions in the equilibrium system. On the other hand, by Nernst's law the potential of a concentration cell depends on the ratio of concentrations, their relative difference, not on their absolute difference. Obviously, therefore, the potential will be greatest when similiions are absent and tend to zero as swamping conditions are approached. This is the same over-all result as in the previous case of dynamic phenomena. Here, however, since no motion is involved in an equilibrium state, the resistance of the solution has nothing to do with it, and friction factors do not enter the picture.

If the gegenions and the similiions have the same valence, the potential causes them to have also the same ratio of concentration but in the opposite direction, so that where the gegenions are twice as concentrated the similiions are twice as dilute.   Under swamping conditions this means that the colloid is half neutralized by an excess of gegenions and half by an equally large deficiency of similiions in the immediate neighborhood.

As always, the potential affects not only the counterions and similiions but also the colloidal ions and, when possible, changes their concentration.   Because of their large charge this can be an important effect, as we shall presently see.

14-9. Sedimentation Equilibrium

Sedimentation equilibrium can be considered as a balance between thermal agitation and gravity and again, the underlying forces remain unaffected.   In the absence of similions, electroneutrality forces the ions to move as a unit on a macroscopic scale.   Hence, the sedimenting forces and the kT terms add for all particles, and we get in analogy with Eq. 7-3.4

$$\ln \mathfrak{C}/\mathfrak{C}_0 = -[m_2(1 - \rho/\rho_2)$$

$$+ pm_3(1 - \rho/\rho_3)]\mathbf{g}(H - H_0)/(p + 1)\mathbf{k}T \quad (14\text{-}9.1)$$

where $\mathfrak{C}$ is the concentration, m the mass of a particle, and ρ its density; H is the height.   The subscript $_0$ denotes the reference level, $_2$ again the colloidal ion and $_3$ the counterion.   Here, too, the gravitational contribution of the gegenions is generally small and can be neglected.   This leads to the expression

$$\ln \mathfrak{C}/\mathfrak{C}_0 = -m_2(1 - \rho/\rho_2)\mathbf{g}(H - H_0)/(p + 1)\mathbf{k}T \quad (14\text{-}9.2)$$

which differs from the relation for uncharged particles (Eq. 7-3.9) by the factor $(p + 1)$.   In view of the large charges which colloids can possess, this factor can have a tremendous effect. Thus a charged colloid free of similiions behaves in sedimentation equilibrium as would an uncharged particle having a particle weight of only $m_2/(p + 1)$.   It would be clearly very misleading to consider this apparent particle weight as the correct value.

On the other hand, as the concentration of similiions increases upon addition of a simple electrolyte, charge effects become negligible, and the behavior approaches that of uncharged particles.

To look at the same phenomenon from a potential point of view: In order to maintain electroneutrality, the concentration of gegenions must (in the absence of similiions) change in the same ratio as that of the colloid.   The potential producing this effect will, however, affect the colloid much more because of its larger charge.   As a result, the equilibrium concentration of the colloid in the gravitational field is disturbed relatively much more than that of the small ions.   As a simple salt is added, the ratio of gegenion concentrations can come closer to unity, the potential becomes less, and the distribution of the colloid can approach the one it would have if uncharged.[3]

The reader may find it profitable to develop the same results from the point of view of a balance of diffusion and sedimentation in analogy with Section 7-4.

14-10. Colligative Properties

When dealing with uncharged colloids the meaning of a semipermeable membrane was unambiguous (Chapter 6), but when dealing with a colloidal electrolyte we must specify whether the membrane is also impervious to the gegenions or not.   Both types are known.   Thus vapor space, which as we have seen acts as a semipermeable membrane in vapor pressure lowering measurements, is impervious to small ions; on the other hand, cellophane offers practically no resistance to their passage.   Both, of course, retain larger colloidal ions.

In the case of a membrane impervious to small ions, the situation is relatively simple.   Each ionic species, animated by thermal agitation, exerts the same pressure on the membrane as if it were neutral.   On the other hand, electroneutrality requires that for each colloidal ion there be p monovalent ions, so that the colligative property corresponds to $p + 1$ particles, and the apparent molecular weight is, again, $M/(p + 1)$ instead of the real M.   This is, of course, the same behavior as observed in the case of simple electrolytes, where the van't Hoff factor, i (the number of ions formed per mole), is precisely $p + 1$ if one of the ions is monovalent.   The presence of salts has a purely additive effect (neglecting activity coefficient effects) on the colligative property in this case, since it simply adds to the number of particles bombarding the wall.

If the membrane is permeable to small ions, the situation is different.   The osmotic pressure is always due to the net concentration of particles bombarding the membrane, i.e., to the excess of particles on one side of it as compared to the other.   Each species exerts a pressure given by $\mathbf{R}T\,\mathfrak{M}_i$ under ideal conditions (Eq. 6-5.l).   In the absence of similiions, electroneutrality requires that all the gegenions be confined, along with the colloid, on one side of the membrane.   Although the membrane is not retaining them directly, it prevents their passage by restraining the colloidal ions.   Hence the osmotic pressure is given by

$$\pi = \mathbf{R}T(p + 1)\mathfrak{M}_2 \tag{14-10.1}$$

where $\mathfrak{M}_2$ is the molar concentration of the colloidal ion.

One way of visualizing this situation is that an unweighable number of small ions crosses the membrane, thus producing a potential difference across it.   This potential rises until it is sufficient to prevent the exit of more counterions.   This same potential must also press the colloidal ions against the membrane. Alternatively, one may visualize the small ions trying to escape and pulling along the colloidal ones, which are, however, retained by the membrane.   In either view, the tendency of the thermal agitation to distribute all particles uniformly, with 1 $\mathbf{k}T$ per particle, must be counteracted by the membrane through the intermediate of the colloidal ions.   Since there are p counterions for each of these, each is equivalent to $(p + 1)$ particles.

If swamping amounts of small electrolyte are present, the potential becomes negligible and, as we have seen, electroneutrality is obtained half by an excess of gegenions and half by a deficiency of similiions.   This means that the concentration of small ions is equal on both sides and that these do not contribute to the osmotic pressure.   The latter is obviously due to the colloidal ion and is therefore given by

$$\pi = \mathbf{R}T\mathfrak{M}_2 \qquad (14\text{-}10.2)$$

just as for an uncharged particle.

14-11. Donnan Equilibrium

In the above discussions we have considered only the two extreme cases, when the simple electrolyte is either absent or is present in swamping amounts.   The intermediate case, when the simple electrolyte is present in moderate concentration, is particularly interesting for membrane equilibria involving membranes permeable to the small ions.   The problem is then to calculate the distribution of the small ions between the two sides of the membrane and the resulting osmotic pressure.

The distribution of the small ions can be calculated readily from two independent points of view.   One is to remember that the same potential affects both kinds of small monovalent ions, so that their concentration ratios are inverse

$$\mathfrak{M}_3'/\mathfrak{M}_3'' = \mathfrak{M}_4''/\mathfrak{M}_4' \qquad (14\text{-}11.1)$$

where $_4$ refers to similiions while $'$ and $''$ refer to the two compartments.   Rearranging, this gives

$$\mathfrak{M}_3'\mathfrak{M}_4' = \mathfrak{M}_3'' \, \mathfrak{M}_4'' \qquad (14\text{-}11.2)$$

which is generally known as the condition of Donnan equilibrium after the English chemist who developed and emphasized it.

The other point of view simply notes that the Donnan condition is equivalent to stating that the activity of the salt must be the same on both sides of the membranes.   It may be visualized as due to the requirement that whenever an ion crosses the membrane it must be accompanied by an oppositely charged one. Hence, the rate of crossing from one side is proportional to the product of the two concentrations on this side.   At equilibrium, the opposite rates of crossing must be equal, so that the products of concentrations of small ions must also be equal on the two sides, as required by Eq. 14-11.2. This is very similar to the solubility product requirement for electrolytes.

14-12. Osmotic Pressure

The Donnan condition gives us only one equation with four concentrations. The other conditions are, however, directly obtained by applying the requirement of electroneutrality to both sides

$$p\mathfrak{M}_2 + \mathfrak{M}_4' = \mathfrak{M}_3' \qquad (14\text{-}11.3)$$

$$\mathfrak{M}_4'' = \mathfrak{M}_3'' \qquad (14\text{-}11.4)$$

This gives three equations involving five concentrations, so that if any two are known the others can be obtained. Once the concentrations are calculated, the osmotic pressure can be computed directly from the difference in concentration between the two sides

$$\pi = \mathbf{R}T(\mathfrak{M}_2 + \mathfrak{M}_3' + \mathfrak{M}_4' - \mathfrak{M}_3'' - \mathfrak{M}_4'') \qquad (14\text{-}11.5)$$

Thus, if the concentration of colloidal ions, $\mathfrak{M}_2$, and that of the added salt in the same compartment, $\mathfrak{M}_4'$ are known, Eqs. 14-11.2, 14-11.3 and 14-11.4 above give for the other concentrations,

$$\mathfrak{M}_3' = p\mathfrak{M}_2 + \mathfrak{M}_4' \qquad (14\text{-}11.6)$$

$$\mathfrak{M}_2'' = \mathfrak{M}_4'' = [\mathfrak{M}_4'(p\mathfrak{M}_2 + \mathfrak{M}_4')]^{1/2} \qquad (14\text{-}11.7)$$

and for the osmotic pressure this gives

$$\pi/\mathbf{R}T = \mathfrak{M}_2(1 + p) + 2\mathfrak{M}_4' - 2[\mathfrak{M}_4'(p\mathfrak{M}_2 + \mathfrak{M}_4')]^{1/2} \qquad (14\text{-}11.8)$$

The reader can verify that this expression gives the correct limits; $\pi/\mathbf{R}T = \mathfrak{M}_2$ when either $\mathfrak{M}_2$ goes to zero or $\mathfrak{M}_4'$ increases, and $\pi/\mathbf{R}T = \mathfrak{M}_2/(p + 1)$ as $\mathfrak{M}_4'$ goes to zero.

We shall return to this Donnan osmotic pressure later in connection with the swelling of gels (Section 17-11).

14-13. Some Limitations

In all these applications of electroneutrality we have assumed ideal behavior, using concentrations instead of activities. Yet, as well known, electrolytes show large deviations from ideality, and in the case of colloidal electrolytes these are particularly marked and often difficult or impossible to take into account. Hence, although the general principles and qualitative results discussed above are correct, the quantitative aspect may have only a vague resemblance to reality.   An alternative approach is to throw all the non-ideality into the charge and to consider p not as the real charge but as an effective charge giving ideal results in experimental observations, and having perhaps a value very different from the true charge.

An interesting peculiarity is presented by the association colloidal electrolytes (which, as we mentioned, are sometimes simply called colloidal electrolytes).   A solution of a pure association colloidal electrolyte above the c.m.c. contains colloidal ions (the micelles), small counterions, and also small micelle-forming ions. From the point of view of this chapter these small, micelle-forming ions are clearly similiions.   Hence, micelles cannot be studied in the absence of similiions, and, at the c.m.c., the micelles are not only at infinite dilution but also in a swamping electrolyte, even when no salt has been added.

Summary

The electric forces due to the minutest macroscopic separation of ions are enormous and lead to the requirement of electroneutrality for any macroscopic system.   The electric forces are also nondiscriminatory and affect all the ions present according only to their charge.   They can therefore be expressed and, often, measured as potentials.   When swamping electrolytes are present, any potentials are readily dissipated by minute motions of all the ions present, so that the behavior of colloidal ions is essentially unaffected by their charge.   When similiions are absent, i.e., when the colloidal electrolyte is pure, it can be looked upon as a unit whose friction factor and kinetic energy are the sums of those of all the particles forming it.   Under these conditions the behavior of the colloidal ion is markedly affected by its charge.

References

1. T. Svedberg and K. O. Pedersen, *The Ultracentrifuge*, Oxford University Press, London, 1940, p. 23.
2. J. R. Vinograd and J. W. McBain, *J. Am. Chem. Soc.*, **63**, 2008 (1941) (N indicates moles, not equivalents).
3. J. S. Johnson, K. A. Kraus, and G. Scatchard, *J. Phys. Chem.*, **58**, 1034 (1954).

Problems

84. If a solution has a concentration $\mathfrak{M}_2$ of colloidal ions having a charge p and $\mathfrak{M}_4$ of similiions having a charge z_4, then the concentration of counterions if they have a charge z_3 is (1) $(\mathfrak{M}_2 + \mathfrak{M}_4)/z_3$; (2) $(\mathfrak{M}_2/\mathfrak{M}_2) + \mathfrak{M}_4 z_4$; (3) $\mathfrak{M}_4 z_2$; (4) $p\mathfrak{M}_2/z_3$; (5) $(p\mathfrak{M}_2 + z_4\mathfrak{M}_4)/z_3$, (6) none of these.

51. The diffusion coefficient of the H^+ ion is close to 10^{-4} cm.^{2}/sec and that of the Cl^- ion close to 2×10^{-5} cm.^{2}/sec. under swamping electrolyte conditions. On this basis, the diffusion coefficient of pure HCl in the same units should be close to (1) 10^{-4}, (2) 6×10^{-5}, (3) 3.3×10^{-5}, (4) 2×10^{-5}, (5) 10^{-5}.

58. If a negatively charged colloidal particle sediments through a column of swamping electrolytes having no tendency to sediment themselves, there will be (1) no motion of small ions, (2) anions moving downwards, (3) only cations moving, (4) cations moving upward, (5) none of these.

54. If an ideal system contains 10^{-3} molar ten-valent colloidal cations separated by a membrane permeable to small ions from pure water and the system is at equilibrium, the osmotic pressure in atmospheres between the compartments is, at room temperature, about (1) 0.275, (2) 0.25, (3) 0.0275, (4) 0.025.

60. If one compartment of an ideal Donnan equilibrium system contains 0.1 M NaCl and the other 0.1 M of a monovalent colloidal cation, then the concentration of Na^+ ion in the other compartment is _____ M.

86. If an ideal Donnan equilibrium system contains 1 mmole/liter of a colloid carrying nine positive charges per particle and 3 mmoles/liter of Na^+ in the same compartment, possible concentrations of Cl^- ion in the two compartments in m moles/liter are (1) 3 and 3, (2) 27 and 9, (3) 12 and 12, (4) 12 and 6, (5) all of these.

82. A solution of a pure colloidal electrolyte is divided into two portions A and B. Some salt is added to B but no flocculation occurs. Both portions are then allowed to reach sedimentation equilibrium. The concentration of the colloid will be more uniform in (*1*) A, (*2*) B, (*3*) no appreciable difference.

CHAPTER XV

The Double Layer

In the last chapter we have seen that electroneutrality requires the presence of a neutralizing amount of counterions in the immediate vicinity of any macroscopic amount of colloidal ions. Hence, in macroscopic motions the electric forces are overwhelming. Electroneutrality does not specify, however, how the counterions should behave while within this immediate vicinity. We need now a more detailed picture of the behavior and distribution of the small ions within this microscopic region surrounding a colloidal ion. Here the electric potentials are no longer overwhelming but become commensurate with thermal agitation. It is the balance between these two factors, the former attracting the gegenions and repelling the similions, the latter, as always, tending to cause a uniform distribution, which is of primary concern. For the time being we shall neglect any other forces which may affect the behavior of these ions, and we will not inquire into the origin of the charges causing the potential. These will be discussed in the chapter after next.

15-1. The Infinite Plane

The electric field intensity around an ion or a point charge changes rapidly with distance. This complicates somewhat the discussion. We can simplify it considerably, without losing any essentials, by considering first an infinite, uniformly charged plane. A small charge in the vicinity of such a plane is subject to a constant force. This results from the fact that the charges acting within any small solid angle increase with the square of the distance from the plane, while the force exerted by each decreases, according to Coulomb's law, at the same rate (Fig.

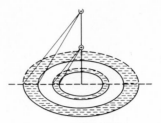

Figure 15-1. The force exerted by an infinite charged plane upon a point charge is independent of distance because the charge acting within a fixed solid angle increases as its effectiveness decreases, with the square of the distance.

15-1). The electric field intensity is thus constant, the potential decreases linearly with distance (Fig. 15-2), and equipotential surfaces are plane and parallel to the charged plane.

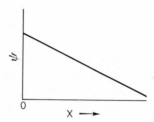

Figure 15-2. The potential changes linearly with the distance from an isolated infinite plane because the force on a point charge remains constant. (If the potential is measured with respect to infinity it is also infinite.)

15-2. Electric and Gravitational Fields

The electric field near an infinite charged plane thus exerts a constant force of constant direction. It is therefore identical in form with the gravitational field over laboratory scale distances. Hence a single electronic charge will behave near such a plane as a small particle behaves in the gravitational field. In particular, the probability of finding it at any distance from the attracting plane is given by the Boltzmann distribution which we developed in Chapter 7)

$$\mathcal{P} = \mathcal{P}_0 e^{-w/\mathbf{k}T} = \mathcal{P}_0 e^{-\epsilon(\psi - \psi_0)/\mathbf{k}T} \tag{15-2.1}$$

in which the work term w is given by the product of the electronic charge, ϵ, times the potential difference. Since the latter is proportional to the distance from the plane, the probability decreases exponentially with distance, just as in the barometric formula.

This analogy with the gravitational field breaks down, however, as soon as we begin to consider another small charge in the vicinity of the first one. This breakdown is caused by two basic differences between the gravitational and the electric field.

1. Gravitational forces between two small particles, even when they are so close to each other that they touch, are completely negligible when compared to the field of the earth. We know from everyday experience that they are negligible for macroscopic laboratory objects. It can be easily shown that this is even more true for the smaller particles of interest to us since the product of their masses is proportional to r^6, while at the closest approach the effect of the distance is proportional to r^{-2}. Hence the force between them varies like r^4. On the other hand, the gravitational effect of the earth upon each particle varies with the mass of each, i.e., with r^3. The interparticle effects therefore decrease faster with decreasing size than does the effect of the earth. On the other hand, as we have seen, the potentials around even a single electronic charge become of the order of volts at distances of the order of atomic dimensions. Hence even in water, where the potentials are greatly reduced, they remain commensurate with the maximum possible potential of some 2 v.

Thus in practice the effect of one charge upon another cannot be neglected because the charges of interest are too large compared to the original field. In other words, the field acting upon each charge is not the simple field of the infinite plane, but the sum of the fields of all the other charges superimposed upon that of the plane.

2.   Gravitational forces are always attractive and therefore always add when combined.   Electric forces may be either attractive or repulsive, depending on the signs involved, and consequently may add or subtract.   Hence, the electric field can be reduced by interposition of opposite charges, whereas the gravitational one can only be increased by interposition of masses.

Thus, the study of a group of particles in an electric field must take into account the interactions of particles.   This makes it much more complicated than the corresponding problem for a gravitational field.   We will begin by developing a qualitative picture with numerical illustrations and later turn to the quantitative bases underlying these illustrations.

15-3. The Diffuse Double Layer

Let us consider a box containing a solution of a simple electrolyte supplying counterions and similiions which are uniformly distributed (Fig. 15-3).   To investigate the effect of a charged plane, let us now assume that one of the walls of the box becomes charged, while an equivalent number of counterions appears in the solution to maintain electroneutrality.   Our problem is to describe the new distribution of the ions in the solution.   In general terms, the counterions will be attracted and the similiions repelled by the wall, while thermal motion will tend to distribute both uniformly throughout.

If thermal motion were absent, or small compared to the electrical forces, an equivalent amount of counterions would be attracted by the wall and would cover it, exactly neutralizing its charge (Fig. 15-4).   The wall and these neutralizing counterions would form a "double layer."   The rest of the solution would not be affected further since the double layer as a whole is electrically neutral, the counterions screening the wall completely.   The electric potential would drop to zero within the double layer.

If thermal agitation is present, it will generally prevent the formation of such a compact double layer.   If we neglect any effects on the similiions, the counterions instead of forming a compact layer will now only tend to concentrate near this wall. They behave in the electric field somewhat as they would in a gravitational field (Fig. 15-5).   However, the extra counterions near the wall will screen those further away from its full effect, so that the field instead of being constant will decrease with distance.   Hence there will be less tendency for the counterions to concentrate further away, and their concentration will fall off faster than it would in a gravitational field.   Because of the screening effect of the counterions the electric field intensity will decrease, rapidly near the wall and more slowly further away. The potential will therefore decrease rapidly, especially near the wall.

On the other hand, if we assume that the counterions are unaffected by the wall, the effect upon only the similiions will be the opposite from the above.   They will be repelled by the wall and their concentrations will be decreased especially near it (Fig. 15-6).   The removal of each similiion has the effect of leaving an additional counterion to screen the charge of the wall. Hence, the reduction in similiion concentration has, essentially, the same effect as if the concentration of counterions were increased; the electric field intensity and the potential decrease with distance, as discussed above.

In reality, the wall affects both the counterions and the similiions, so that the double layer is formed by both an increase in the concentration of counterions and a decrease in the concentration of similiions near the wall (Fig. 15-7).

There is, however, a basic difference in the behavior of counterions and of similiions.   The concentration of counterions can be increased many-fold, and therefore their screening effect can be very great.   The concentration of similiions, on the other hand, cannot be reduced below zero, and therefore the screening effect of their removal is limited.   In fact, in the relatively highly charged systems generally encountered in colloids, it turns out

SCHEMATIC   DOUBLE-LAYER STRUCTURES.

⊖ added counterions
× removed similiions
⊖ ⊕ unchanged ions

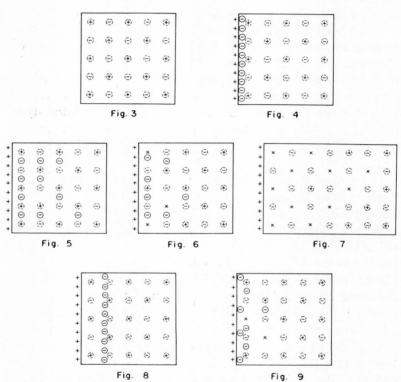

Figure 15-3. Solution undisturbed by a charged wall.

Figure 15-4. Formation of a compact double layer when wall becomes charged in the absence of thermal agitation.

Figure 15-5. Formation of a diffuse double layer by counterions alone.

Figure 15-6. Formation of a diffuse double layer by both counter- and similiions.

Figure 15-7. Formation of a diffuse double layer by similiions alone.

Figure 15-8. A Helmholtz simplified double layer.

Figure 15-9. A combination compact and diffuse or Stern and Gouy double layer.

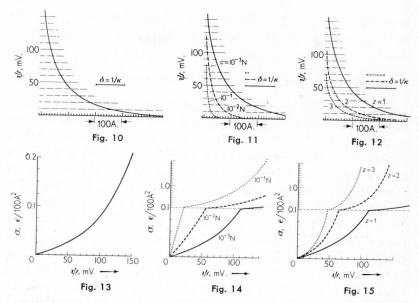

Figure 15-10. The decay of potential with distance in a flat diffuse double layer in the presence of $10^{-3}N$ monovalent ions. Note that the abscissa has no origin. This has to be placed according to the base potential (ψ_d) whose decay is to be estimated.

Figure 15-11. The effect of concentration of monovalent ions upon the decay of potential in a flat diffuse double layer. $\delta \propto 1/\sqrt{\mathfrak{N}}$.

Figure 15-12. The effect of valence of ions upon the decay of potential in a flat diffuse double layer at constant equivalent concentration $(10^{-3}N)$. $\delta \propto 1/\sqrt{z}$.

Figure 15-13. The relation of charge density and potential for a flat diffuse double layer of $10^{-3}N$ monovalent ions.

Figure 15-14. The effect of the concentration of monovalent ions upon the relation of charge density and potential in a flat diffuse double layer. (Note the shift of scale.)

Figure 15-15. The effect of valence of ions at constant equivalent concentration $(10^{-3}N)$ upon the relation of charge density and potential in a flat diffuse double layer. (Note the shift of scale.)

that the similiions have only a very small effect compared to the counterions.

Thus, the effect of thermal agitation is to create a "diffuse" double layer, sometimes called a Gouy or Gouy-Chapman double layer, in honor of the men who first considered it in detail. The potential within such a diffuse double layer decreases gradually from the wall to infinity, at first rapidly then more and more slowly.

15-4. The Decay of the Potential

Figure 15-10 shows how the potential decreases in a plane diffuse double layer of monovalent ions when the concentration of the solution is 10^{-3} M. It may be noted that the abscissa of this figure shows a scale but no origin, whereas the ordinate carries the usual divisions. This makes a single curve apply to any potential at the wall. The specific value of this potential simply gives the highest point up to which the curve should be used, and this point, corresponding to the wall, also determines the origin for the abscissa. In other words, the potential of a plane locates its position on the abscissa of the figure, and the decay curve depends only on this potential. It does not matter whether this plane is at the wall or is located anywhere within the diffuse double layer. A plane screened from a highly charged wall by some ions behaves exactly like a wall with a correspondingly lower charge. This again is due to the lack of discrimination by the electric forces.

On the other hand, the ordinate scale in Fig. 15-10 is fixed and cannot be shifted or expanded. This is because not only the absolute rate of decay of the potential but also its relative rate of decay decreases as the potential becomes lower. The

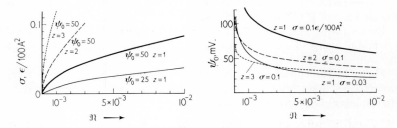

Figure 15-16. The effect of equivalent concentration and of valence upon charge density at constant potential (*left*) and upon potential at constant charge density (*right*) in a flat diffuse double layer.

distance over which the potential halves from 100 mv. to 50 mv. is somewhat shorter than that over which it halves from 50 to 25.   Below this, the decrease is practically exponential, i.e., changes by the same fraction over the same distances.   Above 100 mv. the steepness increases much more rapidly.   This compaction of the double layer at higher potentials results basically from the exponential rise of screening-ion concentration with the potential according to the Boltzmann distribution.

15-5. The "Thickness" of the Double Layer

The diffuse double layer has no sharply defined end point but slowly becomes negligible.   It is nevertheless very convenient for approximate considerations to assign to it a thickness which is designated by δ.   This thickness is generally taken as the distance over which the potential drops to a certain fraction of its value, specifically to $1/e = 0.37$ of that value.

As we have just seen in connection with Fig. 15-10, this distance is not quite constant even within a given double layer.   It is therefore generally taken as corresponding to the rate of decay of the low potential end of the curve, where it is also readily computed (Eq. 15-10.2).   This thickness changes greatly with the concentration and valence of the ions present in the solution, as we will see shortly, and these variations summarize conveniently the effect of the composition of the solution upon the nature of the double layer.

15-6. The Helmholtz Double Layer

The diffuse character of the double layer complicates appreciably its study and interpretation.   A very useful approximation is to consider all the neutralizing counterions of the double layer to be located in a single plane, as shown in Fig. 15-8.   If the distance between the wall and this plane is made equal to the thickness δ of the diffuse double layer as defined above, the two structures have clearly many points of similarity.   It turns out that for low potentials predicted effects are often the same for both.   This simplified model is called the Helmholtz double layer after the German physicist who first introduced the concept of the double layer in 1879.[1]

15-7. The Effect of Concentration and of Valence

The potential affects the counterions individually and simply increases the probability of finding them where it is high. Hence, if the concentration in the bulk solution is increased and if the potential were to remain unchanged, this would lead to a corresponding and proportional increase in the concentration of counterions near the wall.   This higher concentration of counterions, however, would also have a higher screening effect; consequently, the potential cannot remain the same but must decay faster.   Thus an increase in the concentration of simple electrolyte leads to a compacting of the double layer, as illustrated in Fig. 15-11 for three concentrations of monovalent ions.

If the charge of the gegenions is doubled, other things being equal, the effect on the double layer is quite drastic.   Thermal agitation continues to have the same effect on the gegenions, but that of the electric field on each is doubled so that they are brought closer to the wall, and the thickness of the double layer is reduced.   The screening effect of a doubly charged particle is also doubled, so that the potential is further reduced, as shown in Fig. 15-12 for ions of three valences at the same equivalent concentrations $(10^{-3}\ N)$.

If the charge of the similiions is doubled, the effect depends on the potential.   At low potentials, when the concentrations near the plane is close to the average concentration, the effect is similar to that produced by the change in the counterion.   In the more frequently encountered case of high potentials, where the similiions are almost completely expelled from the layers close to the wall, a change in their charge has little effect, since further expulsion is not possible and the structure of the double layer is determined essentially by the counterions.

15-8. Charge Density

The above considerations and the curves of Fig. 15-10 to 15-12 permit the estimation of decay of the potential if the composition of the solution and the potential of the charged wall are known.   For a solution of given concentration and valence of electrolyte, the potential of the wall is defined by its charge or, more exactly, by its charge density, i.e., the charge, σ, per unit surface. A convenient chemical way of expressing the charge density is in electronic charges per 100 A.,[2] i.e., per 1 mμ^2. A monolayer of average sized ions corresponds to a charge density of the order of five such units. Other things being equal, it is obvious that as the charge density on the wall increases so does the potential. However, the increase of potential is less than proportional and becomes slower and slower as the charge density increases. Conversely, to increase the potential by a certain amount, the charge density must be increased more than proportionately, especially if it is already high. Figure 15-13 shows this relation graphically.

The reason for the more rapid increase of charge density as compared to potential is that the potential is measured by work, i.e., by the product of force times distance. The force is determined by the charge density, whereas the distance is related to the thickness of the double layer. When the charge density is doubled, the force also doubles, but the double layer becomes somewhat more compressed, as we have seen (Section 15-4), so that the work, and hence the potential, is less than doubled.

The effect of increasing the concentration or the valence of the counterions is, as we have seen, to reduce the thickness of the double layer. Hence, in order to maintain the same potential, the charge density has to be increased. Again, the increase has to be more than proportionate, as shown in Figs. 15-14 and 15-15.

Considering Figs. 15-10 to 15-15 together, or Fig. 15-16 which summarizes them, if the charge density on the wall is maintained constant, the effect of increasing either the concentration or the valence is to reduce enormously the potential in the solution because such a change not only decreases the potential at the wall but, in addition, speeds up its decay with distance from the wall. On the other hand, if it is the potential at the wall which remains constant, only this second factor tends to reduce the potential in solution. This constancy of potential thus requires a rapidly increasing charge density at the wall. We shall see in Chapter 17 that the constancy of potential is more generally encountered in practice than a constancy of charge density.

It should be noted that the charged plane and its double layer, taken together, are electrically neutral.   Hence, the charge density of the plane is also the charge density of the diffuse double layer.

15-9. Effect of Shape

If instead of considering an infinite plane, we consider a charged sphere, the situation is somewhat more complicated.   In the absence of any counterions, the field intensity decreases with the square of the distance from the center of the sphere, so that the potential is as we have seen (Eq. 14-2.2) inversely proportional to it.   Hence, even in the absence of screening effects, the electrical effects will be particularly large near the sphere.   From the above discussion of the flat double layer, we can see that screening effects will still further emphasize this tendency. Otherwise the nature of the effects upon the small ions will be essentially the same as near a plane.   A diffuse double layer will form, and its thickness will vary with the concentration and with the valence of the ions in the same direction.   The differences will be quantitative rather than qualitative.

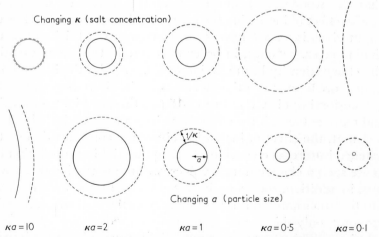

Figure 15-17. The meaning and variation of κa, the ratio of particle radius to double layer thickness.   When κa is large, the double layer is almost flat; when it is small, the particle may be considered as a point charge

If the thickness of the double layer around a sphere is small compared to its radius, the difference of curvatures between the inner and outer parts of the double layer will be small, and its structure will differ little from that of a completely plane double layer.   This, as we shall see shortly, is the case for colloidal systems of larger particles in not too dilute solutions of monovalent ions.   Hence, the infinite plane is not only the simplest model but has also a considerable range of applications.   It is only when the particle becomes quite small or the solution very dilute that the curvature effects become important (Fig. 15-17).

15-10. Quantitative Aspects of the Diffuse Double Layer

The exact quantitative treatment of the double layer is a complicated and as yet unfinished problem.[2]   Even the simplest case of the plain double layer is beyond the scope of this book.   We can, however, consider some of the simplifications that have to be introduced into the calculations and some of the results obtained.

In the qualitative discussion above, we have already introduced implicitly a simplification which is constantly used.   Instead of considering individual charges and their instantaneous positions, we have spoken about layers.   This means that we have averaged the charges both in space and in time so that the charge distribution can be considered to be continuous function of distance from the plane and to be independent of time.   This is similar to the use of concentration in the barometric formula, despite the fact that this concentration is due to individual particles and therefore varies discontinuously and fluctuates with time.

The continuous charge has also a continuous effect on the potential.   The quantitative expression for this variation is known as Poisson's equation and, in the simple case of the infinite plane, reduces itself to

$$d^2\psi/dx^2 = -4\pi\rho/\vartheta \qquad (15\text{-}10.1)$$

where ψ is the potential at x, ρ the volume charge density (concentration) at the same point, and ϑ is the dielectric constant. This is simply a quantitative expression of the screening effect that we have used heretofore.   When the charge density is zero, the second derivative is zero and the potential is linear, as we have seen previously.   In the presence of charges, the potential versus distance plot is curved, the curvature increasing with the charge density at any level.

The probability of finding a particle animated by thermal agitation at any point is still given, of course, by the Boltzmann distribution, and the work term is still given by the product of charge and potential difference, as in Eq. 15-2.1.   The potential difference is, however, dependent on the charge density by Poisson's equation 15-10.1, and that, in turn, depends on the probability of finding a charge at any point.   Thus, the two conditions are intimately interwoven and have to be satisfied simultaneously.   In other words, the mathematical problem is to find a simultaneous solution to both equations, satisfying also the boundary conditions set by the physical situation.   In our case, these boundary conditions are that the potential must have a constant value, ψ_0, along the surface of the particle or of the wall and must vanish at infinity.

In all these calculations an important role is played by the quantity κ which is equal to the inverse of the thicknesses δ of the double layer when the potential is low.   It is defined for the case of equal valence of counterions and similiions by

$$\kappa^2 = 1/\delta^2 = 8\pi\mathfrak{n}\varepsilon^2 z^2/\vartheta \mathbf{k} T \qquad (15\text{-}10.2)$$

where $\mathfrak{n}$ is the number of ions per cubic centimeter, z their valence, and ε the electronic charge, esu-c.g.s. units being used throughout.

In water at room temperature $\delta = 1/\kappa$ is approximately $3 \times 10^{-8}/z\sqrt{\mathfrak{M}}$ where $\mathfrak{M}$ is the molar concentration of the gegenions beyond the double layer.   Hence, in the case of monovalent ions the thickness, δ, of the double layer is, in 0.1 M solution, approximately $3 \times 10^{-8}/0.31 = 10^{-7}$ cm. or 10 A.   It increases to 100 A. in a 0.001 M solution, and becomes 1000 A. in slightly contaminated water of 10^{-5} molarity.   For spherical particles, $\kappa a = a/\delta$, the ratio of radius to the thickness of the double layer gives a measure of the curvature within the diffuse double layer as shown in Fig. 15-17.   When κa becomes 10, the thickness becomes one-tenth of the radius, and the double layer can be considered for most purposes as flat.   The concentration above which this becomes true depends on the valence of the counterions and on the size of the particle.   Typical values are given in Table 15-1. On the other hand, when the double layer thickness becomes some ten times the radius, $\kappa a = 0.1$, the size of the particle can be frequently neglected;   it acts as a point charge.   This occurs at concentrations 10^4 times lower than those listed in the table.

The exact and explicit solution of the Boltzmann-Poisson equations has been obtained in the case of the infinite plane.   The final expression may be put into the form

$$x = (1/\kappa) \ln (e^{ze\psi/2\mathbf{k}T} + 1)/(e^{ze\psi/2\mathbf{k}T} - 1) \qquad (15\text{-}10.3)$$

where ψ is the potential at a distance x.   In order to locate the origin of the x axis at the charged plane, a value of x_0 given by Eq. 15-10.3 for ψ_0 has to be subtracted from x.

TABLE 15-1
Concentrations of Electrolyte Below Which the Spherical Shape of Particles
Becomes Important
(Values of $\mathfrak{M}$ for $\kappa a = 10$)

Radius a, A.	Conc. $\mathfrak{M}$ (moles/liter)		
	$z = 1$	$z = 2$	$z = 3$
10	12	2.9	1.3
50	0.47	0.12	0.052
100	0.12	0.029	0.013
500	4.7×10^{-3}	1.2×10^{-3}	5.2×10^{-4}
1,000	1.2×10^{-3}	2.9×10^{-4}	1.3×10^{-4}
5,000	4.7×10^{-5}	1.2×10^{-5}	5.2×10^{-6}
10,000	1.2×10^{-5}	2.9×10^{-6}	1.3×10^{-6}

A frequently used approximation assumes that the electric work term is small compared to $\mathbf{k}T$, which means that the potentials are small compared to 0.025 v. for monovalent counterions.

This is the so-called Debye-Huckel approximation, used by these physical chemists (Debye was trained to be an electrical engineer) in their justly famous treatment of the interaction of small ions in extremely dilute solutions. In the case of most colloids this turns out not to be a very good approximation, however, because of the very high charges prevailing in these systems. The D-H approximation permits, however, a relatively easy solution to the case of spherical particles, and can, of course, also be applied to the plane.

We have frequently seen how very useful the spherical model is in the study of colloids. Hence, a solution of the Boltzmann-Poisson equation for a highly charged sphere would be very desirable in the study of colloidal electrolytes. Unfortunately, this equation cannot be solved explicitly. Numerical solutions have been obtained, however, for special cases, especially recently by means of electronic computers.[3] In addition, graphical methods of interpolation give a good insight into most situations.[4]

The case of ellipsoids and other shapes, especially when they are highly charged, is, of course, even more complicated, and little is known about them.

15-11. The Stern Layer

We have mentioned earlier that in the absence of thermal agitation the double layer would be formed simply by a very compact layer of gegenions. It is thermal agitation, overcoming in part the electrostatic attractions, which causes the diffuseness of the double layer. If the electrostatic forces are too strong, however, or if they are reinforced by van der Waals forces, thermal agitation is not able to overcome them, and part of the gegenions remains in such a compact layer on the charged surface (Fig. 15-9). This compact part of the double layer is called the Stern layer, after the German chemist who first emphasized its existence.

The compact Stern layer is in dynamic equilibrium with the diffuse Gouy layer and is formed by gegenions. Thus, both may be considered as forming the outer part of the double layer. On the other hand, the ions of the Stern layer are attached to the charged surface, in the same sense that any adsorbed particles are attached to the adsorbent.   In this sense the Stern layer is an integral part of the charged surface or particle.

15-12. The Different Potentials

As we have seen (Section 14-1), an electrostatic potential at a point is measured by the work (against electrostatic forces) which is required to bring a unit charge from infinity to that point. For an infinite charged plane in vacuum, the potential becomes infinity, because the field intensity is constant and independent of the distance.   In the presence of a solution, however, the screening effect of the ions reduces the field intensity to a negligible amount within a rather short distance—a few double layer thicknesses.   Hence, we can consider the "bulk" solution, far enough from the charged surface, as having zero potential.   The electrostatic work of transporting a charge from this bulk solution towards the surface then measures the potential at each point.

The only electric charges which we can have in aqueous solution are, of course, ions, more specifically, hydrated ions.   As long as they stay in solution we may consider them as relatively stable entities, and their movement can involve only electrostatic forces.   Whenever we try to transport them across a phase boundary, however, their nature changes more or less radically, e.g., from the hydrated Ag^+ ion in solution to the silver atom in the $Ag^+ + \epsilon \rightleftharpoons Ag$ electrode reaction, or to the anhydrous Ag^+ ion of AgI crystals.   This change in nature generally involves considerable forces which are not purely electrostatic. Hence the work and the potential measured under these conditions are not the electrostatic potential which interests us here.

Electrode reactions always involve such crossing of phase boundaries, and we shall not consider them here.   We will examine only the potentials defined by the work of transporting an ion up to the phase boundary, but always while the ion remains within the solution so that its nature remains unchanged.   As this ion crosses various layers of the solution, the corresponding work defines the potentials at these layers.

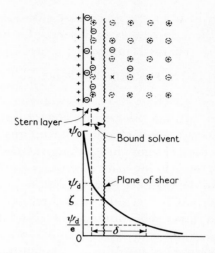

Figure 15-18. The structure of a double layer and the corresponding potentials. ψ_0 is at the wall, the ψ_d at the beginning of the diffuse double layer, ζ at the hydrodynamic plane of shear. In the diffuse double layer the potential decays by a factor of $1/e$ over a distance $\delta = 1/\kappa$ for low potentials.

There are three layers whose potential is of particular interest. One is at the surface of the particle itself and measures the total potential of the double layer. This is called psi, ψ, and is sometimes distinguished as ψ_0. Another is the boundary between the Stern and the Gouy (diffuse) part of the double layer and is called ψ_d. The third interesting layer is formed by the boundary between the solvent adhering to the particle in its motion and that which can move with respect to it. This "plane of shear" essentially separates the water of hydration from free water. The potential of this plane is called the zeta, ζ, potential. The zeta potential, therefore, does not include the Stern layer but only that part of the Gouy layer which is not within a firmly bound solvent layer nor within crevices and hollows. As the bound layer is of the order of a molecule in thickness, ζ will be closer to zero than ψ_d, but not by much. Figure 15-18 shows these relations.

In the next chapter we will discuss the methods used to measure experimentally the ζ potential. Frequently this gives a good approximation of ψ_d. Measurement of ψ_0 is probably impossible in principle, although reasonable approximations can be obtained in special cases, and changes in its value can often be measured. Without being able to discuss this interesting point in detail,[5] we can indicate the principles of such a measurement: Silver iodide crystals in fine suspension can repel each other when charged either positively or negatively, by adsorption of Ag^+ or I^- ions respectively. When they show the least tendency to repel each other and flocculate most readily, their ψ_0 can be assumed to be zero. Thus an absolute value of ψ_0 is determined. On the other hand, the easily measured changes of the potential of electrodes, such as a silver electrode, are presumably due to variations of their ψ_0.

Summary

The charge on a wall or on a particle attracts counterions and repels similiions. Some of the counterions may be immobilized in the Stern layer, while the rest of the ions form a diffuse Gouy layer. The decay of potential within this double layer is measured by its thickness, which is very sensitive to the concentration and valence of the counterions. The surface charge density corresponding to a given potential is also very sensitive to these factors. Potentials at three points are of special importance: ψ_0 at the surface of the wall or particle, ψ_d at the boundary between the Stern and the Gouy layers, and ζ at the hydrodynamic plane of shear.

References

1. L. F. Helmholtz, *Ann. Physik*, **7** (3), 337 (1879). This paper and M. Smoluchowski's article in L. Graetz, ed., *Handbuch der Elektriziẗt und des Magnetismus*, Leipzig, 1921, have been translated in P. Bocquet, *Two Monographs on Electrokinetics* (Engineering Research Bulletin No. 33), University of Michigan, Ann Arbor, 1951.
2. E. J. W. Verwey and J. Th. G. Overbeek, *Theory of the Stability of Lyophobic Colloids*, Elsevier, New York, 1948.

3. N. E. Hoskin, *Trans. Faraday Soc.*, **49,** 1471 (1953).

4. D. Stigter and K. J. Mysels, *J. Phys. Chem.*, **59,** 45 (1955).

5. E. A. Guggenheim, *J. Phys. Chem.*, **33,** 842 (1929); **34,** 1540 (1930). *Thermodynamics*, North-Holland Publishing Co., Amsterdam, 1957. Chap. 9; J. Th. G. Overbeek in H. R. Kruyt, ed., *Colloid Science.* Elsevier, New York, 1952, Vol. I, Chap. IV.

Problems

72. The density of the primary charge depends on (*1*) the concentration of potential-determining ions, (*2*) the concentration of similiions, (*3*) the valence of counterions, (*4*) all of these, (*5*) none of these.

91. The distribution of ions near a charged particle or wall may be described in terms of a Boltzmann expression in which the work term (*1*) is the same for divalent and monovalent ions, (*2*) involves only the charge and potential and therefore is independent of the presence of other ions, (*3*) tends to increase if similiions approach the particle, (*4*) is unaffected by temperature.

99. In order to maintain the same ψ_0 as the concentration of salt increases, the charge density must (*1*) increase, (*2*) decrease, (*3*) remain the same, (*4*) it depends on the valence of the salt.

123. If the surface charge density on a plane wall is σ, the charge density of the ions forming the Helmholtz double layer must be (*1*) $-\sigma/\mathbf{e}$, (*2*) $-\sigma$, (*3*) $-\sigma\mathbf{e}$, (*4*) none of these.

125. If the potential of the wall in a Helmholtz double layer is ψ_0, the potential in the space between this wall and the layer of ions is (*1*) ψ_0, (*2*) 0, (*3*) linearly decreasing from ψ_0 to 0, (*4*) decreasing but not linearly and not to zero, (*5*) decreasing to zero but not linearly.

CHAPTER XVI

Electrokinetics

In the previous chapter we saw that a colloidal ion is surrounded by a double layer within which the potential increases as the surface of the particle is approached. The value of this potential at the plane of shear which separates the particle and any solvent rigidly fixed to it from the rest of the liquid, the zeta potential, is most directly accessible to measurements. These measurements are based on the electric and mechanical phenomena connected with the relative motion of the liquid and the particle. Hence the name electrokinetics which is given to them. Electrokinetics is part of the broader subject of electric transport phenomena, some of which, such as conductivity, transference, and to a lesser extent mobility, are generally considered in the study of small ions. For colloids, it is mobility and allied phenomena that acquire particular importance and will be the main subject of this chapter after being placed in relation to the broader field and especially to conductivity.

16-1. Conductivity

Simple electrolytes are in general easily prepared in pure form, so that their conductivity can be measured with high accuracy even at high dilutions. Hence measurements of this property play a large role in the study of small ions. The preparation of correspondingly pure colloids is generally very difficult; as a result, their conductivities are seldom known, and the method is seldom used in their study. The association colloidal electrolytes are a striking exception. They can often be prepared in a state of high purity and have high, easily measured,

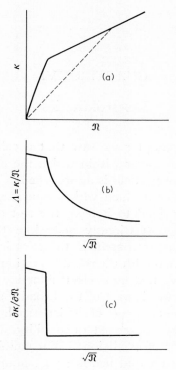

Figure 16-1. Typical conductivity of an association colloidal electrolyte. (*a*) the measured conductivity as a function of concentration; (*b*) the equivalent conductivity, which is the slope of the dashed line of (*a*); (*c*) the differential conductivity which is the tangent of the curve of (*a*). Note the drastic departure from the behavior of a simple electrolyte, corresponding to the presence of micelles above the c.m.c.

and characteristic conductivities which are shown schematically in Fig. 16-1.

Figure 16-1*a* shows how the conductivity $\varkappa$ of a solution of an association colloidal electrolyte changes with concentration. The increase is rapid at first, then, rather suddenly, it becomes much slower. The corresponding changes in the equivalent conductivity are shown in Fig. 16-1*b*. As for simple electrolytes, it is almost constant at low concentrations, then decreases sharply to a lower value. The abrupt change of slope corresponds to the critical micelle concentration above which, as we have already seen (Section 6-11), added material forms micelles. The change of slope clearly shows that these micelles (and their counterions) conduct less well than the unassociated ions.

When all the particles formed by an electrolyte are present in constant proportion (e.g., the Na^+ and Cl^- ions of NaCl), the equivalent conductivity gives a good insight into the change of their conducting ability with concentration. In the present case, however, the proportions change markedly with concentration (the micelles being absent at low and predominating completely at high concentrations), and the equivalent conductivity, which is an average over-all species, becomes more difficult to interpret. Differential conductivity $\partial x/\partial \mathfrak{C}$, shown in Fig. 16-1c, is quite useful in this case, since it shows as a first approximation the conducting power of the added material (a small effect of the added material on that already present is included). The upper part shows the conductivity of the simple ions, the lower that of the micelles and their counterions.

16-2. Mobility and Conductivity

Let us now consider the general relation of mobility to conductivity and some of the factors affecting the relative usefulness of these two properties.

The mobility, or more specifically the electric or electrophoretic mobility, v, of an ion is by definition its velocity in a field of 1 v/cm. If its valence is z, the charge it carries is $z\mathbf{F}/\mathbf{N}$ coulombs. If the concentration of the ions is $\mathfrak{n}/cm.^3$, their flux j in unit field is $v\mathfrak{n}$, and this produces a current flow of jz electronic charges or $jz\mathbf{F}/\mathbf{N} = v\mathfrak{n}z\mathbf{F}/\mathbf{N}$ coulombs/sec. (i.e., amperes) across a unit cross section. The total current flow, being the sum of the current carried by all ions, is given by $\Sigma(\mathbf{F}/\mathbf{N})v_i\mathfrak{n}_iz_i$. This current, flowing through unit cross section of the solution in unit field, is also by definition the conductivity x of the solution

$$x = \Sigma(\mathbf{F}/\mathbf{N})v_i\mathfrak{n}_iz_i \qquad (16\text{-}2.1)$$

It may be noted that, if the sign of z corresponds to the charge and that of v to the direction of motion relative to the field, the products $v_i z_i$ are all positive.

Thus conductivity is intimately connected with the mobilities, charges, and concentrations of all the species present in the solution. It is a property of the whole solution, the resultant of its whole composition. Mobility, on the other hand, belongs to a single species. It can therefore serve to characterize this species from an analytical point of view, and it can also supply clues as to the structure of this species. Hence mobility is of more immediate interest in the study of the composition of colloidal systems and of the nature of colloidal particles.

For simple cases, as for the association colloids discussed above, conductivity can be interpreted directly. In more complicated systems most interpretations require some information about mobilities. In order to calculate a given mobility from the measured conductivity with the help of the above equation, one requires a knowledge of all the other mobilities and of all the charges and concentrations. Such abundance of information is seldom available in colloidal systems. On the other hand, a direct measurement of mobility gives the desired characteristic without further ado.

Another major factor in the importance of mobility is that, as we shall now see, it is readily interpreted structurally and can be measured even in quite complex systems.

16-3. The Electrokinetic Approach

The term "electrokinetics" could cover, in principle, all phenomena involving both motion and electricity and thus could be synonymous with "electric transport phenomena." In practice it is generally restricted to colloids and surfaces where the following special aspects become important.

In experiments with simple electrolytes it is possible to immobilize the solvent but not the ions of one kind. On the other hand, experiments with immobilized charged surfaces are readily performed and are of great help in the understanding of colloids whose behavior depends on their charged surface.

The charge of simple ions is generally known from chemical considerations and tends to remain constant. Among colloids, chemical considerations are generally of little help and the charge tends to change readily, as we shall see in more detail in the next chapter. Hence the charge of a colloid does not have the same basic importance as that of a simple ion. On the other hand, the potential around a simple ion seems to be of minor importance, whereas among colloids it is highly significant, being sufficient to characterize the structure of the double layer.

Interactions between oppositely charged ions are relatively small among simple electrolytes and can be eliminated by extrapolating to infinite dilution, or calculated by the Debye-Hückel theory for high dilutions. Among colloids, with their high charges, the extrapolation is impractical and the approximation insufficient, so that the interaction with gegenions—the double layer—is ever present. As a result, the experiments are most directly interpreted in terms of the double layer and its potential, as we shall see shortly.

There is, of course, a direct relation between the potential and the charge of the particle, but it involves the knowledge of such factors as the size and shape of the particle and the concentration and valence of all ions in the solution (Section 15-8). Even if these can be taken into account, the calculation is often far from simple (Section 15-10). Hence the electrokinetic approach is primarily concerned with the potential and not with the charge.

16-4. Basis of Electrokinetic Phenomena

Electrokinetic phenomena are based on the fact that, although the diffuse double layer is bound to the charged surface by electric forces which prevent its escape into the bulk of the solution, the main part of this layer is within the free solvent and is capable of moving along the surface. This motion along the surface may be caused either by electric forces acting on the

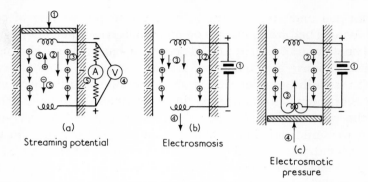

Figure 16-2. Electrokinetic phenomena at a fixed plane. *1* the applied stress; *2* the resulting motion of the double layer or of the solution; *3* the consequent entrainment of the solution or of the double layer; *4* the measured effect of the latter; *5* additional paths of dissipation of potential. *V* voltmeter; *A* ammeter.

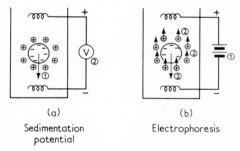

Figure 16-3. Electrokinetic phenomena of particles. *1* the applied stress; *2* the observed effect.

charges or by mechanical forces acting on the liquid and the surface.

One way in which the relative motion may be produced is by fixing the surface and making the liquid flow along it. The liquid then entrains the ions of the double layer, causing a bulk motion of charges, hence a potential (the "streaming potential"), and finally a neutralizing current, carried by the ions in the solution and in the surface, as well as by any outside conductors available (Fig. 16-2a). An alternative but less important way of producing relative motion is to drag the particle through a stationary solution by gravity or centrifugation. The sedimentation potential, which we mentioned in Chapter 14, thus results (Fig. 16-3a).

The application of an electric field along a fixed surface exerts a force on both parts of the double layer. Only the ions of the diffuse part can move under its influence, and they in turn tend to carry the solvent along and thus cause its flow. This is "electroosmosis," which is the reverse of streaming potential (Fig. 16-2b). As in ordinary osmosis, net flow may be prevented by application of proper hydrostatic pressure, and electroosmotic pressure is thus obtained (Fig. 16-2c).

The opposite process, the motion of a surface with respect to an immobile solution can be observed when the surface is that of a particle. In this case the electric field pulls the charged particle in one direction and the counterions in the opposite one so that both move with respect to the observer. This is "electrophoresis" (Fig. 16-3b). The observed velocities measure the electrophoretic mobilities, and among these that of the particle is of particular importance to us.

16-5. The Zeta Potential

Thus we have three principal electrokinetic phenomena: streaming potential, electroosmosis, and electrophoresis, which all depend on the relative motion of the surface and of the diffuse double layer. Obviously, however, only that part of the double layer matters here, which is within the liquid that can flow with respect to the surface. We have already mentioned that the plane of shear is said to delimit this part, and that the potential at this plane is called the ζ potential. Hence electrokinetic experiments can give us information only about the ζ potential and say nothing directly about ψ_0 and ψ_d, although the latter is generally only slightly larger (Section 15-12).

The exact theory of electrokinetic effects involves both the theory of flow and of the double layer, so that it is quite complicated and still incomplete.[1] However, by using the Helmholtz approximation of the structure of the double layer (Fig. 15-8) and assuming that the plane of shear is at the surface, the theory is greatly simplified yet gives considerable insight into the phenomena and indicates how they are related to the ζ potential.

The Helmholtz double layer is analogous to a condenser of two equal and opposite charges separated by the double layer thickness δ.   The charges, in turn, are given by the product of the area times the charge density σ.   The potential of such a condenser is our ζ potential.   According to electrostatics, it varies with the dielectric constant ϑ of the intervening medium and is given by

$$\zeta = 4\pi\sigma\delta/\vartheta \qquad (16\text{-}5.1)$$

This relation permits us to replace the product $\sigma\delta$ which will occur in our considerations by

$$\sigma\delta = \zeta\vartheta/4\pi \qquad (16\text{-}5.2)$$

The product $\sigma\delta$ is called the electric moment per unit surface and is sometimes used in electrokinetic discussions.[2]   It has the advantages of being derived from experiments without any assumptions about the value of the dielectric constant ϑ within the double layer.   Its use may help to emphasize that it is not only the charge density of the particle (σ) but also the spread of the double layer into the solution (δ) that is important in character- izing the double layer.

16-6. Streaming Potential

Theory

Let us consider a tube with a Helmholtz double layer along its walls (Fig. 16-4).

As the liquid is driven through the tube by a pressure P, the flow will be laminar and will obey the equations which we developed for these conditions in Section 12-5.   The mobile charges of the Helmholtz double layer will all be in a single

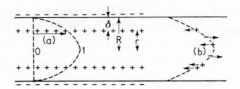

Figure 16-4. The generation of streaming potential. *0* indicates the initial position of a layer of water, *1* its position after a short time of flow. (*a*) shows how the mobile part of the double layer is moved by the flow, (*b*) how the resulting current is neutralized by the motion of all the ions present.

lamella whose velocity depends on its distance δ from the wall. According to Eq. 12-5.5 the velocity of this lamella is given by

$$u = (P/4L\eta)(R^2 - r^2) \qquad (16\text{-}6.1)$$

where L is the length of the capillary, R its radius, and r the distance of the lamella from the center. For this particular lamella $R - r = \delta$. Furthermore, we can generally take δ to be small compared to R. This permits a simplification since $R^2 - r^2 = (R + r)(R - r) = (R + r)\delta \approx 2R\delta$ under these conditions. Hence, the velocity of the ions of the double layer is

$$u = PR\delta/2L\eta \qquad (16\text{-}6.2)$$

The intensity I_f of the electric current produced by this flow of the counterions is the electric charge crossing a cross section of the tube in unit time. If the charge density on the wall is σ, that of the neutralizing layer of ions is $-\sigma$. The perimeter of this layer is $2\pi(R - \delta)$ or, neglecting again δ as small compared to R, it is $2\pi R$. Hence this current is given by

$$I_f = -\sigma 2\pi R(PR\delta/2L\eta) = -\pi R^2 P\sigma\delta/L\eta \qquad (16\text{-}6.3)$$

We see here the appearance of the electric moment $\sigma\delta$, σ stemming from the surface density of the flowing charge and δ from the velocity of its motion. If ζ is now introduced from Eq. 16-5.2, we obtain the equivalent expression

$$I_f = -R^2 P\zeta\vartheta/4L\eta \qquad (16\text{-}6.4)$$

According to the principle of electroneutrality, this current must be neutralized by a current I_n flowing through all the available conductors. By Ohm's law there must therefore be a potential difference E causing this current and given by

$$E = I_n\Omega = -I_f\Omega = R^2 P\zeta\vartheta\Omega/4L\eta \qquad (16\text{-}6.5)$$

where Ω is the net resistance of all the conductors available. This result can be made more specific when there are no conductors except the liquid in the capillary, i.e., when the tube itself is an insulator and the measuring instrument draws no current. (For the opposite extreme, see reference 3.) The resistance of this liquid is inversely proportional to its conductivity $\varkappa$, to its cross section πR^2, and directly to its length L.

$$\Omega = L/\pi R^2 \qquad (16\text{-}6.6)$$

This gives for the streaming potential

$$E = P\zeta\vartheta/4\pi\eta\varkappa \qquad (16\text{-}6.7)$$

in terms of the potential, and

$$E = P\sigma\delta/\eta\varkappa \qquad (16\text{-}6.8)$$

in terms of the electric moment.

In water at 25 °C. Eq. 16-6.7 becomes

$$E = 10^{-5}\zeta P/\varkappa \qquad (16\text{-}6.9)$$

where E and ζ are measured in same units, P in cm. Hg and $\varkappa$ in ohm^{-1} cm.$^{-1}$. For 10^{-3} M KCl $\varkappa = 1.47 \times 10^{-4}$ so that $E = 7.0 \times 10^{-2}P\zeta$. In other words, a pressure of some 15 cm. Hg is required to give a streaming potential equal to the ζ potential in such a solution.

When the conductivity is very low, the streaming potential can reach spectacular heights and cause the formation of sparks. This is the basis for the need to ground trucks which dispense gasoline through a hose.

Experimental

To produce streaming potentials, the solution is pressed by a known pressure through a capillary (Fig. 16-5) or, occasionally, through a diaphragm of compressed particles.   Reversible electrodes close to the ends of the capillary are connected to a potential-measuring instrument of very high resistance.   The resistance of the liquid should be measured in the capillary in order to take into account the contribution to conductivity of the adsorbed ions, or so called "surface conductivity,"[4] which can become important in narrow channels and dilute solutions. Surface conductivity introduces additional complications[5] if the channels of a diaphragm are not very uniform, since it increases the electrical conductance of narrower capillaries relatively more, thus causing electric short circuiting of some parts by others.

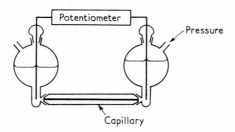

Figure 16-5. Principle of a streaming-potential measurement.

16-7. Electroosmosis

Theory

Again we can consider a capillary with a Helmholtz double layer (Fig. 16-6).   Application of a potential E at its ends creates a pull upon all the counterions.   The counterion layer tends therefore to move as a unit, a smaller tube of counterions within the larger capillary.   This motion is counteracted by the friction within the liquid between the two tubes.   (The streaming potential produced by this motion introduces a correction for "electroviscosity"[6] which we shall neglect.)   When a steady-state is

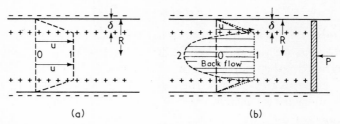

(a)   (b)

Figure 16-6. The generation of electroosmotic flow (a) and of electro-osmotic pressure (b). *0* indicates the initial position of a layer of water, *1* its position after a unit time in the absence of a balancing pressure and *2* in the presence of this pressure. The velocity of electroosmotic flow is given by *u* and its volume by the area between *0* and *1* and also between *1* and *2* in (b).

attained, this friction must be equal to the driving force. The bulk of the liquid in the tube is surrounded completely by the counterions and is carried along at the same rate offering no resistance.

If we consider a unit surface and remember that the thickness of the double layer is very small, we have for the driving force $\sigma E/L$ and for the resisting force $\eta u/\delta$. Hence the terminal velocity is

$$u = \sigma\delta E/L\eta = (\zeta\vartheta/4\pi)E/L\eta \qquad (16\text{-}7.1)$$

the two equivalent expressions being again in terms of the electric moment and of the ζ potential. Since δ is small, this is the velocity with which all the liquid in the tube flows. Hence the volume flowing in time t is

$$V = u\pi R^2 t = (\zeta\vartheta/4\pi)(E/L\eta)\pi R^2 t \qquad (16\text{-}7.2)$$

If this flow is to be prevented, a pressure P must be applied and a return path provided. If the tube itself is the only return path, this pressure is given by Poiseuille's law (Eq. 12-5.8)

$$V = (\pi/8)PR^4 t/L\eta \qquad (16\text{-}7.3)$$

since the volume flowing by electroosmosis must all return by laminar flow (Fig. 16-6). Comparison of the two equations gives

$$P = (\zeta\vartheta/4\pi)8E/R^2 \qquad (16\text{-}7.4)$$

For water at 25 °C. when the potentials are measured in volts, pressures in centimeters of Hg, and the radius and length in centimeters, this becomes

$$u = 7.8 \times 10^{-3}\ \zeta\ E/L \text{ cm./sec.} \qquad (16\text{-}7.5)$$

$$P = 4.2 \times 10^{-8}\ \zeta E/R^2 \text{ cm. Hg} \qquad (16\text{-}7.6)$$

Thus for a ζ potential of 100 mv., about 1500 v./cm. would be required to give a velocity of 1 cm./sec., and 1 v. can give pressures of 1 cm. Hg only in capillaries of slightly less than 1 μ in radius.

Experimental

It is generally the rate of flow which is measured in an apparatus such as shown in Fig. 16-7. The potential is supplied by

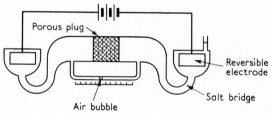

Figure 16-7. Principle of electroosmotic flow measurement. The capillary with the moving air bubble provides the principal path for return flow. Note that one end of the apparatus is closed.

reversible electrodes and salt bridges, and the transport of liquid across the capillary or diaphragm is measured by the motion of an air bubble in a capillary providing the main return path.

16-8. Electrophoresis

Theory

In electroosmosis the surface is immobilized, hence the liquid moves upon application of an electric field. In electrophoresis, the opposite is true, but it is caused by the same forces and opposed by the same resistances, so that the relative velocity must still be given by Eq. 16-7.1, which we may rewrite as

$$u = (1/4)(\zeta\vartheta/\pi)(E/L)(1/\eta) \tag{16-8.1}$$

In electroosmosis the velocity of the bulk liquid is equal to that of the counterions.   In the present case the bulk liquid is immobile, hence this relative velocity is also the electrophoretic velocity of the particle.

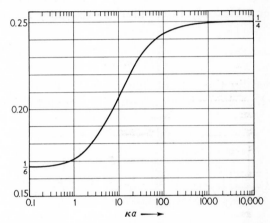

Figure 16-8. The variation of the numerical factor in the equation for electrophoretic velocity (Eq. 16-8.1) with particle radius a and double-layer thickness $1/\kappa$.   Note that the change occurs mainly between κa values of 1 and 100.   (*After D. C. Henry, Proc. Roy. Soc. (London),* **A133,** *106 (1931).*)

In the derivation of the above equation, we neglected the curvature of the surface and of the double layer and any end effects.   It is therefore strictly applicable only to cases where the thickness of the double layer is really quite small in comparison, with the radius (κa of the order of 100 or more).   The effect of the curvature has been computed[7] and turns out to amount to only 33% at most, changing gradually the one-fourth factor to one-sixth when the double layer thickness becomes of the same order as, or larger than, the radius.   Figure 16-8 shows this variation.

We can also note that the diffuse double layer cannot stay concentric with the particle as it moves, but must lag behind because of the time required for it to re-form, by conduction and diffusion.   The lagging, oppositely charged double layer exerts a retarding force on the particle.   This is generally called the "relaxation effect."[8]   This effect can be neglected when considering a tube or a very elongated particle because it would be noticeable only at the ends, but it can become significant for spherical particles.   The magnitude of this relaxation effect has been calculated approximately for this case[9] and has been found marked mainly for high ζ potentials and for intermediate κa values between about 1 and 10.

Thus, as could be anticipated, the theory of electrophoresis of colloidal particles is more complicated than that of streaming potential or electroosmosis in capillaries, although the principles are essentially the same.   Yet the electrophoresis is the only one strictly applicable to colloidal particles.

Although the relation between the electrophoretic velocity u and ζ is thus more complicated than suggested by Eq. 16-8.1, there is no doubt that for usual values, u is strictly proportional to E/L, the applied potential gradient.   For this reason, electrophoretic results are generally expressed in terms of electrophoretic mobility $v = u/(E/L)$, i.e., the velocity in a potential gradient of 1 v./cm.

On the basis of Eq. 16-8.1 we can write for the mobility

$$v = \zeta \vartheta / 4\pi\eta \qquad (16\text{-}8.2)$$

or conversely

$$\zeta = (4\pi\eta/\vartheta)v \qquad (16\text{-}8.3)$$

In most cases, electrophoretic mobility is of the order of 10^{-4} cm.^{2}/v.-sec.   It is therefore conveniently expressed in such units, which are also equal to $(\mu/\text{sec.})/(\text{v./cm.})$ or μ-cm./v.-sec.   Expressing v in these units and ζ in millivolts, the above equations become for water at 25 °C.

$$v = 7.8 \times 10^{-2}\zeta \qquad \text{and} \qquad \zeta = 13v \qquad (16\text{-}8.4)$$

For ordinary ions, the mobility varies between about 5 and 11 μ-cm./v.-sec.   (At infinite dilution: $H^+ = 36.6$, $Cl^- = -7.9$, $Na^+ = 5.2$, $Li^+ = 4.0$).   For colloids, it ranges from close to zero for low ζ potentials to about 1 for proteins and about 6 for micelles and AgI suspensions.   For emulsions of a hydrocarbon in dilute base, values of 12 μ-cm./v.-sec have been reported.[10] Thus, if we calculate ζ potentials on the basis of Eq. 16-8.4, we obtain values of about 13–70 and up to some 160 mv.   This equation being most valid for low potentials (proteins) and large particles (emulsion), these extreme values can be taken as about correct.   In the case of the small particles of high mobility (micelles and AgI), the equation should not be applied without corrections, and their ζ potentials are in fact some 50–100% higher, i.e., about 130 mv.

Experimental

Observation of electrophoresis always involves the application of an electric potential to a solution supported by a solid. This leads to two complications.   One is the presence of electro-osmosis, which tends to cause a flow of the solution as a whole if possible, or a flow of the center in the opposite direction to that at the walls.   The other complication is Joule heating by the passing current, and the consequent necessity of dissipating this heat.   Dissipation of heat requires temperature gradients to which correspond density differences which in turn tend to cause convection currents.

A large number of techniques have been developed to deal with these difficulties.[11]   We can examine some of the principles involved in terms of three main groups: the microscopic electrophoresis (often called microelectrophoresis) methods, the moving boundary frontal methods, and the anticonvectant electrophoresis zonal methods.

16-9. Microscopic or Microelectrophoresis

The electrophoretic mobility of particles which are large enough to be perceptible with a microscope can be determined

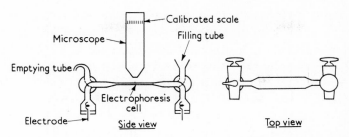

Figure 16-9. Principle of a microscopic method of measuring electrophoretic mobilities.

directly, by observation of the motion in a small horizontal flat cell[12] connected to two electrodes (Fig. 16-9). The rate of motion is measured by timing the passage of a particle across a few microns on an ocular scale.   The electric field is computed from the measured current intensity, the known dimensions of the cell, and the separately determined conductivity of the solution. In this microelectrophoretic method, convection currents are negligible because of the small height of the cell, but electro-osmosis is very important.   The liquid near the walls streams in one direction, while in the middle it streams in the other, as already shown in Fig. 16-6.   There are, therefore, two layers which are immobile.   A relatively simple calculation shows that these are located at 21.2% of the total height from each wall[13] for an infinitely wide cell.   Hence very wide cells are generally used, and measurements are made at these levels.

16-10. Moving Boundary Methods

For particles which cannot be individually perceived, one faces the same problem as in the determination of transference of simple electrolytes, and one must depend on the detection of the movement of macroscopic amounts by indirect methods.   The Hittorf method is seldom, if ever, used, because of its inherent difficulty and the added problem of finding reversible electrodes for the colloid.   The moving boundary method, on the other hand, has been widely adapted.

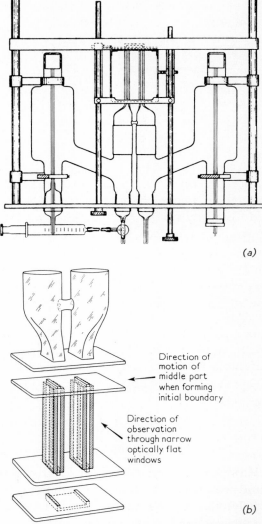

(a)

Direction of
motion of
middle part
when forming
initial boundary

Direction of
observation
through narrow
optically flat
windows

(b)

Figure 16-10. Cell of the Tiselius apparatus for electrophoresis. (a) Over-
all view showing the electrode compartments, mechanism for making boundary
by shearing and syringe for shifting it. (*From L. G. Longworth, Chem. Revs.*, **30,**
225 (*1942*).) (b) Detail of central part. The cell is kept near 2°C. and the
boundaries are observed by a schlieren method.

The most commonly used type of apparatus is shown in Fig. 16-10. It was developed by the Swedish biochemist Tiselius. The solution containing the colloid is denser than the other solution and is therefore at the bottom of a U-tube connected to two large electrode vessels. This permits the passage of considerable current before electrode products affect the solution. The cross section of the U-tube is very elongated (Fig. 16-10b). It has provisions for forming a sharp boundary by shearing along its narrow dimension. The motion of the boundary is observed at right angles to the shearing direction, generally by a schlieren method. This gives the rate of electrophoresis directly. Ascending and descending boundaries can be observed in the opposite arms of the U-tube. Disturbance of the boundary by electroosmosis is prevented by the density difference, which is kept sufficient to confine electroosmotic flow to each solution separately. In other words, the density difference provides the electroosmotic pressure. The effects of Joule heating are minimized by the narrowness of the U-tube, by operation at a temperature near that of the maximum density, and by limits on the applied potential.

A complication generally present in moving boundary experiments stems from the difference in conductivity and therefore in potential gradient at each boundary.[14] These "boundary anomalies" can often be minimized by making all solutions as equal as possible and limiting the concentration, and hence the conductivity contribution, of the colloidal ions. In some cases these difficulties can be completely avoided by using a tagging technique to form a boundary between two essentially identical solutions. However, this removes also the stabilizing density differences and requires a complete redesign of the apparatus.[15]

If the particles studied have different mobilities, each will form a boundary moving with a corresponding speed. Hence, the method may be used for analyzing and characterizing mixtures. It is a frontal method, however, so that it can be used for separating completely only the fastest and the slowest components.

16-11. Anticonvectant Electrophoresis

In the typical moving boundary method, convection is avoided by the density differences at each boundary, the density increasing with concentration towards the bottom of the U-tube.   If one wishes to obtain each component of a mixture as a separate zone, other means for preventing convection must be used.

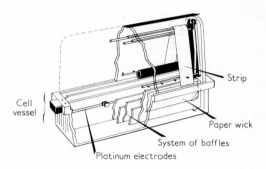

Cell vessel
Strip
Paper wick
System of baffles
Platinum electrodes

Figure 16-11. A paper electrophoresis apparatus.   One of several strips of paper is shown.   It is supported by a removable frame which supports it also during drying and staining.   The sample is applied at the top.   The strip rests on wicks dipping into electrolyte in a baffled compartment leading to platinum electrodes.   (*Courtesy Spinco division, Beckman Instruments, Palo Alto, Calif.*)

Thus, electrophoresis can be conducted in a medium stabilized by a density gradient produced by the addition of sugar or the like.[16]   Generally, convection is prevented by entrapping the solution in a porous matrix, the anticonvectant.   Filter paper is by far the most widely used anticonvectant, and one generally speaks of paper electrophoresis.[17]

Paper electrophoresis uses very simple equipment, such as the apparatus shown in Fig. 16-11, and the procedure is also straightforward.   Basically, a strip of filter paper is saturated with a conducting solution, a very small amount of the colloid is deposited as a spot or stripe, and the potential is applied between the ends of the paper which are in contact with electrode vessels.   After some time, during which each component has moved along the paper through a distance determined primarily by its electro-

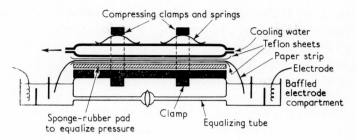

Figure 16-12. Principle of another type of paper electrophoresis cell Evaporation is prevented by compressing the filter paper between two teflon sheets. (*Based on materials courtesy Dr. S. M. Raymond, E-C Apparatus Co., Swarthmore, Pa.*)

phoretic mobility, the current is stopped and the position of the spots or stripes on the paper detected by appropriate methods— color reactions, radioactive counting, etc.—just as in chromatography.

The method has the advantages of being simple and using only minute amounts of materials, which makes it of great value in analytical and micropreparative work and accounts for its wide routine clinical applications. But it is not well suited for absolute determinations of mobility, because of the complexity of processes occurring during electrophoresis. Thus, the flow of current and of the ions does not follow straight lines but a tortuous path among the fibers of the paper; this can be corrected for by using a pilot ion of known mobility. The filter paper does not immobilize the solvent as far as electroosmotic flow is concerned, and the applied potential generally causes a significant flow of solvent, so that only differences of mobility are generally obtained unless an immobile component, such as sugar, is added to the mixture. The paper is often not completely inert but may adsorb the ions and thus reduce their mobility, just as it reduces their motion in chromatography. This can be obviated or reduced by proper choice of solvent, but is not easy to establish. Joule heating is an important factor and, if the paper has an exposed surface, it leads to evaporation of water, hence to flow of solution from the ends towards the center. This results in a gradual increase in the concentration of simple electrolytes and therefore in a reduced potential gradient. These factors tend to reduce the rate of motion with time and towards the ends of the paper and may even lead to a reversal of motion. Evaporation can be prevented by enclosing the strip between impervious, preferably nonwettable (teflon) surfaces (Fig. 16-12) or by submerging it in an insulating liquid.

Summary

Electrokinetic phenomena—streaming potential, electro-osmosis and electroosmotic pressure, and electrophoresis—all depend on the same property of the surface, the ability of the double layer to participate in the flow of the liquid with respect to this surface. This can be expressed as the electric moment or as the ζ potential of the surface. These in turn are related to the surface charge density and to the composition of the solution. The electrophoretic mobility of a colloidal ion can serve as a basis for characterizing it, for separating it, and for estimating the ζ potential describing its double layer. A variety of experimental methods have been developed for these purposes.

References

1. J. Th. G. Overbeek in H. Mark and E. J. W. Verwey, eds., *Advances in Colloid Science*, Vol. III, Interscience Publishers, Inc., New York, 1950.
2. L. A. Wood, *J. Am. Chem. Soc.*, **68,** 432 (1946).
3. R. M. Hurd and N. Hackerman, *J. Electrochem. Soc.*, **102,** 594 (1955); **103,** 316,700 (1956); A. S. Buchanan and E. Heyman, *J. Colloid Sci.*, **4,** 157 (1949).
4. J. Th. G. Overbeek in H. R. Kruyt, *Colloid Science*, Vol. I, Elsevier, New York, 1952, p. 235.
5. J. Th. G. Overbeek and P. W. O. Wijga, *Rec. trav. chim.*, **65,** 556 (1946); A. J. Rutgers and R. Jansen, *Trans. Faraday Soc.*, **51,** 830 (1955).
6. G. A. H. Elton, *Proc. Roy. Soc. (London)*, **A194,** 259 (1948).

7. D. C. Henry, *Proc. Roy. Soc. (London)*, **A133,** 106 (1931).

8. L. Onsager, *Physik. Z.*, **28,** 277 (1928); outlined in, e.g., D. A. MacInnes, *Principles of Electrochemistry*, Reinhold Publishing Corp., New York, 1939, p. 326; or in R. A. Robinson and R. H. Stokes, *Electrolyte Solutions*, Butterworths Scientific Publications, London, 1955, pp. 128 ff.

9. J. Th. G. Overbeek, *Kolloid Beih.*, **54,** 287 (1943); F. Booth, *Proc. Roy. Soc. (London)*, **A203,** 514 (1950).

10. A. J. Taylor and F. W. Wood, *Trans. Faraday Soc.*, **53,** 529 (1957); this reference also discusses possible corrections for the fluidity of the particle.

11. R. Audubert and S. de Mende, *Principes de l'Electrophorese*, Presses Universitaires, Paris, 1957.

12. H. A. Abramson, L. S. Moyer, and M. H. Gorin, *Electrophoresis of Proteins*, Reinhold Publishing Corp., New York, 1942, p. 45; D. R. Briggs, *Ind. Eng. Chem. (Anal. Ed.)*, **12,** 703 (1940).

13. M. Smoluchowski, ref. 1 of Chap. 15; H. A. Abramson, *Electrokinetic Phenomena*, Chemical Catalog Co. (Reinhold), New York, 1934, p. 70.

14. V. P. Dole, *J. Am. Chem. Soc.*, **67,** 1119 (1945); R. A. Alberty, *J. Chem. Educ.*, **25,** 619 (1948).

15. H. W. Hoyer, K. J. Mysels, and D. Stigter, *J. Phys. Chem.*, **58,** 385 (1954).

16. M. K. Brakke, *Arch. Biochem. and Biophys.*, **55,** 175 (1955); A. Kolin, *J. Phys. Chem.*, **22,** 1628 (1954).

17. R. J. Block, E. L. Durrum, and G. Zweig, *Paper Chromatography and Paper Electrophoresis*, Academic Press, Inc., New York, 1955.

Problems

79. If streaming potentials cause corrosion of a pipeline, it may be advisable to (*1*) introduce magnesium plugs into the pipe at regular intervals, (*2*) increase the conductivity of the liquid, (*3*) reduce the ζ potential between pipe and liquid, (*4*) increase the pipe diameter for the same delivery rate, (*5*) all of these, (*6*) none of these.

73. Evaporation will have the greater effect on electrophoretic mobility in paper electrophoresis if (*1*) the concentration of buffer is higher, (*2*) the time of the experiment is shorter, (*3*) the paper is thinner, (*4*) all of these, (*5*) none of these.

95. The cross section of a Tiselius electrophoresis cell is that of a narrow rectangle. This offers the advantage of (*1*) providing a larger optical path for a given volume of solution, (*2*) permitting the formation of a sheared boundary by a short motion which gives a sharp boundary, (*3*) providing a large periphery for a given cross section so that heating effects are minimized, (*4*) all of these, (*5*) none of these.

97. If electrophoretic mobility is computed from measurements performed in the middle of a microelectrophoretic cell, the result will be (*1*) too high, (*2*) correct, (*3*) too low, (*4*) depends on the relative signs of the charge on the particle and on the cell wall.

94. Electrokinetic phenomena depend most directly on (*1*) the charge and thickness of the double layer beyond the plane of shear, (*2*) the primary charge density of the particle, (*3*) the presence of simple salt in the system, (*4*) charge of the Stern layer.

74. By referring to the data given in this chapter and assuming that the theory of electrophoretic mobility applies to simple ions, one can readily calculate that as a first approximation the ζ potential of the Cl^- ion is about —— mv.

124. A better approximation to the answer of problem 74 would be —— mv.

129. Electroosmotic phenomena are sometimes used in construction work when the seepage of water is stemmed and the soil made firmer by the passage of electric current between properly placed electrodes. The economics of this method become more favorable when the (*1*) water is brackish, (*2*) structure of the soil is coarser, (*3*) ζ potential of the soil particles is larger, (*4*) all of these.

CHAPTER XVII

Some Charge Effects in Colloids

In the past three chapters we have reviewed successively the effects of charges in some macroscopic transport and equilibrium phenomena, the structure of the double layer around a particle, and the information gained from electrokinetic experiments. We shall now conclude the study of charge effects by considering how colloidal ions become charged and how they interact with other ions, both ordinary and colloidal. We will look at the interaction with different ions and with similar ions and even at the interaction of an ion with itself. The main macroscopic phenomena which we will thus cover are flocculation by added electrolytes, which we have mentioned often previously, ion exchange, such as that used in the treatment of water, the unusual viscosities exhibited by long chain ions, the so-called polyelectrolytes, and the swelling of electrolytic gels.

17-1. The Origin of the Primary Charge

Thus far we have spoken of a charged plane, particle, or surface without inquiring into the origin and nature of the charge. Since our systems are always conducting to some extent and neutral as a whole, the excess or deficiency of electrons on a particle must be chemically stabilized, that is, must be present in the form of ions. These ions, in turn, must be attached to the particle considered. Overall electrostatic forces cannot be responsible for the attachment of these charges to the particle, because before acquiring its first charge the particle is neutral, and once it has acquired the first charge it becomes similarly charged and can only exert electrostatic repulsion on any additional charge. Hence other forces—covalent bonding, van der Waals' forces, or highly

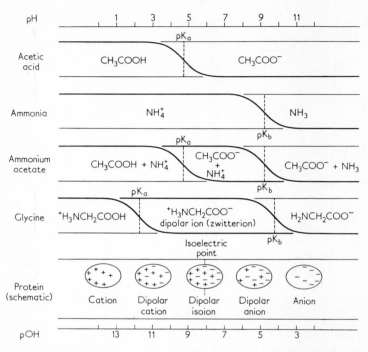

Figure 17-1. The variation of charge with pH for a protein and for some simpler systems. The formation of dipolar ions and the acquisition of net charge by a protein involves the same principles as the ionization of simple acids and bases.

localized electrostatic ones—must be responsible for charges of colloidal particles. The details of this picture are sometimes quite clear but often still unknown. We will briefly review a few examples.

Proteins are formed by long chains of amino acids joined by peptide linkages. Some of these amino acids carry an additional carboxyl or amino group, and these may remain free and exposed to the solvent. Thus they can form COO^- and NH_3^+ ions which are covalently attached to the particle. The degree of ionization of these groups is not greatly influenced by their incorporation into the large molecule; they behave essentially

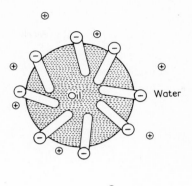

Figure 17-2. An oil droplet can acquire a charge by adsorption of amphipathic ions through van der Waals' forces.

like the ions of ammonium acetate would behave at the same pH. The carboxyl group tends to ionize at pH values above about 4, and the amino group below about 10. Hence, in acid solutions the particle becomes positively charged because of the presence of NH_3^+ and COOH groups, and in basic solution it becomes negatively charged because of NH_2 and COO^- groups (Fig. 17-1). Near neutrality, both NH_3^+ and COO^- groups are present, so that the net charge is small. In fact, there must be a pH value, called the isoelectric point, at which the net charge is zero. This corresponds to the presence of equal amounts of oppositely charged groups on the particle. Such a neutral structure of charged groups is called a dipolar ion or, from the German, a zwitterion.

There are porous solids which have built-in acidic or basic groups. These include some naturally occurring silicates, particularly the zeolites with SiO^- groups exposed, and many synthetic materials. The latter are generally based on crosslinked long chains, an insoluble network, to which are attached ionizing groups. These can be either weakly acidic carboxyl groups or strongly acidic sulfonic acid groups, or weakly basic amino groups or strongly basic quaternary ammonium groups. The ionization of these groups gives these solids a charge which has to be neutralized by counterions in their immediate vicinity.

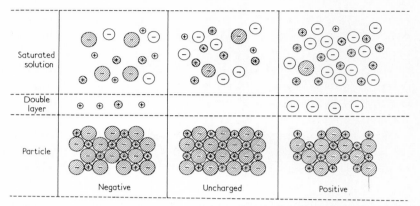

Figure 17-3. Schematic presentation of the variation of charge of an AgI particle with the concentration of potential-determining ions in the saturated solution.   The concentrations of the Ag^+ and I^- ions in solution change from left to right while their product remains constant.   Note that ions are missing from the lattice of the charged particles.

Because of their insolubility these solids are used widely for re-moving certain ions from solutions and are called ion exchangers. We shall shortly return to their mode of action.

Thus, in these two cases, the charge-giving ions are clearly held by covalent bonds.

Tiny crystals of gold, produced by sudden chilling of gold vapor from an electric arc, adsorb hydroxyl and chloride ions very strongly, presumably forming a surface complex analogous to $AuCl_4^-$, and thus acquire a negative charge by chemisorption.

The water–oil interface adsorbs ions with long hydrophobic tails, such as fatty acids, long chain sulfonates or sulfates, etc. Thus, droplets of emulsions acquire a charge by adsorption of such ions upon their surface (Fig. 17-2) which is based on purely van der Waals' forces.

Minute crystals of AgI can be in equilibrium with a saturated solution in which the product of the two ionic concentrations is roughly 10^{-16}.   The two ions differ greatly, however, in the strength with which they are held in the lattice, the more polariz-able iodide being held more strongly despite its larger size.

Hence, when the concentrations of the two ions in solution are equal, the Ag^+ ions escape more readily and the particle is charged negatively (Fig. 17-3).   It is not until the Ag^+ concentration is increased to somewhat above 10^{-6} and the I^- concentration correspondingly lowered somewhat below 10^{-10} that the crystal becomes neutral.   At higher concentrations of Ag^+ and lower of I^-, it becomes positively charged.

Here, it is the fitting of an ion into the localized electric field of the surface of the crystal that seems to be responsible for the specific interaction causing the adsorption and giving the charge to the particle.

17-2. The Magnitude of the Charge

The above examples illustrate that the attachment of an ion to a surface is always due to a specific interaction.   In a few cases the primary charge is thus determined by the nature of the particle, and substantially without regard to the composition of the solution.   This is the case of an ion exchanger with strongly acidic groups.   These are always fully ionized and thus give a constant primary charge to the particle.

In other cases, however, the charge varies and is mainly determined by an equilibrium between certain ions at the surface and in the solution.   Thus, the charge of AgI crystals must depend on the concentration of Ag^+ ions in the solution, and the charge of a protein on the pH of the solution (Figs. 17-1 and 17-3).   The charge is always limited to some extent by the nature of the particle.   For example, after the pH has been lowered sufficiently to attach an H^+ ion to each polar group of a protein, no further increase in charge is likely.   Similarly, one cannot imagine more than a monomolecular layer of extra Ag^+ ions on an AgI crystal.

Within these chemical limits, however, and in addition to them, there is another factor which determines the charge attached to a particle by the specific interactions.   This is the repulsion exerted by the charge itself.

To see how this comes about let us consider an AgI particle in
the presence of excess Ag^+ ions.   The charge on its surface is the
result of a dynamic equilibrium as some Ag^+ ions leave the surface by thermal agitation while others deposit on it from the solution.   As in all such dynamic adsorption equilibria, it is the concentration of the depositing species, the Ag^+ ions, that plays a
major role.   If this concentration is increased, the amount adsorbed at equilibrium will be larger.   The adsorption of the Ag^+
ions leads, however, to a local disturbance of electroneutrality,
the particle becoming positive as more Ag^+ ions attach themselves to it.   This makes it more difficult for additional ions to
deposit on and makes it easier for the adsorbed ones to leave the
surface.   The measure of the extra electric energy required for
depositing, or gained by leaving, is, by definition, the potential
ψ_0 of the surface.

Equilibrium involves, therefore, not only the concentration of
Ag^+ ions in the solution and on the surface, but also the potential.
If the concentration in the solution is changed, the amount adsorbed, and hence the potential, will change until equilibrium is
restored.   Conversely, if the potential is changed at constant Ag^+
ion concentration in the solution, adsorption will also change in
the direction of restoring the potential.   Inspection of Fig. 15-14
shows clearly how addition of any inert electrolyte reduces the
potential if the charge (absorption) remains constant.   As discussed in Section 15-8, this is due primarily to the decrease of the
double layer thickness, δ (Fig. 15-11).   Hence, such addition
makes it easier for ions to deposit from the solution and harder
for them to leave the surface, with a resulting increase of their
number in the surface and a corresponding growth of the charge
until the rising potential restores a steady-state.

Thus, as long as the concentration of the Ag^+ ions in solution
remains the same, it is the potential of the surface which tends to
remain the same, and the charge adapts itself to this requirement.   On the other hand, a change in the concentration of the
Ag^+ ions changes this ψ_0 potential.   For this reason, Ag^+ (or I^-)
ions are called the "potential-determining" ions in this case.

The role of potential-determining ions becomes particularly clear if we consider a silver electrode in a solution of Ag^+ ions. From Nernst's law we know that its potential depends only on the $[Ag^+]$, which are, therefore, the potential-determining ions. We also know that this potential is independent of the presence of other inert salts (except for minor activity corrections). This electrode potential must vary in the same way as the ψ_0 of the electrode surface for the process of crossing this surface should not depend on the nature of the solution (Section 15-12). Again, Figs. 15-14 and 15-15 show that, at constant charge, ψ_0 is very sensitive to the concentration and valence of the other electrolytes. But, in order for the electrode potential to remain unaffected, ψ_0 has to remain constant. These "inert" salts therefore must greatly change the charge density of the electrode, i.e., the number of potential-determining Ag^+ ions adsorbed on it.

17-3. Stabilizing Effect of Charge[1]

In discussing stability, we considered in Section 4-13 the case of diuturnal colloids whose particles tend to attract each other with short range van der Waals' forces but are prevented by electric interactions from getting close enough to each other for these forces to become effective. We are now in a position to consider somewhat more in detail the question of these repulsive forces.

A particle with its double layer is electrically neutral, so that it exerts no net coulombic force upon another. This is the situation at sufficiently large distances between particles. As the particles approach, however, the double layers interpenetrate and interact. When the two surfaces finally touch, there can be no more diffuse layer in between. It is the work required to thus distort and finally destroy a part of the diffuse double layer which causes most of the repulsion.

The details of the destruction of the diffuse double layer are not completely clear and may vary considerably from case to case. Some possibilities are shown schematically in Fig. 17-4. One, indicated by (a), is that the gegenions are simply pushed

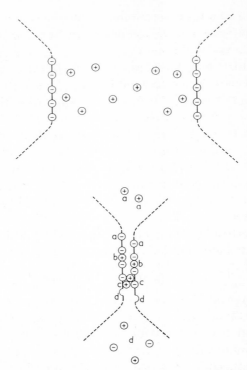

Figure 17-4. Schematic fates of double layer ions of two particles (*above*) during flocculation (*below*). (*a*) The counterions alone are squeezed out; (*b*) the counterions enter the surface; (*c*) the counterions enter the Stern layer; (*d*) the counterions are squeezed out along with some of the ions originally charging the surface.

out into the bulk of the solution and their screening removed, leaving two charged surfaces repelling each other. This, however, would create large local potential differences, and can account for only a small number of counterions. In order to destroy the double layer without producing such large potentials, the counterions must either be driven into the surface (b) or its Stern layer (c), or must leave along with similiions removed from the surface (d). Thus, in the case of a surface whose charge is due to COO⁻ groups, one can expect that these will be neutralized by the squeezed-in counterions; whereas, in the case of

Ag$^+$-charged surface, one may expect the passage of many Ag$^+$ ions from the surface into the bulk solution along with the squeezed-out counterions.

Whatever the particular details of the mechanism of destruction of the double layer, it involves the overcoming of forces, electrical and others, which were originally responsible for the formation and existence of the double layer.   The more counterions involved, the greater the work of disposing of them and the stronger the resulting repulsion between the particles.   The further out the double layer extends, the greater the distance at which this repulsion becomes important.

As mentioned above, the attractive van der Waals' forces extend over a short range only, but they do extend into the solution. In order to prevent them from causing flocculation, it is most important to prevent an approach to within their effective range because at closer range much larger repulsions become necessary.   The effectiveness of the repelling forces in preventing flocculation increases, therefore, not only with their intensity but also with their extension into the solution.   Hence, stability will tend to increase with both the potential and the thickness of the diffuse double layer, i.e., with both ψ_d and δ.

Increasing ψ_d and increasing δ both tend to increase the ζ potential of the particle (Fig. 15-18).   Therefore, stability correlates to some extent with this potential.   Exact correlation would be expected only if the ζ potential were measured at the point where the attractive forces become effective, at the hump of the potential energy curve (Fig. 4-4).   It is likely, however, that the attractive forces extend appreciably beyond the plane of shear at which ζ is measured, so that this measurement is not a completely reliable indication of stability.

We can now consider some aspects of the flocculating action of electrolytes and interpret them in terms of the above ideas.

17-4. Flocculation Value

The transition from a diuturnal to a caducous system is a gradual one, since it depends greatly on the time of observation and the sensitivity of the method of observation.   Under standard conditions, however, a system can generally be classified as one which is flocculating (or has flocculated) or one which appears fully dispersed.   Thus, starting with an apparently stable colloid, one can vary conditions and determine the point at which it becomes clearly unstable.

One of the common ways of performing such an experiment is to prepare a series of test tubes containing equal portions of a sol and add to each, with vigorous stirring, a different and gradually increasing amount of a solution of a simple electrolyte. After some time of resting, the mixtures are again agitated, and, after another short period of rest, they are observed for signs of flocculation.

The tubes can then be classified into two groups, one showing no sign of flocculation and the other showing at least some such signs; alternatively, they may be classified into one showing complete flocculation and the other at least some deflocculated material.   In either case the separation between the two classes is generally quite sharp, and, by repeating the experiment with a narrower range of additions, one can generally establish quite precisely the limiting concentration at which the system becomes unstable.   The intermediate agitation serves to destroy the weakest interparticle bonds and to bring small particles in contact with larger ones, both factors increasing the sharpness of separation between flocculated and unflocculated systems.

The limiting concentration, thus established, is called the "flocculation value" of the additive.   Although, as already stated, the absolute magnitude of the flocculation value varies greatly with experimental conditions and is therefore of minor significance, the relative ranking of various flocculating agents and the approximate orders of magnitude are quite significant.

The sharpness with which flocculation values can be determined corresponds to the great effect at this point of a small increment of electrolyte upon flocculation.   The reason for this lies in the large magnitude of both the attractive and repulsive energies. They just balance each other at the flocculation value, and a small percentage change in the repulsive forces caused by the increment of salt can shift the balance completely, i.e., produce a change large compared to kT in the hump of the potential energy (Fig. 4-4).

17-5. Nonspecific Flocculation

Let us first consider the case where there is no specific interaction between the added electrolyte and the particle.   The added electrolyte simply supplies the counterions and similiions in the bulk of the solution (or increases their concentration), and these enter into the double layer and determine its nature.

If there is truly no interaction with the particle (Fig. 17-5), its charge remains constant, but the thickness of the double layer will decrease and the potential will drop, according to Figs. 15-11 and 15-14.   Hence, flocculation will be facilitated.   Furthermore, these effects will greatly increase if the valence of the electrolyte, particularly the valence of the gegenion, increases, as shown by Figs. 15-12 and 15-15.   Hence, to obtain the same ease of flocculation, a much lower concentration will be required for divalent counterions than for monovalent ones, and a still lower for trivalent ones.

Such an ideal case is not readily observable, however, because of the ubiquitous presence of the potential-determining ions whose ionization or adsorption is responsible in the first place for the charge of the particle.   We have seen above that as the potential is lowered by the added electrolyte, these ions tend to restore it to the original value.

The maintenance of a more or less constant potential by the potential-determining ions does not affect the decrease of the thickness of the double layer caused by the addition of the electrolyte nor the significance of valence in the process.   Hence, we can still expect a corresponding decrease in the ζ potential, which is measured at the plane of shear and therefore somewhat away from the particle (Fig. 17-6).   We can also expect a great effect upon the ease of flocculation and upon flocculation

SCHEMATIC EFFECT OF ADDITION OF SALT UPON THE DOUBLE LAYER AND
ITS RELATION TO THE "RANGE" OF VAN DER WAALS ATTRACTION.

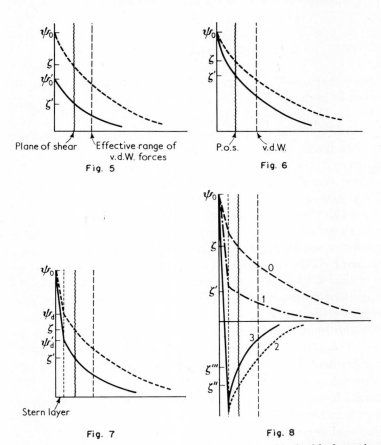

Fig. 5

Fig. 6

Fig. 7

Fig. 8

Figure 17-5. In the absence of any interaction, the double layer is compressed and both ψ_0 and ζ are lowered.

Figure 17-6. In the diffuse double layer, if ψ_0 is maintained constant, the double layer is compressed and, therefore, ζ is lowered.

Figure 17-7. In the presence of a Stern layer, and with constant ψ_0, ζ is lowered by both a lower ψ_d and a compression of the double layer.

Figure 17-8. An adsorbed polyvalent counterion causes the original potential (0) to decrease until the first flocculation value is reached (1). This is followed by a reversal of sign giving the second stability region (2) and finally by the second flocculation value (3) as the double layer is compressed.

values, since these are primarily determined by the distance to which the repulsion is effective.

The effect of the potential-determining ions is to some extent neutralized by the existence of the Stern layer, which can be counted as part of the particle when considering either the ζ potential or flocculation. As the concentration of gegenions increases, more of them are adsorbed in the Stern layer, according to simple laws of equilibrium. Thus, although ψ_0 may remain constant, ψ_d decreases, and ζ decreases even more, as shown in Fig. 17-7. As the valence of counterions increases, the attractive force increases also, while thermal agitation remains the same and adsorption is greatly favored.

17-6. Schulze-Hardy Rule

Although the flocculation effect of electrolytes is not so simple as one might at first expect for the absence of specific interaction, it is clear from the above discussion that addition of electrolytes must tend to change diuturnal systems to caducous ones, and that valence must have a great effect. Table 17-1 shows clearly how large this effect really is and that it is confined to the counterions. Thus, for the negative As_2S_3 sol, essentially the same concentration of Na^+ or K^+ ions is required whether they are used as chlorides, nitrates, or sulfates, whereas Ca^{2+}, Mg^{2+}, and Ba^{2+} also differ little from each other but suffice in about one-hundredth of the amount required for monovalent ions. Trivalent aluminum and cerium are as effective at concentrations almost another ten times lower, but their action probably involves other factors, as we shall shortly see.

This great effect of valence of the counterions upon flocculation is called the Schulze-Hardy rule, after the men who first emphasized it. It is a most effective basic tool in the control of dispersion and flocculation in sols, suspensions, and emulsions. Its effects are seen in soil conditioning, in the control of consistency of drilling muds and of other clay systems, in many filtration and precipitation procedures, etc.

TABLE 17-1

Flocculation Values of Some Simple Electrolytes[a]

Negatively charged As_2S_3			Positively Charged Fe_2O_3		
Salt added	Millimoles per liter	Relative conc.	Salt added	Millimoles per liter	Relative conc.
NaCl	51	100	NaCl	9.25	100
KCl	49.5	97	KCl	9.0	97
KNO_3	50	98	$^1/_2 BaCl_2$	9.6	104
$^1/_2 K_2SO_4$	65.5	128	KNO_3	12	130
LiCl	58	107			
			K_2SO_4	0.205	2.22
$MgCl_2$	0.72	1.41	$K_2Cr_2O_7$	0.195	2.12
$MgSO_4$	0.81	1.55	Tl_2SO_4	0.22	2.38
$CaCl_2$	0.65	1.28			
$ZnCl_2$	0.68	1.32			
$AlCl_3$	0.093	0.182			
$Al(NO_3)_3$	0.095	0.186			
$Ce(NO_3)_3$	0.080	0.156			

[a] After J. Th. G. Overbeek, in H. R. Kruyt, ed., *Colloid Science*, Vol. I, Elsevier, New York, 1952, Chap. VIII.

17-7. Specific Effects

We shall now consider a number of ways in which specific effects of the added electrolyte are felt during flocculation. Some of these are minor and appear only in very careful experiments, others are large enough to obliterate the Shulze-Hardy rule, to lead to quite new phenomena, and to obscure the concept of the primary charge of the particle.

The Hofmeister Series

Ions of the same sign and valence often have somewhat different flocculation values, as shown by the data of Table 17-2. On this basis, one can arrange the ions into a series of increasing effectiveness, and this series reappears in a variety of other phenomena. It is called the Hofmeister series after its discoverer.

TABLE 17-2
Effect of Ionic Radius on Flocculation Values

Salt added	Flocculating value,[a] mM./liter	Ionic radius	
		Hydrated[b]	Crystal
Negatively charged AgI			
$LiNO_3$	165	2.31	0.78
$NaNO_3$	140	1.76	1.00
KNO_3	136	1.19	1.33
$RbNO_3$	126	1.13	1.48
$Mg(NO_3)_2$	2.60	3.32	0.75
$Zn(NO_3)_2$	2.50	3.26	0.83
$Ca(NO_3)_2$	2.40	3.00	1.05
$Sr(NO_3)_2$	2.38	3.00	1.20
$Ba(NO_3)_2$	2.26	2.78	1.38
Positively charged Fe_2O_3			
KCl	9.0	1.17	1.80
KBr	12.5	1.15	1.96
KI	16	1.16	2.20

[a] After J. Th. G. Overbeek, in H. R. Kruyt, ed., *Colloid Science*, Vol. I, Elsevier Press, New York, 1952, chap. VIII.

[b] Calculated from limiting conductance and Stokes' law. Probably grossly erroneous for very small ions.

It is found in many colloidal effects, such as the swelling of gels or the salting out of hydrophilic colloids, but appears also in many simple phenomena, such as the infrared spectrum and viscosity of salt solutions, or the solubility of inert gases therein, and also the heats of hydration of ions, and even the ionization potentials of the corresponding atoms. Thus, the Hofmeister series depends on the structure of the ions and, as indicated by the last two phenomena, it depends especially on their size. This, in turn, affects their interaction with other substances, in particular their hydration in water. This again determines how strongly they are attracted by a charged surface at the point of closest approach. From what we have learned about the mechanism of flocculation it is not surprising that ions which can approach closer should have lower flocculation values although their valence is the same.   Other effects of the Hofmeister series can be interpreted along the same line, but occasionally more complicated mechanisms cause some deviations from the normal order.

The Hofmeister series in order of decreasing flocculating power is for monovalent cations approximately

$$Cs^+, \; Rb^+, \; NH_4^+, \; K^+, \; Na^+, \; Li^+$$

and for the anions

$$F^-, \; IO_3^-, \; H_2PO_4^-, \; BrO_3^-, \; Cl^-, \; ClO_3^-, \; Br^-,$$

$$NO_3^-, \; ClO_4^-, \; I^-, \; CNS^-.$$

Potential-Determining Ions

As explained above (Section 17-2), these are the ions whose concentration tends to determine the potential ψ_0 of the surface. Since all other properties of the double layer depend largely on this potential, it is obvious that these ions play a basic role in flocculation.   Thus a negatively charged AgI sol whose potential is determined by the presence of 10^{-8} molar Ag^+ ions will become uncharged and flocculated if this concentration is raised to about 10^{-6}.   Other monovalent ions require concentrations which are some 10^5 times larger to produce the same result. Of course, this tremendous effect of potential-determining ions makes imperative a close control of their concentration in any experiments.   Thus, in work with proteins the pH is of primary importance, and constant-pH buffers are much used.

In some cases the potential-determining function can be filled by a number of chemically equivalent ions.   Thus stannic oxide can form a stable, negatively charged sol when treated with KOH.   Presumably, its surface is covered by stannic acid groups related to SnO_3^{2-}.   It can be discharged and flocculated by addition of an amount of HCl equivalent to the KOH used in preparing it, but requires five to ten times larger amounts of sodium or potassium salts.   This shows the potential-determining function of the H^+ ions.   However, salts of Ag^+, Ca^{2+}, and Al^{3+} all flocculate at the same equivalent concentration as HCl.[2] Hence, they too must destroy the primary charge. This is readily understood when one remembers that, in contrast to the alkali metals, these all form insoluble stannates.

Van der Waals' Adsorption

The adsorption of ions into the Stern layer is caused by all the forces which can cause adsorption. The coulombic ones which we have considered thus far are often the most important ones. In some cases, however, van der Waals forces may become important, or even predominant. Thus, many large organic counterions have a flocculating value much below that corresponding to their valence. For benzidine it is one-sixth of the value for calcium, though both are divalent. This and other similar values are open to some suspicion, because of possible polymerization of these molecules in solution under the influence of the same forces which would cause their adsorption. Very convincing evidence of the importance of van der Waals forces is, however, given by the stabilizing effect of some similiions.[3] Thus, with negatively charged As_2S_3 sols, the flocculation value of potassium chloride and nitrate is about 5×10^{-2}, but that of potassium formate is 70% higher, for the acetate it is more than double, and for the citrate it is almost five times as high. It appears that, despite their similar charge, these anions become adsorbed and incorporated into the Stern layer, thus increasing ψ_d and the stability of the dispersion.

Reversal of Charge

We have mentioned previously that over-all electrostatic forces cannot be responsible for the primary charge of the particle, although they cause, of course, its reduction by the Stern layer. They cannot cause a reversal because once the charge sinks to zero there is nothing left to attract the counterions. Other adsorptive forces, however, cause a reversal of charge. We have seen how this happens in AgI sols as the Ag^+ concentration changes and in proteins as the pH crosses the isoelectric point (Section 17-1). A similar phenomenon occurs sometimes with metallic ions of high valency, such as tetravalent cerium or trivalent aluminum. As shown in Table 17-1, these flocculate negatively charged suspensions at very low concentrations. At higher concentrations (three times the flocculation value or so), they may give a stable but positively charged system which does not flocculate again until the oppositely charged monovalent ion reaches its flocculation value for this positive sol (Fig. 17-8).

This reversal of charge, or "irregular series," shows that specific forces are effective in the interaction of such highly charged ions with colloids. Whether this is due to the ions themselves or (as is more likely) to their products of hydrolysis is uncertain. In any case it seems unlikely that their first flocculation values would be due to nonspecific interactions alone.

17-8. Irridescent or Schiller Layers

In the above discussion of flocculation we have placed great emphasis on the repulsion between particles and the effect of inert salts upon it, but our evidence was rather indirect. A very direct demonstration of the existence of such repulsion is often provided by aged dilute solutions of ferric chloride[4] or tungstic acid which deposit a highly irridescent sediment. Such irridescence can be produced only by the interference of light reflecting from regularly spaced layers of transparent material, and the spacing of the layers can be estimated from the observed colors. This spacing changes in the presence of salt, as would be predicted by the theory of the double layer. The formation of these irridescent layers is therefore attributed to the sedimentation of lath-like particles of the sol (Fig. 2-6) under the influence of gravity until they reach a distance at which their mutual repulsion stops further settling.[5] The identity of the double layer of all the particles accounts for the uniformity of the spacing over macroscopic distances.

17-9. Ion Exchange

The specific and nonspecific effects in the flocculation by electrolytes brought into play a large number of factors involved in the structure of the double layer.   We are now in a position to predict which ions will be found in the double layer if two kinds of counterions are present in the system.   This is the problem of ion exchange.   It pertains only to counterions because, as we have already seen, the similiions are generally expelled and play only a minor role, unless specifically adsorbed.

Briefly stated, at equal concentrations and in the absence of specific effects, valence is the primary consideration.   The divalent ion is attracted twice as strongly while only the same kinetic energy tends to keep it in the bulk solution.   Furthermore, its double charge permits it to screen twice as effectively, thus reducing the attraction for the monovalent ions.   At equal valence, smaller size favors closer approach and, hence, stronger attraction, and van der Waals forces can also cause preferred adsorption.   Potential-determining ions have, of course, always a high priority.   Differences in concentration, if large enough, can reverse any of these effects.

In agreement with these considerations it is found that the flocculating effect of divalent ions is substantially unaffected by the presence of equal amounts of monovalent ions.   Also in agreement, during the familiar titration of chloride the dichlorofluorescein anion does not become adsorbed until the $AgCl$ suspension becomes positively charged by the Ag^+ ions present at the end-point, and its adsorption is favored over the other anions present by specific, probably van der Waals, factors. In this case specific interaction is sufficiently strong to change the color of the dichlorofluorescein ion and thus make it serve as an indicator.

The same considerations explain the functioning of the ion exchangers of commerce, the porous solids with reactive groups. The solid always keeps its neutralizing double layer in its immediate vicinity for reasons of electroneutrality, but the composition of this double layer is determined mainly by the concentration and charge of the ions in solution.   Thus, in the oldest application of water softening, divalent calcium ions are withdrawn from dilute solution while monovalent sodium ions are released into it until almost completely exhausted.   By treatment with a small volume of very concentrated NaCl solution, the process is reversed, however, and the exchanger is regenerated.   The efficiency and completeness of the exchange is further increased by using a frontal chromatographic method, passing the solution through a column of finely divided exchanger.   This permits exchange even if the equilibrium at each state is quite unfavorable.

For exchangers with weakly acidic or basic groups, the H^+ ions are potential-determining and are relatively very firmly held.   For those with strong groups, these ions are readily exchanged.   This permits the "deionization" of water by exchanging all cations for H^+ ions of an acid solid and all anions (of strong acids) for neutralizing OH^- ions of a basic solid. Regeneration, of course, uses a strong acid and a strong base at high concentrations acting separately on the two solids.

A limitation—and a means of attaining added selectivity—of ion exchangers lies in the size of their pores, which limits the access of large ions.   Thus proteins can be freed of small ions without being retained themselves.

17-10. Electroviscous Effects

Charge always increases the viscosity of dilute colloidal solutions, just as it contributes to the viscosity of ordinary electrolytes. In the case of rigid particles this may be visualized as due to an increase of the effective volume of the particle by its double layer.[6] In flow through capillaries it may be ascribed to the fact that flow creates a streaming potential which, in turn, creates an electroosmotic pressure opposing the flow.[7]   These effects are significant but not spectacular, except for highly dilute solutions in very narrow spaces.   On the other hand, remarkably large effects are observed for flexible long chain ions, the polyelectro lytes.

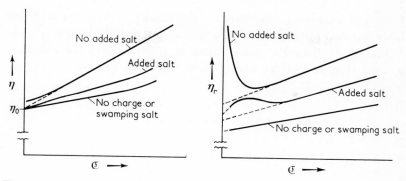

Figure 17-9. The viscosity (*left*) and reduced viscosity (*right*) of polyelectrolyte as affected by concentration and by the presence of salt.

We have seen (Section 13-5) that the intrinsic viscosity $[\eta]$ is very sensitive to hydration and shape, increasing with the cube of the radius and roughly with the square of the axial ratio. The same is true of the reduced viscosity, η_r, at low concentrations. For any given shape, however, η_r tends towards a constant value—the intrinsic viscosity—at low concentrations. This is the observed behavior of uncharged particles, including the polymers. Polyelectrolytes, on the other hand, give reduced viscosities which seem to increase without limit when the concentration is lowered. In other words, although their viscosity decreases with dilution, it tends to decrease more and more slowly (Fig. 17-9).

Upon addition of simple salts, this behavior is radically modified. For any given concentration of polyelectrolyte the η_r is lowered. If the concentration of polyelectrolyte is lowered at constant salt concentration, the reduced viscosity first decreases, then increases to a maximum, and finally decreases (Fig. 17-9). At higher salt concentrations the maximum decreases and shifts to higher concentrations until, under swamping electrolyte conditions, the behavior becomes substantially normal. The effectiveness of added electrolyte also obeys the Shulze-Hardy rule, so that the abnormal viscosity of polyelectrolytes must be due to their charge and double layer. In fact, it can be interpreted very satisfactorily in terms of what we have learned about long chains and about double layers.

We know that the interaction of particles always increases η_r and that the effect decreases upon dilution.   This can ac-

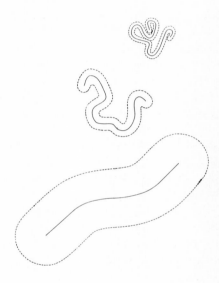

Figure 17-10. A charged flexible chain assumes an increasingly stretched configuration as the thickness of the double layer increases and there is less shielding against the mutual repulsion of the charges.

count for the initial decrease in all cases, and for the final decrease in the presence of salt.

The increase in η_r can be explained by a change of shape of the random coil corresponding to less compact coiling or even a straightening out. This, in turn, is due to the mutual repulsion of the charged segments. The range of these repulsions depends on the thickness, δ, of the double layer and, therefore, on the concentration of the gegenions. The higher the gegenion concentration, the thinner the double layer, the shorter the effect of mutual repulsion of the segments, and the less distended the coil (Fig. 17-10).

When the solution is relatively concentrated, the concentration of gegenions is high, so the tendency to expand is small. In addition, because of the crowding by segments of neighboring molecules, the coil would gain little by expanding. Hence the polyelectrolyte behaves rather normally. In a pure polyelectrolyte, with increasing dilution, the concentration of the gegenions decreases, δ increases, and the coil acquires more room to expand, with a resulting continuous rise of η_r. Even at the highest dilutions, however, the polyelectrolyte is not yet fully expanded, and as a result no maximum is reached.[8] In the presence of salt, the situation is different. At medium concentrations, the gegenions supplied by the polyelectrolyte are a significant part of the total, so that dilution has some effect in increasing δ and expanding the coil. Thus η_r increases, but less markedly. At higher dilutions (or higher salt concentrations), however, the total gegenion concentration does not change significantly as the polyelectrolyte is diluted, so that δ and the shape of the coil remain constant. Hence η_r decreases because of smaller particle–particle interaction. The maximum in η_r marks the transition between these two effects—roughly where the simple electrolyte becomes swamping.

By changing the concentration of salt as the polyelectrolyte is diluted, so as to keep the gegenion concentration approximately constant, it is possible to obtain straight line plots of η_r versus $\mathfrak{E}$, so that extrapolation to infinite dilution is easy and intrinsic viscosities are obtained. These indicate, as would be expected, that the shape of the polyelectrolyte coil varies markedly with the counterion concentration.[9]

17-11. Swelling of Electrolytic Gels

A closely related phenomenon is that of the effect of simple electrolytes upon the swelling of gels whose network carries charges.   Gelatin and structured proteins are typical gels of this kind for which H^+ is the principal potential-determining ion. Here the size of the gel is determined by an equilibrium between the elasticity of the network, which is primarily a rubber elasticity, on one hand, and the expanding electric forces on the

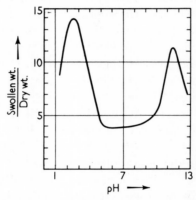

Figure 17-11. The effect of pH on the swelling of fresh muscle.   Small concentrations of acid or base charge the protein and increase swelling whereas additional amounts act as inert electrolytes and reduce it.   (*After D. Jordan Lloyd and A. Shore, Chemistry of the Proteins, J. and A. Churchill Ltd. London, 1938.*)

other.   The electric forces may be looked upon as due to repulsion of double layers of the segments of the gel or, equivalently, as the result of a Donnan osmotic pressure of the gegenions held within the confines of the gel by electroneutrality.   It may be remembered that the membrane of the standard Donnan equilibrium (Section 14-11 and 14-12) also retains the counterion only by electroneutrality, so that the analogy is quite complete.

Thus, it is understandable that such gels show a minimum volume at their isoelectric point but swell in both dilute acids and dilute bases (Fig. 17-11).   Simple salts reduce this swelling.

Excess acid, above that necessary to fully charge the gel, also reduces swelling, since it acts only as a simple electrolyte, having lost its potential-determining power. Besides these main effects, one can also observe specific effects due to adsorption of small ions and due to a weakening of the gel structure by a number of electrolytes which destroy the crosslinks.[10]

Summary

Over-all electrostatic forces cannot cause the net charge on a particle. Specific interactions are required, and these explain the importance of potential-determining ions. The protective action of the charge is due to the energy required to destroy during flocculation some of the double layer surrounding it. It increases with the potential and with the extent of the double layer. In flocculation as in ion exchange, the effectiveness of the ions is primarily determined by their valence and concentration, but specific effects due to the size and adsorbability can be important and become overwhelming for potential-determining ions. The interaction of double layers can also acount for the remarkable viscosity effects of polyelectrolytes and the swelling of electrolytic gels.

References

1. E. J. W. Verwey and J. Th. G. Overbeek, *Theory of Stability of Lyophobic Colloids*, Elsevier, New York, 1948.
2. R. Franz, Dissertation, Göttingen, 1913; E. Heinz, Dissertation, Göttingen, 1914; through H. R. Kruyt, *Colloids*, John Wiley & Sons, Inc., New York, 1930, p. 105.
3. H. R. Kruyt (see ref. 2), p. 74.
4. H. Zocher and W. Heller, *Z. anorg. Chem.*, **186,** 75 (1930).
5. P. Bergmann, P. Löw-Beer, and H. Zocher, *Z. physik. Chem.*, **A181,** 301 (1938).
6. F. Booth, *Proc. Roy. Soc. (London)*, **A203,** 533 (1950).
7. G. A. H. Elton, *Proc. Roy. Soc. (London)*, **A194,** 259 (1948).
8. H. Eisenberg and J. Pouyet, *J. Polymer Sci.*, **13,** 85 (1954); B. E.

Conway, *J. Polymer Sci.*, **18**, 257 (1955) report maxima below 10 mg./100 ml.

9. D. T. F. Pals and J. J. Hermans, *Rec. trav. chim.*, **71**, 433 (1952).
10. A. Küntzel, *Biochem. Z.*, **209**, 389 (1929).

Problems

92. The addition of a small amount of a reagent to a sol causes flocculation, but addition of a larger amount has no effect. One could conclude that (*1*) the reagent is a protective uncharged colloid and the sol is originally close to flocculation, (*2*) the sign of the particles of the sol is different before any addition and after addition of the larger amount, (*3*) insufficient information to decide which one of these, (*4*) none of these.

76. In order to increase the swelling of a gel you would not (*1*) increase the concentration of potential-determining similiions, (*2*) reduce the crosslinking, (*3*) add a better solvent, (*4*) add an inert electrolyte.

71. In order to determine the sign of the charge of a silver iodide sol, you would not (*1*) add increasing, very small amounts of $AgNO_3$ to it, (*2*) add increasing amounts of Na_2SO_4 to one portion of it and of $MgCl_2$ to another portion, (*3*) observe its electrophoretic mobility on paper saturated with a phosphate buffer, (*4*) all of these, (*5*) none of these.

77. If NaCl has the same flocculation value (FV) with respect to sols *A* and *B* whereas $MgCl_2$ has a much lower FV for *A* than for *B*, it is likely that (*1*) NaCl and $MgCl_2$ have about the same FV with respect to *B*, (*2*) they have about the same FV with respect to *A*, (*3*) something is wrong with the experiment, (*4*) mixtures of *A* and *B* are likely to be stable in all proportions.

93. The lowest flocculation value with respect to a positive AgI sol may be expected from (*1*) $CaCl_2$, (*2*) NaCN, (*3*) Na_2SO_4, (*4*) $MgSO_4$.

88. The addition of $NaNO_3$ to an AgI sol will affect least the (*1*) ζ (*2*) ψ_0, (*3*) σ, (*4*) δ.

78. Flocculation will be favored by (*1*) increased range of van der Waals forces, (*2*) reduced thickness of the double layer, (*3*) reduced ψ_d, (*4*) all of these, (*5*) none of these.

75. The reason divalent counterions have lower flocculation values

than monovalent ones is that (*1*) they have a lower kinetic energy, (*2*) their screening effect is lower, (*3*) they are attracted more strongly, (*4*) all of these, (*5*) none of these.

101. Other things being equal, the effect of pH (between 2 and 12) on the viscosity of a dilute solution of the Na salt of a linear high polymer carrying only COO^- groups can be expected to be (*1*) negligible, (*2*) higher viscosity at high pH, (*3*) higher viscosity at lower pH, (*4*) maximum viscosity at intermediate pH, (*5*) minimum viscosity at intermediate pH.

106. Among the following pairs, the one in which the first member should have a much lower flocculation value with respect to a positive $Fe(OH)_3$ sol is (*1*) $MgCl_2$ and $NaCl$, (*2*) Na_2S and Na_2SO_4, (*3*) $(C_8H_{17}NH_3)_2SO_4$ and Na_2SO_4, (*4*) all of these, (*5*) none of these.

109. In order to form a highly permeable filter cake it might be most advisable to add to a suspension of negatively charged particles (*1*) Na_2SO_4, (*2*) $MgSO_4$, (*3*) $NaCl$.

80. An isoelectric protein does not have (*1*) any electric charges, (*2*) equal equivalent concentrations of similiions and gegenions, (*3*) zero electrophoretic mobility, (*4*) zero ζ potential, (*5*) all of these, (*6*) none of these.

103. Assuming that the van der Waals forces among particles and between particles and solvent remain unchanged during addition of an inert salt, if flocculation is caused by this addition, the original sol may be considered as (*1*) stable, (*2*) caducous, (*3*) metastable, (*4*) diuturnal.

107. If the viscosity of a solute varies as indicated in the table, it is likely that

$\mathfrak{B} \times 10^2$:	0	0.5	1	2
η:	5	5.75	6	6.5

the solute is (*1*) spherical, (*2*) uncharged, (*3*) rigid, (*4*) all of these, (*5*) none of these.

127. The isoionic point is defined as the pH of a solution obtained by dissolving a pure protein, free of ions such as Cl^- or Na^+, in pure water. This point must be (*1*) equal to the isoelectric point, (*2*) above 7, (*3*) below 7, (*4*) between 7 and the isoelectric point, (*5*) further from 7 than the isoelectric point.

CHAPTER XVIII

Optical Phenomena: I. Refraction and Schlieren

Just as in everyday life our eyes and vision are perhaps our best source of information about the outside world, so are optical methods among the most valuable tools in the study of colloids. Our everyday experience with the behavior of light is, however, often insufficient or misleading in this study because of the small size of colloids, and a relatively good understanding of the principles of optics is frequently required. The present book cannot attempt to present properly this prerequisite. The reader must therefore be referred to textbooks of optics for further explanation.[1]

In these last chapters we shall consider the use of optical methods to measure the concentration changes of solutions, to see the individual particles and to estimate their sizes and masses. The first and probably the simplest aspect, involving only geometrical optics, is that of the schlieren methods treated in the present chapter. We will then come to topics involving the wave theory of light.

Schlieren methods have wide and growing applications in the visualization and measurement of gradients of concentration, pressure, and the like. We have already encountered their application several times. A brief examination of the principles underlying their operation should be of value in using them, in interpreting their results, and in estimating the limits of their applicability. The same principles will also be found in a variety of other optical methods beyond the scope of this book.

18-1. The Refractive Index Gradient

It is well known that light is refracted when it passes abruptly from one medium to another having a different refractive index,

ν.   We will be more interested, however, in what happens to it as it passes through a solution having a continuously varying concentration and, therefore, in general, a continuously varying refractive index.

For dilute solutions, the refractive index, ν, generally does not differ much from that of water (1.333 at room temperature) or, more generally, from that of the solvent.   The difference, $\Delta\nu$, between the solution and the solvent is usually called the refractive increment of the solute (in the particular system). It is generally directly proportional to the concentration, so that the ratio $\partial\nu/\partial\mathfrak{C}$ is a constant characteristic of a given solvent–solute system at a given temperature.   The value of this constant depends, of course, on the units used in measuring concentration.   Very frequently, $\mathfrak{C}$ is measured in grams of solute per cubic centimeter of solution (which is 1/1000th of the customary units) to give the specific refractive increment.

Thus, as concentration changes within a solution, the refractive index changes proportionately.   If we consider a column of solution of nonuniform concentration, such as we have encountered in connection with sedimentation, diffusion, and electrophoresis, it is obvious that to the concentration gradients correspond refractive index gradients and that there is a simple proportionality between the two.   Hence by measuring the refractive index gradient we determine the concentration gradient.   This measurement by the schlieren method depends on the bending of light in the refractive index gradient.

18-2. The Bending of Light

Let us consider a ray of light crossing obliquely a change in refractive index, as shown in Fig. 18-1a.   Let x and $x + \Delta x$ denote two planes between which the change in ν is confined. If this change is abrupt, there is a corresponding abrupt change in the direction of the ray, in accordance with Snell's law of refraction.   For small changes in ν, the change in direction will also be small and proportional to $\Delta\nu$ as long as the angle of incidence α is the same.   If we now introduce a

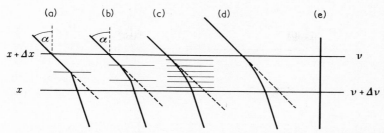

Figure 18-1. Light bends as much when the refractive index changes gradually as when it changes abruptly. The bending increases with the angle of incidence.

sharply delimited layer of intermediate refractive index, as shown in Fig. 18-1b, the light will be bent twice but each bending will be half as effective, so that the total change of direction is substantially the same. If the number of intermediate layers is increased, as shown in Fig. 18-1c, the path of the ray approaches a continuous curve, but the total deflection remains the same. Finally, when the change in refractive index becomes continuous, Fig. 18-1d, the path becomes a curve without changing the deflection.

Thus, a ray of light is curved in a refractive index gradient, and the total change in direction increases with the total length of the optical path in the gradient and with the magnitude of the gradient. In addition, this change depends on the angle of incidence.

A ray entering a refractive index gradient perpendicularly to layers of equal v is, of course, unaffected as to direction (Fig. 18-1e). As it becomes more oblique, the angle of incidence increasing, it becomes more deflected (Fig. 18-1d). Hence, the deflection should be greatest when the ray is initially parallel to layers of equal v. This loose conclusion may seem to be contrary to the intuitive impression that a ray travelling within a single layer should not deviate at all. This intuitive view neglects the fact that neighboring possible paths affect the course of a ray by Fermat's principle. Exact analysis confirms that the deflection is maximum for the parallel ray and the fact that it

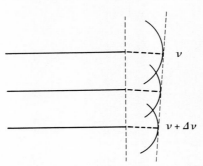

Figure 18-2. Huygens' construction showing that light travelling parallel to the layers of a refractive index gradient is bent.

is deflected can be shown by Huygens' construction, illustrated in Fig. 18-2.   Rays parallel to the layers have originally a wave front perpendicular to them.   The next wave front is tangent to circles having radia inversely proportional to the refractive indices.   Since these are unequal, the wave front must be inclined and therefore the rays must be deflected to stay perpendicular to the wave front.

The deflection of a ray of light in a refractive index gradient, although shown as very large in the illustrations, amounts in fact to very little.   Thus, if a protein solution (specific refractive increment = 0.18) changes in concentration by 1% over a height of 1 cm., it affects the direction of a horizontal ray of light by about 0.1 °/cm. of width.   Hence, cells are generally designed to give optical paths as long as possible in order to increase the deflection, and sensitive methods are needed to detect these deflections.

The deflection-detecting systems involve combinations of lenses, and we must first review some of the properties of these.

18-3. Lenses

A spherical convex lens is essentially an optical instrument for collecting the light emanating from one point and focussing it at another point.   These two points are called conjugate.   In the graphic method of finding these points, certain special rays, e.g. one parallel to the axis and one passing through the optical center, are used (Fig. 18-3). It is important to note, however, that all and any rays emanating from a point and passing through the lens meet at its conjugate point. In fact, in our schlieren systems, there will generally be only an extremely narrow bundle of rays emanating from one point and used to produce an image at the conjugate one.

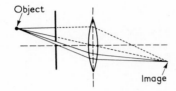

Figure 18-3. A spherical lens forms an image with any bundle of rays coming from the object.

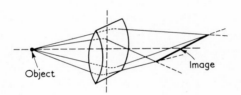

Figure 18-4. A cylindrical lens focuses in only one plane. A point object gives a line image.

Although the surfaces of most familiar lenses are approximately spherical, there exist also cylindrical lenses whose special properties we will have occasion to use. As the name indicates, these have cylindrical surfaces instead of spherical ones. The body of a simple bottle, when filled with water, forms such a cylindrical lens (though of very poor quality). As shown in Fig. 18-4, a cylindrical lens leaves the rays of light essentially unaffected in one plane but collects them effectively at right angles to this one. Hence, light emanating from a point is collected into a line parallel to the axis of the cylinder.

18-4. The Basic Schlieren System

Let us consider a cell C and a photographic lens L which forms an image I of the cell on a photographic plate P (Fig. 18-5a). Thus C and P are in conjugate planes.   This image will form

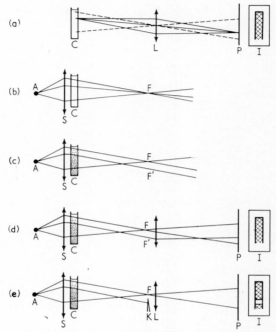

Figure 18-5. The simple (Töppler) schlieren system. (a) photographic part; (b) illuminating system in the absence of gradient; (c) a gradient deflects the rays passing through it; (d) the combination of illuminating and photographic parts gives an image of the cell and a separation of deflected and undeflected rays; (e) a knife edge intercepting the deflected rays obscures that part of the image where the gradient exists.

even if only very few rays from the cell reach the plate as long as these all pass through lens L.

Let us now consider a narrow horizontal source of light A, and a large lens S placed very close to cell C (Fig. 18-5b). This lens will cause all the light crossing the cell to collect at F to give an image of the source, i.e., a horizontal line. This is true, however, only if the contents of the cell are homogeneous. If there is a refractive index gradient in the cell (Fig. 18-5c), the rays passing through that region will be deflected downwards (if ν increases in this direction, as is usually the case), and will converge on a horizontal line located at F' in the same plane as F but slightly lower. If the refractive index gradient is not uniform, there will be a continuous blur extending from F downward to a distance determined by the greatest gradient.

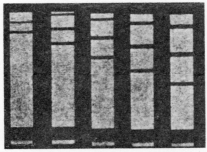

Figure 18-6. Successive simple schlieren patterns obtained at five minute intervals during the ultracentrifugal sedimentation of haemocyanin of *Limulus*. Each shifting dark band corresponds to the boundary of a sedimenting component. (*From T. Svedberg, Ind. Eng. Chem. (Anal. Ed.) 10, 116 (1938).*)

We can now combine this illuminating system, formed by the horizontal light source and the large lens S (the schlieren lens), with the photographic system previously mentioned. This requires that lens L collect the light which passed through the cell C, and is accomplished by placing it near F as shown in Fig. 18-5d. It should be noted that as far as the formation of the photographic image is concerned, it does not matter at this stage whether the light has been deflected while passing through the cell or not. It forms the image as long as it comes from the cell and goes through lens L.

The light coming from the gradient region is clearly separated from that coming from the rest of the cell at F'.   One can therefore act upon it here, and thus one can affect the corresponding part of the image.   The simplest method of accomplishing this is to bring a sharp knife edge K up from below until it reaches F' and thus cuts out the most deflected rays (Fig. 18-5e).   These rays are therefore no longer able to reach the corresponding point on the plate P, and there will be a dark, horizontal band in the image of the cell at the point of greatest gradient, as shown in Fig. 18-6 for successive stages of sedimentation of a three-component system.

This simple method therefore permits locating the position of the gradients within the cell and, when the position of the knife edge is known, also an estimate of their magnitude.   To each position of the knife edge corresponds, however, only one gradient, so that a very incomplete picture of the state of the solution is obtained.   A number of modifications have therefore been introduced to overcome this drawback.   The one most commonly used is based on the combination of an inclined knife edge and a cylindrical lens.

18-5. The Philpot Method

In the above simple schlieren system (Fig. 18-7a), it really did not matter whether the light source was a point or a horizontal line—the image obtained would be the same in either case. An additional possibility is opened, however, by the fact that it is a line and that the light from each point of this line passes through the whole cell before being brought together again at a single point of the line F in the absence of gradients (or to a short vertical line between F and F' in the presence of a gradient). This possibility is utilized by placing a cylindrical lens Q next to the photographic lens L (Fig. 18-7b).   This cylindrical lens is oriented so that it does not affect at all the action of the photographic lens L in the vertical plane (Fig. 18-7c).   A narrow horizontal layer in the cell is still imaged in a definite horizontal layer on the plate.

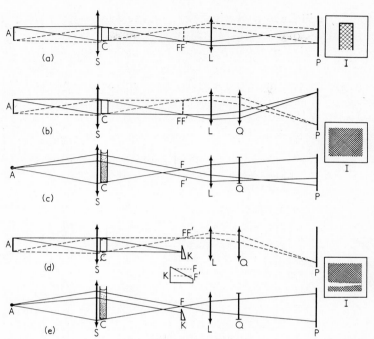

Figure 18-7. A Philpot schlieren system. (a) top view of the simple schlieren system of Fig. 18-5; (b) the effect of introducing cylindrical lens Q; (c) side view of same; (d) an inclined knife edge intercepting the deviated rays obscures a part of the image corresponding to the level of the gradient and extending from one side of the image according to the steepness of the gradient.

In the horizontal plane (Fig. 18-7b), however, the image of the cell is thrown completely out of focus, so that rays coming from any point within a layer in the cell form a horizontal line on the plate. The ends of such a line are indicated by the pair of solid and dashed rays coming from a side of the cell (Fig. 18-7b).

In order to produce a schlieren system, the curvature of the cylindrical lens Q is chosen so that acting together with the photographic lens L it focuses the plane of FF' on plate P (in the horizontal direction only). Thus light from the far side of

F (or F') will form a vertical line on the near side of the plate (dashed rays of Fig. 18-7b), and vice versa. Of course, light from the far side of F (or F') must have come from the near side of the source A and has passed through the cell.

Thus, rays coming from a given layer in the cell spread over a horizontal line on the plate, whereas those coming from a given point of F (or F') spread over a vertical line. As a result, rays coming from a given layer in the cell *and* through a given point

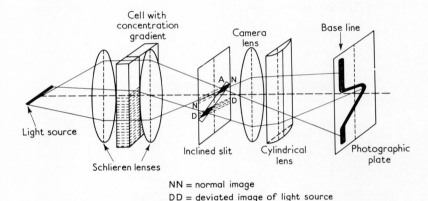

NN = normal image
DD = deviated image of light source

Figure 18-8. Schematic perspective of a schlieren system with twin schlieren lenses and an inclined slit. NN corresponds to F, and DD to F' of Fig. 18-7.   (*From H. R. Kruyt, Colloid Science, Vol. I, Elsevier, N. Y., 1952.*)

of F can reach only a single point of the plate, the one where these two lines intersect.

Conversely, a point on the plate corresponds to light which came from a definite level of the cell and passed through a definite near–far position in the plane FF'. The vertical position of the ray of FF' still corresponds to the refractive index gradient through which it passed. Now, if an inclined knife edge K is introduced into the FF' plane so as to allow all light to pass at the F level but to cut out most of it at the F' level (Fig. 18-7d,e), the effect will be to permit the light to form an image of the cell which is complete where there is no refractive index gradient but which is only a narrow strip at the point of maximum gradient. This gives, therefore, a direct image of the refractive index gradient throughout the cell.

The quality of the schlieren pattern can be brought to a high degree of perfection by proper attention to details of the practical design.[2] For example, sharpness is improved if the light passing

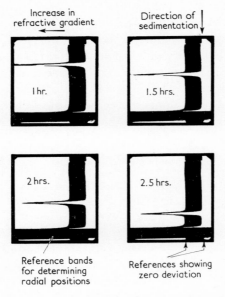

Figure 18-9. Successive schlieren patterns obtained with a cylindrical lens and an inclined slit during centrifugal sedimentation of a monodisperse system. (*From E. G. Pickels, Chem. Rev.* **30**, *351 (1942)*.)

through the cell is as nearly horizontal as possible, so that it is affected only by a very narrow layer of solution. This is generally realized by using two schlieren lenses, and placing the cell between them (Fig. 18-8). The inclined knife is often replaced by an inclined slit, an inclined cross hair, or a similar optical obstacle, so that the schlieren pattern is given by a line rather than by the contour of an area, as shown in Fig. 18-9 for successive stages of sedimentation of a monodisperse system.

Summary

Light passing through a refractive index gradient is deflected, especially if it passes at right angles to this gradient.   Schlieren systems utilize this deflection to affect the photographic image of the cell so as to indicate the gradient.   For this purpose a horizontal line source is used, and the light is brought to focus after passing the cell and before being used to form the image. At this focus the deflected light rays are segregated and can be cut off, thus darkening the corresponding part of the image. With the help of a cylindrical lens different parts of the line source and of its focal image can be made to correspond to a vertical line on the cell image.   Hence a partial obstruction of the light at the focal image can give a line showing directly the refractive index gradient throughout the cell.

References

1. R. W. Wood, *Physical Optics*, The Macmillan Co., New York, 1934; F. A. Jenkins and H. E. White, *Fundamentals of Optics*, McGraw-Hill Book Co., Inc., New York, 1957; J. Strong, *Concepts of Classical Optics*, W. H. Freeman and Co., San Francisco, 1958, etc.
2. R. Trautman, *J. Phys. Chem.*, **60**, 1211 (1956); E. Wiedemann, *Int. Arch. Allergy*, **5**, 1 (1954).

Problems

115. The light from a candle reaches a convex lens through a small diaphragm.   By proper positioning of a screen on the other side of the lens it is generally possible to obtain a sharp image of (*1*) candle flame and diaphragm simultaneously, (*2*) candle flame or diaphragm separately, (*3*) only candle flame but never diaphragm, (*4*) only diaphragm but never candle flame.

119. It is possible to have a refractive index which decreases from top to bottom of the cell. If an ordinary simple schlieren apparatus is used on such a system the results will be (*1*) no gradient will appear, (*2*) the gradient will appear as a dark strip, (*3*) the gradient will appear as a light strip, (*4*) none of these.

113. If the slope of the knife edge in the Philpot method is increased, the effect on the height of a peak of the schlieren patterns will be (*1*) an increase, (*2*) a decrease, (*3*) no effect.

96. In a simple schlieren system the following lie in conjugate planes (*1*) cell and photographic plate, (*2*) knife edge and photographic plate, (*3*) schlieren lens and photographic lens, (*4*) light source and cell.

CHAPTER XIX

Optical Phenomena: II. Interference

We shall now consider some optical phenomena related directly to the fact that light has the character of a wave motion and that two such waves can interact to reinforce or weaken each other, depending on their phase difference, i.e., on whether the crests of one coincide with crests or with troughs of the other.

19-1. Diffracting System and Diffraction Pattern

If light from a point source passes through two pinholes in a screen, the two resulting spreading beams interfere to produce a pattern of dark and light bands if received on a photographic plate (Fig. 19-1). The important fact from our point of view is that the shape of this diffraction pattern is determined by the wavelength, λ, of the light and by the separation, d, of the two pinholes. The angle separating successive light or dark regions increases with λ/d and is of the same order (in radians) as this quantity. Hence, the angle is small when the separation is large compared with the wavelength of light, and becomes rapidly large as the separation becomes comparable to this length.

If additional pinholes are provided, or if they are replaced by slits or other apertures, the diffraction pattern changes accordingly, but it is always completely determined by the wavelength of light and by the nature of the diffracting system of apertures. Since the nature of the light is generally easily controlled, this provides a most useful interdependence between the diffraction pattern and the diffracting system. Thus the diffraction pattern can (in principle at least) be calculated from a complete knowledge of the system of pinholes or slits. Conversely, from a

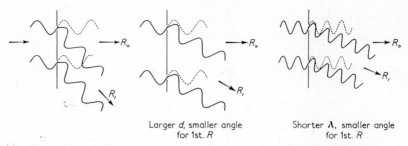

Larger *d*, smaller angle
for 1st. *R*

Shorter *λ*, smaller angle
for 1st. *R*

Figure 19-1. The spread of a diffraction pattern decreases as the diffracting system becomes coarser and as the wave length becomes shorter. *R*'s
indicate the direction of reinforcement.

complete knowledge of the diffraction pattern one can calculate,
in principle, the exact shape of the diffracting system. One
should note the word "complete" in this last statement, because
any lack of information about the diffraction pattern results in a
corresponding uncertainty in the conclusions drawn about the
diffracting system.

As we have noted above, the angle of the diffraction pattern
increases as the distance between diffracting elements becomes
smaller. Hence, information about the large elements is found
already near the center of the diffraction pattern, whereas that
about small ones has to be sought at the periphery.

The chemist's interest in this field comes, of course, from the
possibility of learning about the structure of his systems by obtaining and interpreting the diffraction patterns which they
produce. For this purpose he uses not only visible light but also
other waves, such as x-rays or those associated with electrons or
neutrons. In all cases the diffraction pattern is collected, and
then an attempt is made to reconstruct from it the original
structure.

In the case of x-ray diffraction this procedure is well known
and clearly apparent. A photographic film (or its equivalent)
is used to collect the diffraction pattern, and from the position
and intensity of this pattern conclusions are drawn about the
structure. The photographic technique permits the collection

of the pattern at almost all angles, small regions around the incoming and outgoing beam being the only ones that present some difficulty.   The photographic record, unfortunately, gives no information about a very important property of the diffraction pattern, the relative phases of its various parts.   This information must be supplied from other sources and is frequently impossible to obtain methodically.   It is this which makes much of the interpretation of x-ray diffraction patterns an art, and a very difficult one.

19-2. The Limit of Resolution

The microscope is a system of lenses which may be considered as a machine for collecting a part of the diffraction pattern and using it to reconstruct an enlarged image of the system.   The effectiveness of the use that is made of the collected part of the diffraction system depends on the proper design and execution (correction) of the lenses.   The art of correcting glass lenses used in an ordinary microscope has reached a very advanced stage.   However, the best lens system cannot reconstruct details which do not affect that part of the diffraction pattern which is available to it.   Hence, the size of the smallest detail visible in the microscope—its limit of resolution—depends on how large a portion of the diffraction pattern it uses.

Let us consider now the objective lens of a microscope and a small object (Fig. 19-2).   In order to be visible, the object must be located very close to the focal plane of the microscope, so that its distance from the objective is fixed.   It is clear that of the whole diffraction pattern produced by the object, only that part which strikes the lens can be used by the microscope.   Its extent depends therefore on the diameter of the lens or, more exactly, on the angle which it subtends from the point of view of the object, i.e., twice the sine of the angle α shown in the figure. Thus, if we call δ the resolving power of the microscope, we can see that λ/δ must be of the order of $2 \sin \alpha$, and this is why the resolving power of a microscope is generally given as

$$\delta = \lambda/2 \sin \alpha$$

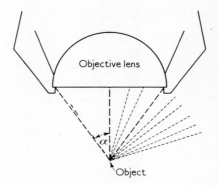

Figure 19-2. Only that part of the diffraction pattern which enters the objective can contribute to the formation of the image. α is the half-angle subtended by the lens from the point of view of the object.

If water or oil replaces air as the immersion medium between the object and the lens, the refractive index, ν, of this immersion medium shortens the effective wave length, so that the refractive pattern becomes more compact, and the expression becomes

$$\delta = \lambda/2\nu \sin \alpha$$

The product $\nu \sin \alpha$ is fixed for a given objective and the particular immersion medium for which it is designed. This is called the numerical aperture and measures the quality of an objective as far as resolving power is concerned.

The difficulty of designing lenses increases with the angle they subtend, but $\sin \alpha$ of 0.95 is obtainable. By using immersion liquids of high refractive index, numerical apertures of 1.6 are reached.

Thus, there is a necessary lower limit to the resolution of a microscope which depends on the wavelength used and on the numerical aperture. For the ordinary light microscope it is of the order of half a wavelength of light, i.e., some 2000 A., but this is attainable only in exceptional cases. The ordinary microscope is therefore useful only at the upper limit of the colloidal range.

19-3. The Electron Microscope

Although x-rays have a much shorter wavelength, they cannot be used in microscopes because there is no good way at present to make the equivalent of lenses for them.   Electrons can, however, be produced with wavelengths of the order of 0.1 A.

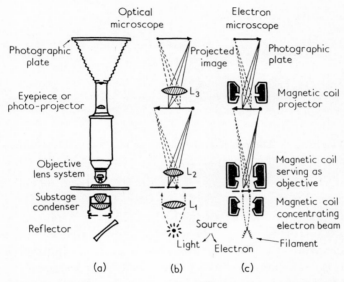

Figure 19-3. Microscopes.   (*a*) outlines the structures of the conventional microscope, (*b*) shows the function of its components, and (*c*) indicates how these are performed in an electron microscope.   (*From E. F. Burton and W. N. Knoll, The Electron Microscope, Reinhold Publishing Corporation, N. Y., 1946.*)

or less, and they can be deflected in electric and magnetic fields in a manner equivalent to lenses.   Such magnetic lenses can be combined along the same lines as ordinary lenses to form an electron microscope (Fig. 19-3), which provides considerably lower limits of resolution than ordinary microscopes.   The limiting factor is the difficulty of correcting lenses of significant numerical apertures.   At present, only lenses with numerical apertures of less than 0.01 are useful, so that the limit of resolu-

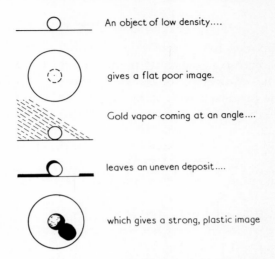

An object of low density....

gives a flat poor image.

Gold vapor coming at an angle....

leaves an uneven deposit....

which gives a strong, plastic image

Figure 19-4. The principle of shadowing in electron microscopy.

tion under best conditions is about 10 A., and occasionally structures due to small molecules become visible.[1]

There are two important factors, other than resolving power, which limit the usefulness of the electron microscope. One is that electrons can travel unhindered only in high vacuum. Hence only specimens having a negligible vapor pressure can be studied. This means, for example, that any aqueous sample must be thoroughly desiccated before it can be observed, and this may frequently introduce distortions or artifacts. The other limitation is that the electron-microscope image is due only to differences in transparency to electrons. Transparency, in turn, depends on the thickness and on the atomic number of the atoms forming the specimen. Hence, organic materials tend to be equally and highly transparent, so that they give pictures having little contrast, whereas heavy metals or thick specimens give too dark an image.

Many ingenious techniques[2] are used to overcome the difficulties connected with the transparency of the specimens. We can mention only some of the principles underlying the main ones. Small particles are generally supported by a very thin (down to 200 A.) plastic film on a small disk of 500 mesh sieve. Soft specimens are sliced into sections which may be as thin as about 200 A. Transparent features are made visible, and three-dimensional effects such as those of Figs. 2-1 and 2-5 are obtained by "shadowing" with a highly opaque material such as gold, as indicated in Fig. 19-4. For this purpose the specimen is placed in vacuum and some gold is vaporized in the same enclosure. The vaporized atoms travel in a straight line because of the vacuum and deposit on exposed surfaces. If the angle at which the vapor arrives is very different from the angle of observation, the result is the same as if the object were illuminated from the side. When surface features are desired, a thin plastic film may be cast on the surface, then stripped therefrom, and the "replica" thus obtained may be shadowed and observed.

As far as resolution is concerned, the electron microscope with its limit of resolution of about 10 A. covers the whole colloidal range. Whenever specimens can be prepared for observation without destruction of original features, it gives unequalled information about size, shape, and structure, as shown by Figs. 2-1 2-2, 2-5, 2-6, 2-7, and 8-11. Unfortunately, unambiguous preparation of specimens is generally difficult and often still impossible.

19-4. Dark Field Microscopy

Small size is not the only limitation on the visibility in an ordinary microscope. Just as in the electron microscope another and important one can stem from lack of contrast, that is, from a lack of difference between the surrounding background and the object. In the extreme case, if the object has the same optical properties as its surroundings, it becomes invisible no matter what its size. This can be readily demonstrated with a glass rod in a mixture of benzene and bromobenzene. Their color is the same, and when the mixture is so adjusted that its refractive index equals that of the glass, the latter disappears from view. Under favorable conditions it can still be perceived, but only

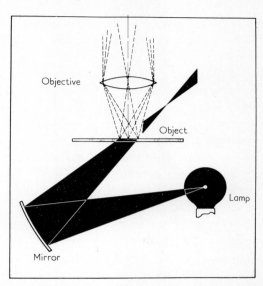

Figure 19-5. Path of light in dark field observation with oblique lighting produced by skewing the mirror in a simple microscope. (*Courtesy of the Bausch and Lomb Optical Co., Rochester, N. Y.*)

because the refractive indices cannot be equated at the same time for all visible wavelengths.

Staining techniques, used by biologists, serve to increase the contrast and visibility of structures which interest them.   Another, more recent approach is that of phase-contrast microscopy, which is basically an adaptation of the schlieren method and serves to make visible small differences in refractive index.

The one which is of particular interest in colloids, however, is dark field microscopy. This depends on controlling the illuminating light so that it does not enter the microscope unless deflected by the object through reflection, refraction, or scattering.   Thus, whereas with ordinary illumination the background seen in the microscope is light, in the dark field microscope it is completely black.   Hence, even objects which deflect but little light can stand out brilliantly against this background.

Dark field illumination can be obtained by skewing the mirror

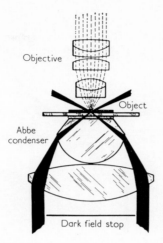

Figure 19-6. Path of light in dark field observation with standard condenser and central stop. The central stop produces a hollow cylinder of light which is transformed into a hollow cone by the condenser. (*Courtesy Bausch and Lomb Optical Co., Rochester, N. Y.*)

of a simple microscope (Fig. 19-5) or by introducing a dark field stop to intercept the central part of the normal illuminating beam (Fig. 19-6).

The amount of light which is deflected by an object and makes it visible in a dark field microscope depends on the intensity of the illuminating light and on the nature of the object, particularly on its refractive index (as compared with the surroundings) and on its size. As the object becomes of colloidal dimensions, the amount of deflected light becomes so small that even under favorable conditions especially intense illumination is needed to make it visible. This special illumination is provided by special dark field microscopes called ultramicroscopes.

19-5. Ultramicroscopes

The ultramicroscope is a good ordinary microscope with a special illuminating system giving a highly intense illumination which normally does not enter the objective. The two principal

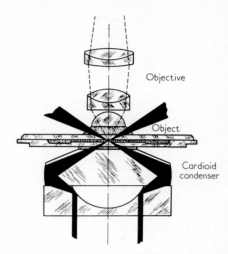

Figure 19-7. Path of light in dark field observation with a cardioid condenser.   Note the use of an immersion liquid to increase the numerical apperture and to reduce stray light.   (*Courtesy of Bausch and Lomb Optical Co., Rochester, N. Y.*)

types are the cardioid and the slit ones.   The cardioid (Fig. 19-7) and similar condensers gather a cylinder of rays into a hollow cone of light surrounding the objective.   The object is located at the apex of this cone, where all the light is concentrated.

The slit ultramicroscope (Fig. 19-8), in contrast to the cardioid one, gives a one-sided illumination of well-defined dimensions. This is obtained by providing an intense illumination (e.g., from a carbon arc) on an adjustable slit, and projecting a greatly reduced image of this slit into the field of view of the microscope inside a special cell.   The lens system for projecting the slit image is a reversed microscopic objective.

An ultramicroscope does not help us in exceeding the limitations imposed by the limit of resolution.   In fact, because of restrictions on illumination and aperture, its resolution limit is generally only fair.   It does, however, permit one to see as a single weak blur, particles which may be much smaller than the

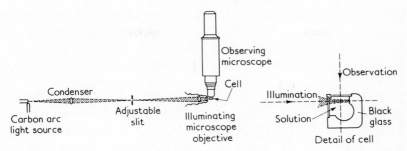

Figure 19-8. Principle of the slit ultramicroscope. *Left:* over-all view showing how the reduced image of an illuminated slit is projected into the cell from one side only. (*From materials courtesy of Bausch and Lomb Optical Co., Rochester, N. Y.*) *Right:* detail of the observation cell showing the path of light. (*From T. Svedberg, Colloid Chemistry, Chemical Catalog Co.* (*Reinhold*) *New York, 1928.*)

limit of resolution.   The lower limit for gold particles (which are exceptionally well visible in water) is of the order of only 20 A. in radius.[3]   Two such particles, in order to be individually visible, however, must be separated by more than the limit of resolution of the microscope (i.e., by several thousand Angstroms), which corresponds to the size of the blur indicating each.   Any finer structure of the particle is therefore completely lost in this blur which stems from all the points of its outline.

Hence the ultramicroscope does not make the particles visible in the usual sense but only makes perceptible their presence and location.   This information can, however, be of great value in many ways.   It assures us in the first place of the particulate nature of the system.   From the aspect of the blurs one can obtain an indication of the uniformity of the particles, and any scintillation indicates that they are far from spherical. Their Brownian motion can be observed or measured, and gives an indication of their size.   From the distribution with height under equilibrium conditions, one can also estimate their size. Flocculation and deflocculation can be observed directly. Finally, if the observed volume of the solution is delimited (by the field of view of the microscope in the horizontal direction and by its depth of focus or, better, the height of the slit in the vertical direction), counting of the particles present in this volume gives their concentration. From the number of particles per unit volume and the analytically determined total concentration, one can calculate the average particle size.

The main limitation on the usefulness of the ultramicroscope is that the particles of many colloidal systems, such as proteins or polymers, do not differ sufficiently from their surroundings to be visible even in the best ultramicroscope. They do not deflect enough light individually to become perceptible. However, their number in a few milliliters of a solution is large enough so that the total amount of light deflected can be measured readily with photoelectric cells and provides valuable information about their nature. We shall discuss this in the next chapter under the heading of light scattering.

19-6. The Gouy Method

Another interesting application of interference is the so-called Gouy method of measuring diffusion (Fig. 19-9). It involves a system identical with the illuminating system of a schlieren apparatus (Fig. 18-5b) applied to a column of liquid in which unlimited free diffusion (Section 5-4) occurs. The concentration gradient has therefore the general shape shown in Fig. 5-2 and indicated inside the cell in Fig. 19-9. Obviously, there are two and only two separate layers in the cell which have the same gradient for each value of the gradient between zero and the maximum. The two light rays passing through any such pair of layers are brought together by the schlieren lens at some point such as F' in Fig. 19-9. The two rays have not travelled the same optical path in order to get to the same point, because they have passed through layers of different refractive index (though of same gradient) and therefore of different optical thickness. The path difference corresponds, of course, to a phase difference which may lead to extinction or to reinforcement. Hence a photographic plate in the FF$'$ plane will register a series of fringes whose position and intensity is deter-

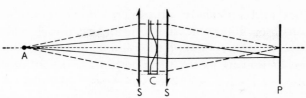

Figure 19-9. Principle of the Gouy method of measuring diffusion. The curve within the cell C indicates the refracting index gradient. Light deflected by two layers of same gradient—one above, the other below the original central boundary—is deflected to the same point on the photographic plate P. Differences in optical path length produce a pattern of interference fringes from which the concentration gradient and the diffusion coefficient can be calculated.

mined by the exact shape of the gradient at any time and therefore by the diffusion coefficient.

It may be noted that in the early stages of diffusion when the gradient is the steepest, the diffraction pattern will be widest, most rapidly changing, and most easily measured. This makes the Gouy method very popular whenever it can be applied. The exact establishment of the relation between the pattern and the diffusion coefficient is a rather complicated problem of optics, which we cannot discuss here but which yields useful results for many cases.[4]

Summary

The diffraction pattern of any radiation provides information concerning the diffracting structure. The smaller the structure in relation to the wavelength of the radiation, the more widely divergent the corresponding pattern. Since a microscope is primarily an efficient instrument for reconstructing the structure from the pattern, it can enable us to see only details which are large enough to produce a pattern capable of entering the objective. This determines the limit of resolution of the microscope. In addition, only features having enough contrast can be observed. The electron microscope greatly extends the limit of resolution of the ordinary microscope, whereas dark field techniques and especially ultramicroscopy greatly lower the minimum observable contrast.   The former, therefore, often permits the observation of details of colloidal particles, whereas the latter can enable us to see their position and motion within a solution.

References

1. V. E. Cosslett, *Endeavour*, **15,** 153 (1956); from J. W. Menter, *Proc. Roy. Soc. (London)*, **A236,** 119 (1956); and I. M. Dawson, *Proc. Roy. Soc. (London)*, **A214,** 72 (1952).
2. R. W. G. Wyckoff, *The World of the Electron Microscope*, Yale University Press, New Haven, 1958.
3. R. Zsigmondy and P. A. Thiessen, *Das Kolloide Gold*, Akademische Verlagsg., Leipzig, 1925, p. 95.
4. G. Kegeles and L. J. Gosting, *J. Am. Chem. Soc.*, **69,** 2516 (1947); L. J. Gosting and L. Onsager, *J. Am. Chem. Soc.*, **74,** 6066 (1952); summarized in R. A. Robinson and R. H. Stokes, *Electrolyte Solutions*, Academic Press, Inc., New York, 1955, pp. 278 ff.

Problems

117. If two very small particles are closer together than the limit of resolution of an ultramicroscope, (*1*) they will appear as a single particle, (*2*) both will become invisible, (*3*) they will both be ultramicroscopically visible, (*4*) none of these.

 98. From the known total concentration (by weight) of a sol and the number of particles per cubic micron determined with an ultramicroscope, one can compute the weight of one particle.   This will in general be (*1*) the actual weight of each particle (*2*) m_n, (*3*) m_w, (*4*) none of these.

102. Examination of the electron micrograph of a highly purified and monodisperse colloid gives a much higher particle weight than sedimentation rate.   This could be due to (*1*) presence of a charge if sedimentation was conducted in a buffer, (*2*) hydration, (*3*) either of these, (*4*) none of these.

CHAPTER XX

Optical Phenomena: III. Scattering

We come now to a brief survey of effects connected with the scattering of light, that is, with the appearance of light away from its normal path because of its interaction with a small particle. This was already involved in our discussion of the ultramicroscope and is part of the familiar sight of dust grains dancing in a beam of sunlight and of the blue sky and the red sunset. When properly understood and used, it is also one of the most powerful tools in the study of colloids.

20-1. Turbidity

The light scattered sidewise by a solution makes it appear turbid. Turbidity is easily seen when intense. When weak, it can be detected more readily by observing, from the side and against a dark background, a well-defined and intense beam of light passing through the solution. The visible path of the beam is sometimes called the Tyndall cone. Photoelectric detection under these conditions shows that even the clearest water has a dectectable turbidity, i.e., scatters some light. Colloidal systems can give turbidities varying from little above that of water to very deep ones, depending on their nature and concentration.

One often uses the term turbidity in a qualitative way as a measure of the light-scattering ability of the solution. It can also be defined quantitatively in the same sense as an extinction coefficient (or absorbancy index) of the solution. Turbidity then becomes τ, the inverse of the length of the solution which will reduce, by scattering, the intensity of a beam of light to $1/e$ of its original value. For purest water this length is about half a mile.

By the above definition, one can also determine turbidity by measuring all the light scattered sidewise and comparing it with the original beam. As we shall see later, the scattering is frequently rather regular with respect to direction so that determination at a single angle, e.g., at $90°$, or at two or three angles only, permits the calculation of the light scattered in all directions and hence of turbidity.

20-2. Experimental

The measurement of light scattering is based on the above considerations. It involves the quantitative comparison of the light entering a solution with that either transmitted or scattered.

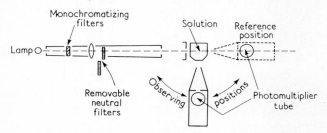

Figure 20-1. The principle of a light scattering measurement.

Since the transmitted light differs appreciably from the incident only for very turbid solutions, its measurement is seldom used. Instead, it is the very weak scattered beam which is ordinarily measured. The photocell measuring the scattered light is generally mounted on a rotating arm to permit observation at several angles (Fig. 20-1). Because of the usually low turbidity of the solutions studied, the weakening of the scattered beam as it passes through the solution can be neglected, and one can compare the scattered light with the transmitted one.

Light-scattering measurements are thus quite simple in principle but in practice encounter many problems. One of them is the need to eliminate all stray light, such as that coming from the walls of the cell. The latter is, therefore, often immersed in a larger container of water having internal light baffles. Another problem is that of standardization, because of the difficulty of determining the exact geometry of the apparatus and the ratio of the two beams. Thus, standard solutions, such as those of sugar,[1] are used frequently for this purpose. One of the greatest problems is the proper purification of the samples, because any large particles, such as dust, cause a great deal of scattering and must be eliminated very thoroughly, yet the particles of the sample itself must be unaffected. Filtration through special filters and high speed centrifugation are generally used.

20-3. Theory

The theory of light scattering is basically an advanced chapter of optics and is subject to quite rigorous though difficult analysis which gives explicit or numerical solutions for most systems.[2] We will be interested only in obtaining a semiquantitative or qualitative insight into the basic effects involved in order to gain an appreciation of the kind of information they can give us about the structure of colloidal systems.[3] Even this will have to involve occasionally optical concepts with which the reader might not be familiar.[4] Skipping such a paragraph or noting only its general conclusion should not prevent, however, an understanding of the main phenomena involved.

What we observe in light scattering can be interpreted as the result of a series of successive interactions, each affecting the final result. As illustrated schematically in Fig. 20-2, the incoming light wave interacts with the individual atoms of each particle and makes them re-emit very weak light of same wavelength. The light thus produced interacts with that produced by all other atoms of the same particle. This is intraparticle interference. The resultant train of waves has to be combined with similar trains coming from all the other particles before reaching our eyes or our phototube. This is interparticle interference.

Thus, the kind of questions to which we will need some answers

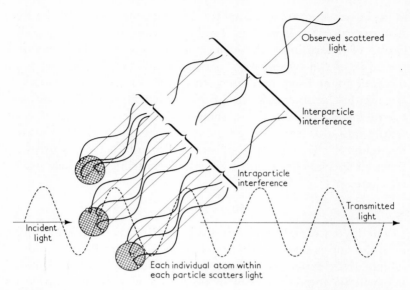

Figure   20-2. Intraparticle   and   interparticle   interference.   Whereas most of the incident light is transmitted, a tiny fraction is scattered by the individual atoms.   After interfering with that coming from other parts of the same particle and with that from other particles, it gives the observed intensity.

are: How does the primary re-emission of light depend on its nature and direction? On the nature of the primary scatterer? How does the shape and size of the particle affect intraparticle interference? How does concentration and ideality of the solution affect interparticle interference? In order to obtain the answers we will have to explore successively the behavior of a number of simple systems.

20-4. Polarization

The intensity of light emitted in various directions can be indicated by curves such as those of Fig. 20-3. The distance of a point on the curve from the center (the source of the light) is proportional to the intensity emitted in the direction of this point. These curves show the effect of polarization of the in-

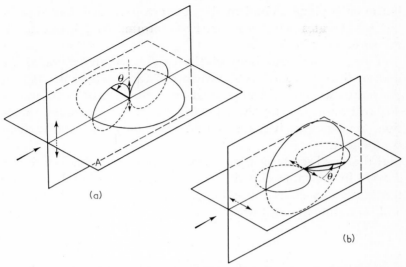

Figure 20-3. Spatial distribution of scattering of polarized light by a small isotropic scatterer. The plane of polarization of the incoming light is indicated by the double arrows on the left, the induced oscillation by those in the center. The distance from the center, as indicated by the solid arm of θ, is proportional to the scattered intensity. This is independent of direction in plane A of (a).

coming light on the intensity scattered by a small isotropic scatterer. Polarization can introduce considerable complication into light scattering, and we are going to ignore it essentially by assuming that we are always located in what corresponds to plane A of the a part of the figure. As the circle on this plane shows, the intensity is here the same in all directions and polarization plays no role.

If we wish to look for a moment at the other plane, the one in the plane of polarization of the incoming light, we see that the intensity varies greatly with the angle θ and becomes zero when this is zero. The over-all distribution of intensities is represented by a slightly flattened doughnut. This is related to the fact that the incoming electromagnetic radiation forces an oscillation of the dipole of the scatterer perpendicularly to its path and in the same plane, as indicated by the arrows.   This forced oscillation generates waves symmetrically around its axis but not in the direction of this axis.

If the primary beam is unpolarized and has both the horizontal and vertical components shown in the two parts of the figure, the scattered light will in general be partially polarized, and at 90° will even be completely polarized; in the horizontal direction, for example, it stems at that angle only from the vertical component.

If the small scatterer is anisotropic, the forced vibration is not exactly in the same direction as the original one, and the scattered intensity shifts accordingly.   This shift can be estimated and taken into account when necessary.[3]

20-5. A Pair of Scatterers

If two identical point scatterers are both scattering the same incoming radiation, the observed result will depend both on their separation and on the direction of observation.   The inter-

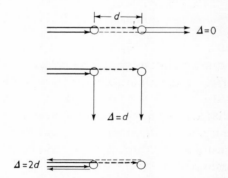

Figure 20-4. Optical path difference of scattered light vanishes in the forward direction and is greatest in the rearward direction.

ference of the scattered waves coming from the two points will depend on the phase difference, which is determined by the optical path difference, i.e., by the extra distance which the light has to travel in order to reach first the scatterer and then the observer.   As shown in Fig. 20-4, this path difference is always zero in the forward direction, because the extra distance travelled by the incoming light to reach the second point is equal to the extra distance travelled by the light scattered by the first one. The difference increases, however, as the angle of observation is shifted, becoming equal to the distance between the points at 90° where the scattered rays travel the same distance but the incoming ones do not.   The maximum path difference is reached for observation from the rear where both the incoming and the scattered light must cover the extra distance to reach the observer from the second point.

If this path difference is an integral multiple of the wavelength, the light from the two points will reinforce.   An additional half a wavelength will cause complete cancellation, whereas intermediate values will give a gradual transition.

20-6. Ordered Scatterers

If identical scatterers are arranged perfectly regularly as in a perfect crystal (Fig. 20-5) and if a certain phase difference is found for a given pair, it will also exist for an infinite number of pairs comprising all the scatterers.   This can be shown as follows: if a and a' form the first pair and b is a third scatterer located in a certain relation to a', there must be (because of the perfect regularity of the structure) another scatterer b' in the same relation to a'.   Hence the relative positions of b and b' must be the same as those of a and a' giving the same phase difference of scattered light.   If the regular arrangement involves several kinds of atoms, it is the repeating unit (the unit cell) which must be taken as the scatterer.

In general, light scattered by neighboring scatterers will have a somewhat different phase.   By going further away this difference is multiplied, and in general (Fig. 20-5a) one can find another scatterer cancelling exactly the first one.   Once this pair is found, we have just seen that all other scatterers can be arranged into such pairs, so there must be complete cancellation in that direction for all scatterers, for the whole ordered assembly.

Conversely, if no such pair is found, there will be no cancellation but only reinforcement in that direction.   This impossibility
of finding a cancelling scatterer is a very exceptional case and
means that the phase differences are all an integral wavelength (if they were not, one could always find cancellation by
going far enough).   For this exceptional case to occur in a three-
dimensional array, there must be a special combination of

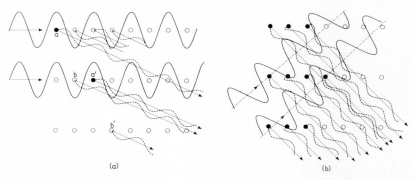

(a)   (b)

Fig. 20-5. Scattering by ordered scatterers.   (a) In general, a small phase
difference produced by neighbors (top row) leads to the existence of a pair
(a and a') which gives complete cancellation.   Other points can then be
similarly paired (b and b') and all scattering vanishes.   (b) For special directions, spacings, and wavelengths, such that neighbors scatter in phase, scattering
is intense.

wavelength, distances and orientation of the scattering array,
and angle of observation.   This is why x-ray diffraction patterns of crystals consist of only a small number of spots or lines
which correspond each to the coincidence of all three of these
factors.

In the case of pure liquids, although the pairing and cancellation is not perfect because molecules are not arranged in complete order, the differences are so small compared to a wavelength that they lead to a very small amount of scattering which is
essentially equal in all directions.

20-7. Amplitude and Intensity

We have thus far spoken of reinforcement in a rather qualitative way and need to make its meaning more precise. In addition to its wavelength, a wave motion is also characterized by its amplitude, A, i.e., the height of its crest and depth of its trough. When two wave trains combine, their amplitudes simply add with due regard for their phase relation. Hence, if two equal wave trains are exactly in phase, they are equivalent to a wave of double amplitude.

If we consider light as due to corresponding oscillations of electric charges, the amplitude corresponds also to the velocity of these oscillations since it takes twice as rapid a motion to cover a double deflection within the same time, i.e., at a constant frequency and wavelength.

Amplitude, however, does not affect directly our eyes or phototubes. These are sensitive to the energy carried by the wave train, i.e., the intensity, I, of the light. This turns out to be proportional to the square of the amplitude

$$I \propto A^2 \qquad\qquad (20\text{-}7.1)$$

This is connected with the fact that the energy of a moving particle is proportional to the square of its velocity and, as we have just seen, amplitude is proportional to the velocity of the oscillations.

Hence if we find that the amplitudes re-emitted by scatterers simply add, i.e., that the resulting amplitude is proportional to their number, we can conclude that the observed intensity will be proportional to the square of this number. On the other hand, if the resulting amplitude is proportional to the square root of the number of scatterers, the observed intensity must be proportional to that number, i.e., is simply additive.

A limiting factor on the intensity of radiation is the limited length of individual wave trains or the impossibility of having completely monochromatic light. This prevents the observation of the quadratic increase for macroscopic objects, very large compared to the wavelength.   This limitation will not enter our considerations.

20-8. Polarizability and Refractive Index

The amplitude and therefore the intensity of the scattered light depends on the nature of the scattering atom or molecule.   In order for this primary unit to act as a source of the scattered light, its electric charges have to oscillate, and these oscillations have to be forced upon them by the incoming light.   The same incoming amplitude will produce different amplitudes of the oscillation and of the scattered light, depending on the electric "softness" or polarizability, α, of the scatterer, that is, the dipole induced in it by a unit electric field.   Hence we can write for the ratio of scattered to incident amplitudes

$$A_s/A_0 \propto \alpha \qquad (20\text{-}8.1)$$

Since the intensities are proportional to the square of the amplitudes we have

$$I_s/I_0 \propto \alpha^2 \qquad (20\text{-}8.2)$$

The polarizability of a molecule is related to its contribution to the refractive index, ν, which increases rapidly above unity as polarization increases above zero, these two values corresponding to vacuum.   The exact relation between these is due to Lorenz and Lorentz and can be written

$$\alpha \propto (\nu^2 - 1)/(\nu^2 + 2) \qquad (20\text{-}8.3)$$

If the small variation of $\nu^2 + 2$ is neglected, this becomes

$$I_s/I_0 \propto (\nu^2 - 1)^2 \qquad (20\text{-}8.4)$$

This applies to scatterers of one kind in vacuum.   For us, liquid solutions of scattering particles are more interesting.   We have already seen that a pure liquid scatters very weakly because of the almost complete cancellation of the effect of each molecule by others.   If some of the solvent molecules were replaced by solute molecules of same refractive index, there would be no effect on scattering. It is only to the extent that the solute molecules have a different polarizability than those of the solvent which they replace, i.e., if they change the refractive index of the system, that they also lead to significant turbidities.

Thus, when considering the effect of solutes we have to look at molecules not in a vacuum of refractive index 1, but in a solvent of refractive index ν_0. It is therefore reasonable that the above relation changes to

$$I_s/I_0 \propto (\nu^2 - \nu_0^2)^2 \qquad\qquad (20\text{-}8.5)$$

where ν is the refractive index of the solution. As long as this is close to ν_0 the above relation can be simplified to

$$I_s/I_0 \propto (\nu - \nu_0)^2(\nu + \nu_0)^2 \approx (\nu - \nu_0)^2 4\nu_0^2 \qquad (20\text{-}8.6)$$

or for a given solvent

$$I_s/I_0 \propto (\nu - \nu_0)^2 \qquad\qquad (20\text{-}8.7)$$

If we introduce the specific refractive increment $\partial\nu/\partial\mathfrak{W}$ we have $(\nu - \nu_0) = \mathfrak{W}\partial\nu/\partial\mathfrak{W}$, so that for small concentrations

$$I_s/I_0 \propto (\partial\nu/\partial\mathfrak{W})^2$$

The turbidity increases with the square of the specific refractive increment.

20-9. Small Particles

If a particle is small compared to the wavelength of light, say less than one-twentieth of it, the maximum phase difference between light scattered by any of its parts cannot exceed twice this value (Fig. 20-4), i.e., one-tenth even in the rearward direction where the difference is the greatest. This is such a small difference that the amplitudes can be considered as simply additive, and the resulting amplitude is proportional to the number of individual scatterers in the particle, i.e., to its mass. Therefore, the resulting intensity must be proportional to the square of the mass of the particle (Section 20-7)

$$(I_s/I_0)_{\text{small}} \propto m^2 \qquad\qquad (20\text{-}9.1)$$

This result is independent of the shape of the particle as long as it remains small in all directions.

20-10. Random Scatterers

If the scatterers are distributed completely at random, the phase relations of the scattered light must also be completely random, the phase relations of the scattered light must also be completely random. The probability of any two cancelling completely is the same as of their reinforcing completely or of interfering in any intermediate way. Such random amplitudes will add somewhat as steps in a random walk (Chapter 5), with the resultant amplitude proportional to the square root of the number of scatterers. The observed intensity must therefore (Section 20-7) be additive and directly proportional to the number of these randomly located scatterers.

20-11. Ideal Solutions of Small Particles

Completely random location of scattering particles means that only thermal agitation affects their distribution with no net forces between them. This is the case of molecules in an ideal gas and of solutes in ideal solutions. In this case, therefore, the intensities of light scattered by each particle are additive, and the intensity of light scattered by a unit volume, hence the turbidity is proportional to the number n of particles in this volume

$$\tau \propto n \qquad (20\text{-}11.1)$$

In the special case when the particles are small compared to the wavelength of light, we have already seen (Section 20-9) that the intensity scattered by each is proportional to the square of its mass. Introducing this into the above result gives

$$\tau \propto nm^2 \qquad (20\text{-}11.2)$$

This relation involves both the number and the mass of individual particles which are generally both unknown. Fortunately, the weight concentration $\mathfrak{W}$, which is readily determined, is given by $\mathfrak{W} = nm$. The above expression is therefore equal to

$$\tau \propto \mathfrak{W}m \qquad\qquad (20\text{-}11.3)$$

which relates the experimentally accessible $\mathfrak{W}$ and τ to the mass of the particle m.   This expression is generally written in terms of the particle weight, M, and the proportionality constant, which includes the refractive index effect, is denoted by H [specifically $H = 8\pi^3(\nu + \nu_0)^2(\partial\nu/\partial\mathfrak{W})^2/3\mathbf{N}\lambda^4)$].   This gives

$$\tau = H\mathfrak{W}M \qquad\qquad (20\text{-}11.4)$$

or, as it is generally written

$$H\mathfrak{W}/\tau = 1/M \qquad\qquad (20\text{-}11.5)$$

This is the fundamental expression for the determination of particle weight by light scattering.   It is valid for ideal solutions of particles which are small compared to the wavelength used.

20-12. Measurement of Particle Weights

Turbidity is an equilibrium property useful in estimating particle weights.   So is osmotic pressure.   Their dependence on the particle weight is, however, in sharp contrast.   For solutions containing the same number of particles per unit volume, osmotic pressure is independent of the particle weight (Eq. 6-5.6); turbidity increases with the square of the particle weight (Eq. 20-11.2).   For solutions of the same weight concentration, osmotic pressure decreases with the particle weight (Eq. 6-10.1); turbidity increases with it (Eq. 20-11.3).   Osmotic pressure is independent of the nature of the particle, turbidity is a function of the refractive index increment.

Thus, as the particle weight increases, light scattering becomes easier to measure (provided a proper solvent can be found), whereas osmotic pressure becomes more difficult.   In practice, particle weights of the order of 10,000 can be determined by light scattering, and a particle remains small in the above sense until its radius reaches some 100 A. and its particle weight about 10^7. We will shortly see that much larger particles can be also studied by slight modifications of this method.

20-13. Averaging

The above equation (20-11.4) was derived with the assumption that all the randomly spaced scatterers of an ideal solution made the same contribution to the observed turbidity.   If the system is polydisperse, the above equation will still apply to each species provided that the solution is ideal, i.e., that the distribution of all particles remains completely random, one kind uninfluenced by the other.   This same distribution assures that there is no special or fixed phase relation between the light scattered by the different species, so that their intensities, i.e., the turbidities are additive.   Hence we can write

$$\tau = \Sigma \tau_i \qquad (20\text{-}13.1)$$

If all the species have the same influence on the refractive index (which is normally the case if they have the same composition), then the proportionality constant H is also the same for all, and

$$\tau = H \Sigma \mathfrak{W}_i M_i \qquad (20\text{-}13.2)$$

If we now calculate an average particle weight from the observed turbidity according to Eq. 20-11.4, this will be

$$M = \tau/H\mathfrak{W} = H\Sigma\mathfrak{W}_i M_i / H\mathfrak{W} = \Sigma n_i M_i^2 / \Sigma n_i M_i \quad (20\text{-}13.3)$$

since $\mathfrak{W} = \Sigma n_i M_i$.   Comparing this expression with the definition of M_w in Section 2-8, we see that light scattering gives us a weight-average particle weight for polydisperse ideal systems of chemically similar small particles.

20-14. The Effect of Wavelength

We are now in a position to establish the effect of the wave length, λ, on the scattered intensity.   Although there are many ways of calculating this, the simplest seems to be a dimensional consideration.   Let us take a small particle of radius r illuminated by light of intensity I_0.   The scattered light will have an intensity I_s when observed at a distance L from the particle.

I_s is of course proportional to I_0, and their ratio I_s/I_0 is a simple number.   This number depends on many factors but should not depend on the yardstick used to measure the linear dimensions involved. Hence only a ratio of these dimensions can enter into the final expression for I_s/I_0.

We know already that I_s is proportional to the square of the mass of the particle and therefore to r^6. I_s decreases also with the square of the distance L of the observer. The only other factor which can be determined with a yardstick is λ, the wavelength of the light. If this enters with a power x, the product $r^6 L^{-2} \lambda^x$ must be a simple ratio; i.e., the sum of the exponents must be zero. Hence $x = -4$ and

$$I_s/I_0 \propto 1/\lambda^4 \qquad (20\text{-}14.1)$$

Therefore, under equal conditions the scattered fraction of light rises rapidly with shorter wavelengths. Within the visible spectrum, which covers the range from about 4000 to 7000 A, this effect amounts to a factor of slightly over 10. If the light incident upon small particles is white, the shorter wavelengths are affected most and the eye sees a blue color in the scattered light. This accounts for the appearance of fine colloidal suspensions of particles which do not themselves absorb the light and for the color of the sky. Conversely, in the transmitted beam, it is the red light which is least disturbed by scattering and gives the dominant hue. This explains the color of sunsets.

20-15. Large Particles

As the particle increases in size, phase differences between light scattered by its various parts become significant and intra-particle interference ceases to be purely additive. This effect will be most pronounced for light scattered in the rearward direction by the front and the rear parts of the particle, since it is here that the path difference of the light is the greatest (Fig. 20-4). This will lead to extinction when the radius becomes $\lambda/4$. Hence, as the particle becomes larger, the intensity of its forward scattering continues to increase with the square of its size, whereas the backward scattering decreases until in fact it reaches zero. Figure 20-6 shows the progressive effects by

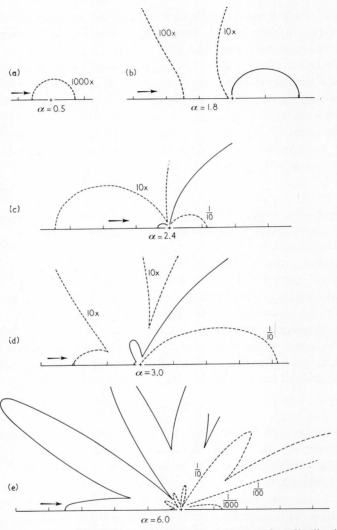

Figure 20-6. The effect of particle size upon the angular distribution of scattered light.   The incident light comes horizontally from the left as shown by arrow.   The distance from the center indicates the intensity of light scattered in any direction.   Solid lines are drawn to same scale, dashed lines are reduced or increased by the indicated factor. α is a measure of the particle size in terms of the wavelength ($\alpha = 2\pi r/\lambda$, $\nu/\nu_0 = 1.33$).   (*Based on tables of scattering functions for spherical particles, National Bureau of Standards, Applied Mathematics Series No. 4, U. S. Govt. Printing Office, Washington, 1949.*)

curves whose distance from the center is proportional to the intensity scattered in that direction.

As the particle becomes still larger, the extinction occurs at an intermediate angle, while some reinforcement may be seen in the rearward direction. With further increases, this reaches a maximum and then again decreases while the maximum moves to an intermediate angle.

Thus, large particles show maxima and minima of scattering (Fig. 20-6e) when viewed at different angles. The number and angular positions of these maxima and minima depend on the ratio of the dimensions of the particles to the wavelength. Hence, using light of known composition, they can be used to determine the size of the particles. If white light is used, the direction of a maximum for, say, red light may correspond to a minimum for, say, green light. In such a case the scattered light is predominantly red. At a different angle it may be predominantly green for similar reasons, and so on. Hence, when observed along an arc the scattered light has a sequence of colors similar to a spectrum which may be repeated several times. This is called a "higher order Tyndall spectrum."

If such large particles are randomly distributed through the solution, the intensities, scattered by each in any given direction, add directly. If the system is monodisperse, or almost monodisperse, a given direction of observation will correspond to the same intensity, which may be a maximum or minimum or the same color, for all particles. Hence the solution as a whole will show maxima and minima or higher order Tyndall spectra. We have already noted their existence in monodisperse sulfur sols (Section 11-13).

If, on the other hand, the particles are not monodisperse, any direction will correspond to minima for some particles and maxima for others, giving only a gradual change in intensity and a constant, substantially white color at all angles.

An exact quantitative interpretation of intraparticle interference is given, in principle, by the so-called Mie theory. This does not lead, however, to explicit expressions but requires the laborious calculation of each intensity, depending on angle, size, and refractive index. The results of such calculations have been tabulated for many cases of special interest.[5]

By extrapolating to zero angle, i.e., to the forward direction, one can eliminate, in principle, as we have seen (Section 20-5) the effect of intraparticle interference. The simple formula (Eq. 20-11.4) can then be used to estimate the particle weight even for large particles.

20-16. Dissymmetry

A particularly interesting situation is presented by particles which are larger than about a tenth of a wavelength yet too small to show a series of minima and maxima. The intensity of their scattered light simply decreases from front to rear (Figs. 20-6a and b). Hence, the ratio of intensities scattered in two directions gives a measure of this decrease and therefore of the size. For convenience, the symmetrical angles of 45 and 135° are generally used. The corresponding ratio (I_{45}/I_{135}) is unity for very small particles and increases with size. It is called the dissymmetry of scattered light and is used in estimating the size.

The size measured by the dissymmetry is the effective extent of the particle with respect to the wavelength. Hence, if the particle weight is also known, it gives an indication of the shape of the particles and can tell us whether they are spheres, rods, random coils, etc.

20-17. The Fluctuation Approach

We have now looked into the effects of size and to some extent of shape upon intraparticle interference and have also seen that interparticle interference results in simple additivity of intensities for ideal solutions in which the particles are randomly distributed. When the solution is nonideal, interparticle interference becomes much more difficult to compute. There is, however, an alternative approach to the theory of light scattering which is particularly adapted to the treatment of nonideal solutions of small particles.

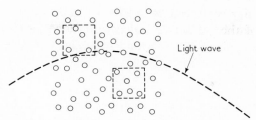

Figure 20-7. In the fluctuation approach to light scattering, concentration fluctuations in volumes of solution which are small compared to the wavelength of light are considered.

This "fluctuation" approach disregards the optical effects of the individual particles and considers instead small volumes of the solution. If these volumes had each exactly the same refractive index, there would be no scattering. If a small volume has a refractive index differing from the surroundings, it will scatter some light just as a small particle would. The main reason for the existence of such a refractive index difference is a difference in concentration between the volume and the surroundings, and this, in turn, is caused by fluctuations resulting from the random Brownian motion of the particles (Fig. 20-7). Thus, the change of refractive index of the small volume and, therefore, the scattering and turbidity, will depend on two factors: (1) the ease of fluctuations and (2) the optical effectiveness of these fluctuations, i.e., the change in refractive index produced by a given fluctuation. We will now consider these factors in more detail.

The small volumes which we consider are small compared to the wavelength. The intensities scattered by each of them bear no relation to each other (although the volumes themselves are in a fixed relation which could be perfectly regular and lead to a definite phase relation). Thus the amplitudes are random and, again, add like steps in a random walk, so that (Section 20-7) the intensities are additive. Hence, the turbidity of a solution is proportional to the average intensity scattered by a small volume

$$\tau \propto \langle I_v \rangle \tag{20-17.1}$$

The intensity scattered by a given small volume depends on the square of the refractive index difference and the square of the volume, v, since this is small compared to the wavelength (Section 20-9)

$$I_v \propto v^2(v - v_0)^2 \qquad (20\text{-}17.2)$$

For a given change in weight concentration $\mathfrak{W}$, the change in refractive index depends on the specific refractive index increment, $\partial v/\partial \mathfrak{W}$, which measures the optical efficiency of a fluctuation in concentration

$$v - v_0 = (\mathfrak{W} - \mathfrak{W}_0)(\partial v/\partial \mathfrak{W}) \qquad (20\text{-}17.3)$$

Thus, the intensity scattered by a small volume is given, after collecting the last two relations, by

$$I_v \propto v^2 (\mathfrak{W} - \mathfrak{W}_0)^2 (\partial v/\partial \mathfrak{W})^2 \qquad (20\text{-}17.4)$$

For a given two-component[6] system $\partial v/\partial \mathfrak{W}$ is fixed so that it can be incorporated into the proportionality constant and we can write for the average values

$$<I_v> \propto v^2 < (\mathfrak{W} - \mathfrak{W}_0)^2 > \qquad (20\text{-}17.5)$$

In our discussion of fluctuations we have already estimated the average square fluctuation in concentration and found it to be (Eq. 10-4.7)

$$<(\mathfrak{W} - \mathfrak{W}_0)^2 > = 2\mathbf{k}T\mathfrak{W}/v(\partial \pi/\partial \mathfrak{W}) \qquad (20\text{-}17.6)$$

Omitting the constant factor $2\mathbf{k}T$ we obtain, therefore

$$<I_v> \propto v\mathfrak{W}/(\partial \pi/\partial \mathfrak{W}) \qquad (20\text{-}17.7)$$

Thus, after taking into account that the extent of fluctuation in concentration decreases with increasing volume, we find that the average intensity of scattering from a small volume of solution is proportional to its size.   Since these intensities are additive, the amount of light scattered is therefore simply proportional to the total scattering volume, as would be expected. Hence the turbidity, which depends on the amount scattered per unit volume, is given by

$$\tau \propto \mathfrak{W}/(\partial \pi/\partial \mathfrak{W}) \qquad (20\text{-}17.8)$$

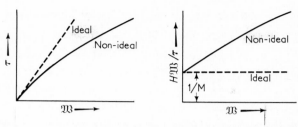

Figure 20-8. The relation of the $H\mathfrak{W}/\tau$ plot to the direct τ plot.

which holds for solutions of small scatterers whether they are ideal or not.

The turbidity increases with the concentration of the solution and also with $1/(\partial\pi/\partial\mathfrak{W})$ which measures the ease of fluctuation. In the special case of an ideal solution, this factor is $M/\mathbf{R}T$ which gives, omitting the constant $\mathbf{R}T$,

$$\tau \propto \mathfrak{W}M \qquad (20\text{-}17.9)$$

just as we have derived earlier (Section 20-11) for ideal small scatterers by considering only interferences. Again, this can be written as

$$H\mathfrak{W}/\tau = 1/M \qquad (20\text{-}17.10)$$

where H takes into consideration such factors as the refractive increment of the solute and the wavelength of light.

For nonideal solutions, however, the osmotic pressure deviates from $\pi = \mathbf{R}T\mathfrak{W}/M$ at finite concentrations, and turbidity deviates correspondingly from the above expression. Hence, unless the nonideality is known, molecular weights can be obtained in such a case only by extrapolating to infinite dilution. For this purpose it is customary to plot experimental values of $H\mathfrak{W}/\tau$ against $\mathfrak{W}$. For ideal solutions they define a horizontal straight line. For nonideal solutions, the line is not horizontal and often more or less curved. It is then extrapolated to zero concentration, and the intercept gives $1/M$ (Fig. 20-8). Conversely, the slope gives a measure of the nonideality of the solution.

20-18. The Breadth of X-ray Lines

Let us consider again for a moment a regular arrangement of scatterers, such as a perfect crystal. We have seen (Section 20-6) that extinction occurs whenever (1) a mutually cancelling pair can be found and, in addition, (2) all other scatterers can be similarly paired. This required both perfect order and infinite extent of the crystal. Scattered x-rays are then extinguished in all directions except a few which satisfy very special conditions, and the diffraction pattern is correspondingly very sharp.

Experimental limitations account for a certain small width of the lines. Among these limitations are the halation of the photographic film and the difficulty of rendering the incoming beam perfectly monochromatic, parallel, and infinitely narrow. Any additional spread must be due to a deviation from the above ideal arrangement of scatterers. This deviation may be due either to an imperfect order of the array, to its limited size, or to a combination of these two factors.

The small size of a crystal reduces the chances of finding the second scatterer of a cancelling pair, and, even if one pair is found, there must be some scatterers along the edges for which the other member of the pair is missing. The extreme case is that of only two scatterers. This pair will give perfect extinction for only certain directions, so that there will be some scattering in almost all directions.

In view of the experimental limitations on the observable width of x-ray diffraction lines, it is generally sufficient to have about 100 scatterers in perfect order in all directions to give the same sharpness of the pattern as an infinite number. Conversely, crystals that are smaller give a measurable broadening of lines, and their size can thus be estimated.

Summary

Whenever light strikes an atom, a tiny fraction of it is re-emitted as scattered light. The magnitude of this fraction is related to the refractive index contribution of this atom, and decreases with the fourth power of the wavelength. Before being observed, the re-emitted light must be combined with that from all other atoms within the field of view, in particular with that coming from other parts of the same particle and with that from other particles. If the particle is small, intraparticle interference gives an intensity increasing with the square of the mass of the particle; for larger particles it leads to dissymmetry and then to maxima and minima as the angle of observation is changed. For ideal solutions interparticle interference leads to an additivity of the light scattered by the individual particles. If small volumes of the solution are considered instead of the individual particles, the turbidity depends on the ease of fluctuations within them and on the optical efficiency of these fluctuations. The ease of fluctuation depends on the slope of osmotic pressure, $\partial\pi/\partial\mathfrak{W}$, and therefore on the ideality of the solution as well as on the particle weight.

References

1. S. H. Maron and R. L. H. Lou, *J. Phys. Chem.*, **59,** 231 (1955).
2. H. C. van de Hulst, *Light Scattering by Small Particles*, John Wiley & Sons, Inc., New York, 1957.
3. K. A. Stacey, *Light Scattering in Physical Chemistry*, Academic Press, Inc., New York, 1956, gives further details with many references.
4. Reference 1 of Chapter 18.
5. Reference 2, pp. 165–171 gives a list of such tabulations.
6. H. C. Brinkman and J. J. Hermans, *J. Chem. Phys.*, **17,** 574 (1949) treat the general multi-component case. Simplified application to charged systems is shown in L. H. Princen and K. J. Mysels, *J. Colloid Sci.*, **12,** 594 (1957).

Problems

111. The intensities will be not additive for light scattered by (*1*) randomly spaced scatterers of equal size, (*2*) regularly spaced scatterers of random size, (*3*) randomly spaced scatterers of random size, (*4*) regularly spaced scatterers of equal size.
114. The accompanying graph shows that (*1*) *a* is a more ideal solute than *b*, (*2*) the turbidity of solutions of *a* is greater than that of solutions

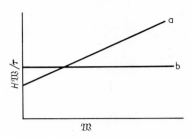

of b, (3) the particle weight of a is greater than that of b, (4) all of these, (5) none of these.

116. If the same solute is dissolved in several solvents in which it forms ideal solutions, one can expect to have for all of them (1) the same turbidity for the same concentration, (2) the same value of H, (3) the same intercept of the $H\,\mathfrak{W}/\tau$ versus $\mathfrak{W}$ plot, (4) all of these, (5) none of these.

120. If a particle swells by solvation while remaining very small compared to the wavelength of light, the amount of scattered light may be expected to (1) increase since it is proportional to the square of the volume, (2) remain the same since it is due to atoms forming the original particle and not those of the solvent, (3) decrease since the refractive increment of solvated particles is less than that of the unsolvated ones.

108. If a system illuminated by white light appears slightly turbid and white (i.e., milky) in all directions, one can conclude that (1) it is polydisperse, (2) it contains particles whose diameter exceeds 2000 A., (3) both of these, (4) neither of these.

105. Many protein molecules are several times larger than the smallest gold particle that has been observed with the ultramicroscope, yet the former have never been thus seen.   This is most likely to be due to the fact that (1) nobody tried to see them, (2) they are below the limit of resolution of the visible light, (3) the numerical apertures used were too small, (4) the optical properties of the particles are too similar to those of water.

ANSWERS TO PROBLEMS

The answers are arranged in numerical order to facilitate location. The problems are numbered randomly to prevent involuntary "peeking" at the answer to the next problem.

1	2	36	1	71	3	106	2
2	3	37	2×10^5	72	4	107	5
3	5	38	3	73	1	108	3
4	17.7 min.	39	4	74	102	109	2
5	8.1×10^{-20}	40	2	75	3	110	1
6	4	41	4	76	4	111	4
7	2,206	42	6	77	1	112	6
8	4	43	3	78	4	113	2
9	4.5 A.	44	C	79	5	114	3
10	100	45	3	80	1	115	2
11	2	46	1	81	4	116	3
12	E and W	47	3	82	1	117	1
13	2	48	4	83	2	118	2
14	10 hr.	49	5	84	5	119	3
15	4.9×10^4	50	4	85	3.3	120	2
16	N and S	51	3	86	4	121	2
17	29 hr.	52	1	87	1	122	3
18	1200	53	4	88	2	123	2
19	2	54	1	89	4	124	153
20	4	55	4	90	3	125	3
21	10	56	EHA	91	3	126	1
22	1	57	3	92	3	127	4
23	2	58	5	93	2	128	1
24	4	59	1	94	1	129	3
25	248	60	0.061	95	4	130	4
26	4	61	4	96	1		
27	5	62	2	97	4		
28	5	63	4	98	2		
29	7	64	3	99	1		
30	2	65	3	100	5		
31	3	66	4	101	4		
32	2	67	1	102	2		
33	2	68	2	103	4		
34	3	69	1	104	3		
35	1	70	1	105	4		

ABBREVIATIONS AND SYMBOLS

I. Small Italics

(mainly microscopic quantities pertaining to individual particles)

a — Constant; radius of particle; distance of closest approach; distance between ion and dipole; half axis of ellipsoid of revolution along axis of symmetry; area of particle.

b — Constant; distance between charges of a dipole; half length of the two equal axes of ellipsoid of revolution.

d — Distance between particles, pinholes.

i — van't Hoff's factor.

f — Force acting on particle.

h — Constant.

j — Flux (number of particles per unit cross-section and unit time).

l — Distance (between particles); average Brownian displacement; characteristic dimension.

m — Mass (or weight) of a particle.

n — Number of (particles).

p — Effective charge of particle in electronic units.

q — Charge in e.s.u.; permeation; amount of monolayer.

r — Radius of sphere; distance from center of tube.

t — Time.

u — Velocity.

v — Volume of particle; small volume of solution.

w — Work term in Boltzmann exponential.

x — Direction or distance along abscissa or radius.

z — Charge in electronic units (may be $+$ or $-$)

II. Capital Italics

(mainly macroscopic quantities)

A — Area; specific area; normalization constant; amplitude of light wave.

E — Electric potential.

F — Force.

D — Diffusion coefficient.

H — Height; light scattering constant $(= 8\pi^3(\nu + \nu_0)^2(\partial\nu/\partial\mathfrak{W})^2/3\mathbf{N}\lambda^4)$.

I — Intensity (of light, electric current).

J — Flux (flow per unit time and unit cross-section).

441

K Constant.
L Length or distance.
M Particle weight; molar.
N Number (of steps, moles); normal.
P Pressure; vapor pressure.
Q Electric charge in coulombs or in e.s.u.; permeation.
R Electric resistance; radius.
T Absolute temperature.
V Volume; electric potential.
W Weight.

III. Roman

A   Angstrom unit (10^{-8} cm.).
c.m.c.   Critical micelle concentration.
k   Kilo (10^3).
ln   Logarithm based on **e**.
log   Logarithm based on 10.
m   Meter, mili (10^{-3}).
v   Volt.

IV. Small Greek

(mainly specific, intensive properties)

α Polarizability; half-angle subtended by microscope objective; revolutions per second; angle of incidence.
γ Microgram (10^{-6} g.); surface tension.
δ Resolving power of microscope; "thickness" of double layer.
∂ Partial derivative sign.
ζ Zeta potential.
η Viscosity.
θ Flory temperature; angle.
ϑ Dielectric constant.
κ Debye-Hückel theory parameter—inverse double layer "thickness"
$\varkappa$ Conductivity of solution.
λ Wave length.
μ Micron (10^{-4} cm.).
ν Refractive index.
π Osmotic pressure.
ρ Density, volume charge density.
σ Surface charge density.
τ Turbidity.
υ Electrophoretic mobility.

φ	Friction factor.
ψ	Potential.
ω	Angular velocity (radians per second).

V. Capital Greek

Δ	Difference; increment; change.
Λ	Equivalent conductivity.
Ω	Electrical resistance.

VI. Bold Face Letters

(numerical constants)

e	Base of natural logarithms (≈ 2.7183).
g	Acceleration of gravity ($\approx 981 \approx 10^3$ cm./sec.^{2}).
k	Boltzmann constant, $\mathbf{R/N}$ ($\approx 1.38 \times 10^{-16}$ erg/degree).
F	Faraday, $\mathbf{N}\epsilon$ ($\approx 96{,}500 \approx 10^5$ Coulombs, $\approx 2.9 \times 10^{14}$ e.s.u.).
N	Avagadro's number, molecules per mole ($\approx 6.02 \times 10^{23} \approx 6 \times 10^{23}$).
R	Gas constant ($\approx 8.31 \times 10^7$ erg/degree mole, $1.98 \approx 2$ cal./degree mole.
STP	Standard temperature and pressure (0° C., 760 mm. Hg).
ϵ	Electronic charge ($\approx 4.8 \times 10^{-10}$ e.s.u., $\approx 1.6 \times 10^{-19}$ Coulombs).
π	Pi (≈ 3.14).

VII. German

(concentrations)

$\mathfrak{C}$	Concentration (amount in any units/volume).
$\mathfrak{M}$	Molarity (moles/liter).
$\mathfrak{N}$	Normality (equivalents/liter).
$\mathfrak{n}$	Number of particles/volume.
$\mathfrak{x}$	Mole fraction.
$\mathfrak{V}$	Volume fraction.
$\mathfrak{Q}$	Amount adsorbed/unit of adsorbent.
$\mathfrak{W}$	Weight concentration (weight/volume).

VIII. Script

(dimensionless numbers)

$\mathscr{H}$	Hydration.
$\mathscr{P}$	Probability.
$\mathscr{R}$	Reynold's number; chromatographic ratio ($\mathscr{R}_f$).

IX. Subscripts

Average; pure solvent; equilibrium; saturation; initial; base level; specific value; at surface of particle; unhydrated; incident.

1	Solvent.
2	Solute; colloidal ions.
3	Counterions.
4	Similiions.
45, 135	Angles of observation.
d	Driving; due to diffusion; of diffuse double layer
f	Produced by flow.
h	Hydrated.
i	Any number; of a fraction.
n	Neutralizing; number-average.
p	Vapor pressure.
R	Radius.
r	Resisting; reduced.
rel	Relative.
red	Reduced.
s	Due to settling; of segment(s); scattered.
spec	Specific.
t	Total.
v	Volume; volume fraction; of small volume; vapor.
w	Weight-average.

X. *Superscript*

$'$	Differentiating index.
$''$	Differentiating index.

XI. *Other Signs*

∞	Infinity.
$\propto$	Proportional to.
$< \ >$	Average.
$[\ ]$	Intrinsic, dominant bracket.
$\approx$	Approximately equal.

INDEX

Parentheses indicate the page to which a literature reference pertains.

N